泰戈特（北京）工程技术有限公司
TECHGART(BEIJING)ENGINEERING LTD

EPC / EPCM for Coal Handling and Preparation Plant
Operations & Maintenances
Vibrating Screens, Magnetic Separator,
Dense Medium Vessel, Centrifuges
Engineering Design, Consulting, Sourcing

Techgart is a leading engineering construction company offering EPC/EPCM based project delivery and operations to coal washing plants. Techgart owns a manufactory in Tianjin, we can provide major coal washing equipment, e.g. screens, centrifuges, dense medium vessel, magnetic separators, etc. Basis on advanced coal washing technology from USA and over ten years rapid development in China; today we own state-of-the-art coal washing technology and its implementation practice. Techgart has rich experiences in CHPP project delivery, operations as well as top quality process equipment.

www.coalepc.com
Email: zhang@techgart.com
Tel: +86 139 1039 3058

www.hot-mining.com

HOT is a leading provider of mining, mineral processing and infrastructure to global resources industry.

We provide engineering design, equipment supply, project delivery and operations services for coal, copper, gold, cobalt, zinc-lead, silver and other base metals.

Mining Project Evaluation, National Instrument 43-101 and JORC reporting
Resource Modelling and Estimation
Open Pit Mine Design, Planning and Engineering
Underground Mine Design, Planning and Engineering
Consulting, Engineering Design, Owners' Engineer of Coal Preparation Plant
EPC/EPCM /FEED project delivery of Mineral Processing Plant
Operations and Consulting for CHPP, and Mineral Processing Plant
Contract Mining for Underground Mines
Coal Shearer, AFC, BSL, Roof Support, Centrifuge, Crushers, Screens, TBS

北京浩沃特矿业技术有限公司
Beijing HOT Mining Tech Co Ltd
www.hot-mining.com
Email: dgzhang@hot-mining.com
Tel: +86 28 8331 1885

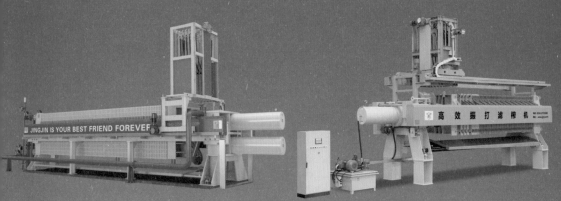

The company
INTRODUCTION

Weihai Haiwang cyclone Co., Ltd. is the national leading and world class manufacturer of cyclone. With 30 years' experience and technical advantages in cyclone classifying and heavy medium separating field, the company can provide high efficient, energy saving and environmental friendly one-stop solution for the R&D, installation, commissioning and technical service of hydrocyclone, heavy medium cyclone, fluidized bed separator and spiral separator, etc.

Haiwang Product Range for Coal Preparation Industry

Our clients include large coal mining groups like Shenhua Group, China Coal, Datong Coal Mine Group, Shanxi Coking Coal Group, Inner Mongolia Yitai Group, Jizhong Energy Group, Yankuang Group and international large coal preparation plants like South Africa Greenside colliery of Anglo Thermal Coal, etc. Also we have agencies and offices in Australia, Russia and South Africa, etc., which can provide localized technical service for global users.

FX hydrocyclone

FZJ two-product heavy medium cyclone with pressured feeding

YTMC three-product heavy medium cyclone with pressured feeding

WTMC three-product heavy medium cyclone with non-pressured feeding

LXA spiral separator for coal

FBS fluidized bed separator

Add: NO.95 Huihe Road, Weihai City, Shandong, China, 264204   Tel: +86-631-5781196   +86-631-5789459
Fax:+86-631-5621557   E-mail: info@wh-hw.com / weihaihw@163.com   Http:// www.wh-hw.com

Line of Sight
Radio Remote Control System

To avoid the danger and improve efficiency in the underground mining process, Alpha applies Radio Remote control system to mine equipment, such as LHDs (Underground Loader), Roadheader, Drilling Rig, Drill Jumbo, Scaling Jumbo, etc. The control system allows equipment drivers can operate machines at a distance (Less than 100m). To create a safer and more comfortable working environment for operators, and achieve efficient mining.

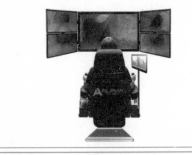

Tele Remote Control System

Alpha Tele Remote Control System allows LHDs drivers to operate in the control centre. Through wireless signal transmission, drivers control remote console to realize all operation of LHDs. And the on-site video data is transmitted to control center through Wireless Mesh Networks, realizing real-time monitoring and operation.

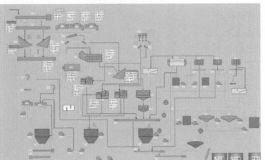

Device Status Wireless Monitoring System of Coal Preparation Plant/Mineral Processing Plant

Wireless monitoring system is mainly used for conventional vibration and temperature measurement of mechanical rotating equipment. It uses built-in acceleration transducer to measure vibration signals in two directions, and thermal resistance temperature sensors for temperature measurement., improving the continuous operation cycle of equipment and reducing the time and cost of shutdown maintenance.

The Miner Intelligent Helmet

Alpha Brain Wave(α wave): Fatigue monitoring, to avoid the first-line miners or operators accident caused by fatigue. **Blood Oxygen Content:** Advance warning of gas inhalation in Coal Mine. **Heart Rate:** Real-time monitoring miners body characteristics, for easy emergency treatment and rescue.

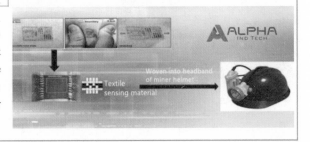

Contact us: Kyle lee

E-mail: kyle.lee@alpha-technology.com.au

Tel/whatsapp: +86 15756875803

Benjamin Yang

benjamin.yang@alpha-technology.com.au

+ 86 18669037219

Manual Knife-shaped Gate Valve

U-shaped seal structure, strong sealing reliability, short in length, light in wight and easy to install. The valve and stem are made of stainless steel to prevent corrosion caused by sealing leakage and durable in use.The guiding head on the stem and body makes the valve plate move correctly, and the extrusion block ensures that the plate is sealed effectively.

Pneumatic Butterfly Valve

With simple and compact construction, it is lightweight and easy to transport, install and dismount. Open/ close quickly in 90° with small torque and operation good texture. Excellent sealing performance with no leakage and durable in use. Through selecting different parts' materials it is applicable to a variety of media.

Industry Application:Coal Washing Plant,Thermal Power Plant,Mineral Processing Plant,Cement Plant

Ceramic Knife Gate Valve

Wear-resistant ceramic knife gate valves are suitable for high hardness particles, soft particles but also corrosive media pipeline to open/close. The valve has a very high wear resistance, corrosion resistance, erosion resistance, and good insulation, thermal expansion.Way of actuation: manual, gear, electric , electronically controlled hydraulic etc.

General Distributor of International Market:
Mine Boss Exploration Mining Holding Co Limited
Want to be the Exclusive Agent in your country?

Contact Us
Email: Sophie.guan@mineboss.cc
Whatsapp/Mobile: +86 1588 8212 8010
Factory Address：Tianjin Jinnan district Beizhakou development zone

CHINA COAL MINING

COAL WASHING PRACTICES

Heng Huang（黄恒）著

CHINA COAL MINING AND COAL WASHING PRACTICES/ Heng Huang-Editor; Nengjun Yu, Yuxiang Zhang-Associate Author. — Hong Kong: Dazhong Publishing House, January 2018

ISBN 978-988-78608-5-3

Ⅰ.①CHINA… Ⅱ.①Huang… ②Yu… ③Zhang… Ⅲ.①Management of coal mining operation—mineral engineering Ⅳ.①TD82-9

CHINA COAL MINING AND COAL WASHING PRACTICES

——————————————————————

Chief Author: Heng Huang
Associate Author: Nengjun Yu, Yuxiang Zhang
Responsible Author: Xuqing Tian

Publishing and issuing: Dazhong Publishing House
Address: ROOM 1607 16/F KOWLOON BUILDING 555 NATHAN ROAD MONGKOK
Printing: Guangzhou DeJia color printing Limited Co.
Website: www.xjcbs.com
E-mail: dzcb@xjcbs.com

Specifications: 16 folio, 27.25 pages
Revision: First edition of January 2018
Impression: First printing in January 2018
Book number: ISBN 978-988-78608-5-3
Price: $ 78

——————————————————————

China Coal Industry Brief

Comprehensive understanding the China Coal Industry with ONE Handbook

Preface

China has maintained a consecutively rapid growth in economy in recent years. However, our previous development has been achieved at the price of sacrificing the environment. As a strategic resource for industrial development, coal performs an indispensable role in China. Reasonable exploitation and utilization of coal, development of clean coal technology and coal chemistry have become hot points in coal industry, which directly determine whether we can firstly accomplish the sustainable development and utilization of coal resource or not, as well as determine the influence of coal on environment in China. The realization of long-term strategic goal of the whole sustainable development in China bases on the sustainable development of coal and fundamental industry of this sort.

This book provides a valuable update on current coal mining practice throughout China, addressing a wide range of subjects including history, exploration; mine planning, safety, coal preparation and marketing. It also covers a number of new topics, reflecting more recent developments in the China coal mining industry.

China coal industry is famous for its "high discharge, big pollution and dangerous as well as low efficiency". As for either utilization of coalbed methane or safety and production efficiency of mine, China is far behind the developed countries, such as Germany, Australia, America, etc. Although world- class equipment and technology have been widely applied in some leading companies of China coal industry e.g. China Shenhua Group, Datong Coal Mine Group, China Coal, etc. since 1998, the entire China coal industry is still in a relatively backward phase. Thus, it will be a long time to upgrade the overall level of China coal industry. Only in this way will the mission of energy conservation and reduction of pollutant emissions be efficiently fulfilled. The coal industry is in urgent need of enhancement in a great many aspects for the purpose of energy conversation and reduction of pollutant emissions, including the application of environmental-friendly hydraulic support equipment, the effective exploitation and comprehensive utilization of coalbed methane, coal preparation prior to further processing, etc. In this handbook, we will mainly focus on the status quo and development prospect of coal mining and coal preparation industry in China.

The clean coal of coal preparation is characterized by low ash and sulphur content, etc., which the firm guarantee of raw material for various types of further is processing. Consequently, coal preparation is a basic and necessary starting point regardless of clean coal technology or coal chemical industry.

The overview of China coal preparation industry is concretely introduced in this handbook, from major processing technologies and equipment, optimized CAPEX and OPEX, and so on. We sincerely expect that this handbook will be helpful for friends active in China coal preparation field to rapidly expand the networking. Meanwhile, we hope it will provide fellows with much more opportunities for exchange and learning so as to promote the development of China coal preparation industry by our joint efforts.

This is the 3rd edition. Due to my personal time limited, most of data cannot be upgraded, please refer to more official data for references.

From this handbook, you can also have brief understanding of the current status and trends of coal mining and preparation technologies in China.

I really appreciate HOT colleagues, and engineers, mining & CHPP managers and senior consultants from China coal industry for the effective help in the compilation of this handbook. However, it is inevitable that there will be some mistakes in the handbook and I am sorry for any errors and please contact us if you notice them. Your contribution to the promotion of mutual communication in China coal mining industry will be highly appreciated.

Any contacts or comments are welcome, please contact me.

Yours truly,

(*Steven*) Heng Huang

Competent Person, Member of the Australasian Institute of Mining and Metallurgy

Sept. 20th 2017, Chengdu, China

Co-Authors Brief

Most of co-authors are from Beijing HOT Mining Tech Co Ltd, Techgart (Beijing) Engineering Ltd, Alpha Industrial Technology Pty Ltd (Australia); some of them are our engineering partners for many years. All theauthors are practicing engineers or mining project managers.

Thanks a lot for their entire job on preparing the original paper, translation and real project case studies. I really appreciate to their contribution of this great handbook.

All names are arranged in random order.

Mr. GuoMin Sun, mechanical engineer

Mr. XiangDong Liu, coal mining and mechanical engineer

Mr. YuXiang Zhang, coal preparation engineer

Mr. NengJun Yu, mining engineer, hydrogeologist, coal gas specialist

Mr. YanFeng Xu, coal preparation engineer

Mr. *Camus* DaoGuo Zhang, mechanical engineer

Mr. ChunAn Tang, rock mechanics and rock engineering

Mr. Jundi Zheng, Master of China Coal Preparation Engineering Design

Ms. Shan Liu, senior engineer, process engineer

Mr. *Steven* Heng Huang, mining and mineral process engineer (***Member of AusIMM***)

Mr. *Luke* Ke Jiao, mining engineer (*https://www.linkedin.com/in/luke-jiao*)

Mr. *Jack* ShuangYin Zhou, coal preparation engineer

Mr. Fei Mao, mining engineer, geologist

(***Member of AusIMM***)

Ms. *Serena* Ling Fu, mining engineer, (*https://www.linkedin.com/in/ serena-fu*)

Ms. *Kira* Jing Zhang, coal mining, mineral processing (*https://www.linkedin.com/in/kira-zhang*)

Mr. *Benjamin* Bo Yang, coal mining engineer

Mr. *Kyle* Lee, graduated mining engineer (*https://www.linkedin.com/in/kyle-lee-8a744513a/*)

Mr. *Jason* Aobo Wang, graduated process engineer, editor of this book.

Heng Huang (Member of AusIMM)

Mr.Heng Huang has over 13 years' experience in mining and mineral processing projects. He focuses on mining and mineral processing industry and related business. From 2005 to present, he had finished many large size projects, especially coal handling and preparation plants, and underground coal mining projects. The total coal washing plants' capacity those are designed or delivered by Mr. Huang is about 100 million ton per annual. Heng shows good understanding of mining and mineral processing business and also has wide net-working in this field.

Heng has previously served as a Project Director at Techgart Global, Beijing, China. Techgart Global is an international engineering and construction firm with expertise in turnkey project engineering design, supply, and construction till commissioning of coal preparation plants and material handling systems. Heng was with Techgart from Dec. 2008 to Oct. 2011. Prior to join Techgart, Heng had set up his own business and act as Co-Founder and Vice President (ADSJ Coal Process Engineering Co Ltd). Heng spent more than 13 years focused on project delivery and business development. He has been involved in funding raising for mining projects.

Heng is the Member of The Australasian Institute of Mining and Metallurgy (MAusIMM)

Heng has experience across Australia, Africa and China in strategic leadership through corporate and operational roles, most recently as Director & Board Member of Beijing HOT Mining Tech Co Ltd. Non-Executive Director & Board Member of 9X Minerals LLC.

Mr. Heng Huang warmly welcomes to contact him for technical seminar and consulting about mining and mineral processing projects.

Official Email: hhuang@hot-mining.com

Personal Email: huanghengwolf5@163.com

Linkedin Page: https://www.linkedin.com/in/stevenhenghuang/

All photos, papers, and drawings have authorized to be used in paper and publication by HOT Mining, Techgart, and Alpha.

HOT Mining, www.hot-mining.com

Techgart, www.coalepc.com

Alpha, www.alpha-technology.com.au

Guide for Readers

"_**China Coal Industry Handbook**_" is the first professional handbook of Coal Industry in China. In this book, the author has introduced the current status, development and trends of China coal industry as well as the newly technologies applied to coal mining sector. How the TOP companies help China coal mining industry to approach the world's leading level within 10 years?

Exclusive advantages of this handbook:

1. This handbook will quickly and efficiently help you to understand the technologies and market of China Coal Mining, Coal Preparation and make you a leading figure prior to other similar organizations—No matter you are an equipment manufacturer, or an engineering contractor, or a mining manager, CHPP manager; the key information of coal mining projects and coal preparation plants in this handbook will be a great help with information and client networking management and with the quick and effective establishment of smooth communication with professionals in the area of coal mining and CHPP with the key authors' email;

2. This handbook will quickly and efficiently help you lock up target markets and potential customers—we provide you with specifically basic materials of China coal mining and preparation industry, such as annual mining production, processing capacity and technology, which can tremendously assist you and other specialists to rapidly pick up potential clients really fit for your products or services;

3. This handbook will make you feel more ease in all kinds of activities in China Coal Mining and CHPP Networking—the history and prospect of China Coal Industry and Coal Preparation Industry are carefully analyzed, which will facilitate favorable recognition in the communication with other experts in this field and hugely help you better hold direction of the development of China Coal Mining Industry.

4. This handbook will help you to approach better investment and project development in mining—Additionally, there are also some case studies and guide for mining investment, how to control risk and how to optimize the mine's value by exploration, mining and process? Before or during developing a mining project, what are the crucial factors shall be concerned? How to do a CAPEX or OPEX modelling? With this book, you can know it.

Proper for professionals:

1. Suppliers / Contractors who are active in China coal preparation industry, e.g. equipment and corresponding auxiliaries manufacturers, turn-key project contractor, design companies, consulting service corporations for coal preparation industry, automatic system and equipment manufacturers and those who have serious aspirations to development of China coal preparation industry.

2. Organizations and individuals who desire to enter the area of equipment supply, technology and engineering service in China coal preparation industry.

3. Operation managers in coal mining and washing plants who can better assist fellows through sharing their experience of operation management, equipment maintenance, operation safety and aspects of this sort with this handbook in hand.

Catalogue

16

COPYRIGHT PROTECTION & WAIVER OF LIABILITY STATEMENT

The copyright of "China Coal Industry Handbook" (later called this handbook) belongs to **HOT Mining**. All the contents and information this handbook contains are business confidential and can only be used with the permit by the original author. Recipients should make a confirmation as soon as they receive this handbook and observe provisions as follows:

1) If recipients do not want to refer to any information this handbook contains, please cooperatively protect the safety of personal privacy in it and cannot use private information included to make any form of contact. Once infringed, related individual has the right to bring a lawsuit against you and hold you totally responsible for liability and consequences caused by your improper behaviour and saying and doing. You must agree that the original author has the right of waiver of liability on all possible issues mentioned above before you confirm your purchase;

2) Recipients must not entirely or partly copy, deliver, photocopy, disclose and distribute this handbook without the written consent from the original author;

3) Recipients should treat all the confidential materials supplied by this handbook as what you do to your own company's confidential materials.

This handbook cannot be used to sales quotation, as well as to purchase quotation. Most importantly, it must not be used to infringe personal privacy and business secret of individuals and organizations involved.

Part 1 Summarization for Coal Resources in China

1. Simple Introduction for Coal resources in China

1.1 Key Characteristic of China Coal Industry

• China is relatively abundant of coal, at the time-being, the depth of coal exploitation is about 400~500m, (in some special cases, it is 600m).

• Alongside with the increase of depth, exploitation cost, safety, etc. are very serious problems.

• Generally speaking, the coal seams with depth more than 1000~1500m are not suitable for exploitation. Because of the difference of absorb ability of CO_2 and CH_4, injection of CO_2 to replace CH_4 is a win-win strategy.

• From aspect of CO_2 sequestration, detailed survey, study and analysis of the deep unminable coal seams will be of significant importance.

China is the largest producer and consumer of coal in the world and is the largest user of coal-derived electricity. However, since 2014 coal as a percentage of the energy mix has fallen, declining from 64% in 2015 to 62% in 2016 according to the National Bureau of Statistics.

Domestic coal production has declined even further, dropping 9% year on year in 2016. Further declines in production were announced in July 2016 when the commission in charge of state-owned enterprises, SASAC, ordered companies under its supervision to cut coal mining capacity by 10% in 2 years and by 15% in 5 years1.

China targets aggressive coal capacity cuts to 2020

Please use the sharing tools found via the email icon at the top of articles. Copying articles to share with others is a breach of FT.com T&Cs and Copyright Policy. Email licensing@ft.com to buy additional rights. Subscribers may share up to 10 or 20 articles per month using the gift article service. More information can be found here.

China aims to cut the capacity of its coal mines by 300m tonnes even as production and consumption of the fuel increases, according to the country's top economic planner. Beijing is targeting output of 3.9bn tonnes of coal in 2020, up from 3.75bn tonnes in 2015, said the National Development and Reform Commission, adding that consumption will rise to 4.1bn tonnes from 3.96bn tonnes over the same period. Under the plan, revealed at the end of last week, the NDRC will cut 800m tonnes of "outdated" and inefficient coal capacity while adding 500m tonnes of "advanced" capacity. The reductions will be concentrated among smaller mines in the north-east. Big producers in the western regions, such as Inner Mongolia and Xinjiang, will boost supplies. Surging coal prices were among the biggest surprises in commodity markets during 2016. After China introduced production curbs in April the price of thermal coal, used to generate electricity in power stations, more than doubled, reaching $110 a tonne in Asia as utility companies were forced to import material. International suppliers include BHP Billiton, Glencore

. . . .

1   1 Source from https://en.wikipedia.org/wiki/Coal_in_China#Coal_production

and Rio Tinto. The price of coking coal, a key ingredient in steelmaking, also surged as a consequence of the supply curbs, to more than $300 a tonne, making it the best performing commodity of 2016s. Those gains have faded as Beijing — alarmed by the spike in price — relaxed the controls. High-quality Australian thermal coal is trading around $94 a tonne, while premium hard coking coal has slipped back to $2242.

China has announced a creation of a high-level body to integrate its energy management supervision and policies, functions that are currently dispersed among many government agencies.

The following are basic information about one of its major energy resources--coal, which accounts for about 70 percent of China's energy use.

Coal reserves stood at 1.03 trillion tons as of 2006, which was the world's third-largest amount, and the country's coal deposits are concentrated in the northern and northwestern parts of the country. Shanxi, the largest producing province, contributes a quarter of the nation's total output.

China, the world's leading coal producer and consumer, saw its raw coal output reach 2.52 billion tons in 2007 and consumption that year stood at 2.58 billion tons, according to statistics from the National Bureau of Statistics.

Coal is largely used to generate electricity, produce building materials like cement and glass and produce steel. This latter demand is

· · · · · · · · · · · · · · · · · ·

2   2 Source from https://www.ft.com/content/3d9d0c78-ce7b-11e6-864f-20dcb35cede2

met by coking coal, which constitutes 27 percent of China's total coal reserves.

China mainly imports coal from southeastern Asian nations such as Vietnam and Indonesia, which supplied 76 percent of its total imports in 2007. It also exports coal, mostly to Asian countries: the Republic of Korea (ROK) and Japan took up about 65 percent of its total exports.

But exports have been falling as China takes steps to keep coal home to fuel its fast-growing economy. The government introduced a series of tax changes starting in 2004 to curb coal exports.

Net exports slid to 25 million tons in 2006 from 45.6 million tons in 2005. The figure plunged to 2.15 million tons in 2007, a mere fraction of the 82.9 million tons exported as recently as 2003.

China reported a 20.2 percent decrease in the number of fatalities caused by coal mine accidents in 2007.

The country's safety watchdog said that 3,786 people were killed in coal mine accidents last year.

2007 was the second consecutive year for the country to report a 20-percent fall in coal mine accident fatalities, Li Yizhong, head of the State Administration of Work Safety (SAWS), said at a national work safety meeting in Beijing.

China has been shutting down coal mines with small capacities and pouring more investment into safety facilities to improve the colliery safety record.

Small coal mines, those with annual output capacity of less than 300,000 tons, accounted for one third of all the coal mines in China, but caused two thirds of the total deaths every year, according to sources with the SAWS.

The country has closed 11,155 small coal mines since it began to shut down small collieries in the second half of 2005.

In recent years, mining safety has been a top concern of the government, which imposed stricter supervision and tougher penalties to restrain illegal operations. Many small mines were closed or merged with larger mines.

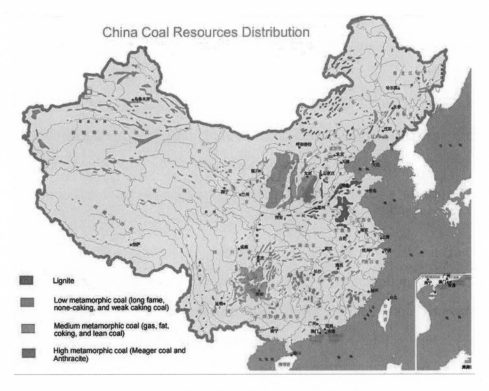

Figure 1.1 China Coal Resources Distribution

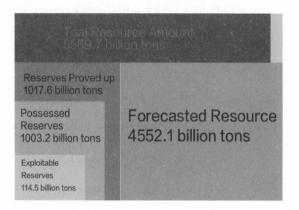

Figure 1.2 Chinese Coal Resources

1.2 The Depth Distribution of Chinese Coal Resource

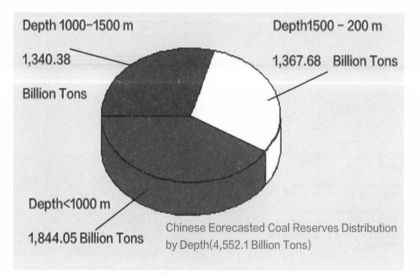

Figure 1.3 The Depth Distribution of Chinese Coal Resource

1.3 Chinese Forecasted Coal Reserves

[1] Shanxi, Inner Mongolia and Hebei = 1675.1 billion tons

[2] Shaanxi, Gansu, Ningxia, Qinghai and Xinjiang = 2359.88 billion tons

[3] Sichuan, Guizhou and Yunnan = 263.86 billion tons

[4] Other provinces = 253.27 billion tons

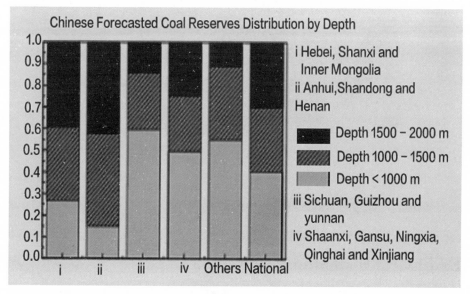

Figure 1.4 Chinese Forecasted Coal Reserves Distribution by Depth

1.4 Chinese Forecasted Coal Reserves (Depth<1000m)

[1] Shanxi, Inner Mongolia and Hebei = 450.46 billion tons

[2] Shaanxi, Gansu, Ningxia, Qinghai and Xinjiang = 1174.21 billion tons

[3] Sichuan, Guizhou and Yunnan = 157.68 billion tons

[4] Other provinces = 61.70 billion tons

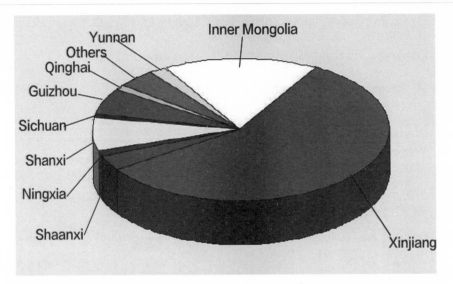

Figure 1.5 Chinese Forecasted Coal Reserves (Depth within 1000m)

1.5 Chinese Coal Mine Exploration Depth

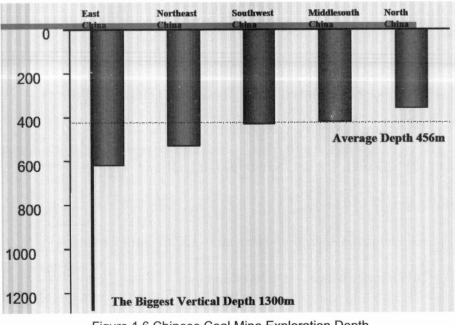

Figure 1.6 Chinese Coal Mine Exploration Depth

1.6 Chinese Coal Production (1949~2004)

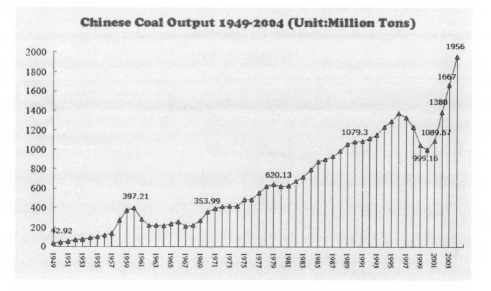

Figure 1.7 Chinese Coal Output 1949~2004

China is the largest coal producer in the world,[12] but as of 2015 falling coal prices resulted in layoffs at coal mines in the northeast.

1.6.1 The composition of coal output of China in 2004

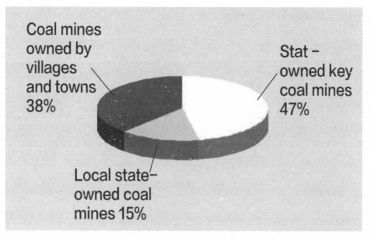

Figure 1.8 The composition of coal output of China in 2004

1.7 Chinese Coal Production (2004-2014)

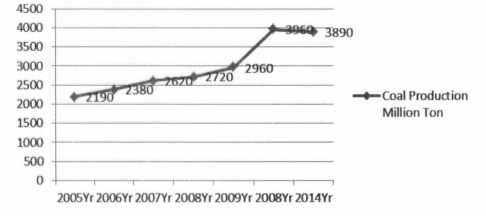

Figure 1.9 The Coal production Million Ton

1.8 China Closed More Than 1,000 Coal Mines in 2016: Energy Bureau[3]

A worker speaks as he loads coal on a truck at a depot near a coal mine from the state-owned Longmay Group on the outskirts of Jixi, in Heilongjiang province, China, October 24, 2015. REUTERS/Jason Lee

BEIJING-China will aim to close more than 1,000 coal mines over this year, with a total production capacity of 60 million tones, as part of its plans to tackle a price-sapping supply glut in the sector, the country's energy regulator said.

. . . .

3   4 Source from David Stanway; Editing by Himani Sarkar, Reuters

China is the world's top coal consumer but demand has been on the wane as economic growth slows and the country shifts away from fossil fuels in order to curb pollution.

In a notice posted on its website on Monday, the National Energy Administration (NEA) said the closures would form part of the plan released earlier this month to shut as much as 500 million tones of surplus production capacity within the next three to five years. (www.nea.gov.cn)

China has a total of 10,760 mines, and 5,600 of them will eventually be required to close under a policy banning those with an annual output capacity of less than 90,000 tones, the China National Coal Association has estimated.

China has promised to stop approving all new coal mine projects for three years in a bid to control capacity. The country produced 3.7 million tones coal last year and has an estimated capacity surplus of 2 billion tonnes per annum.

Last year, the supply overhang dragged down domestic coal prices by a third, but there has been some recovery this year with thermal coal at the port of Qinhuangdao up 2.7 percent at 380 yuan ($58.29) per tone.

Apart from coal, China will also aim to tackle overcapacity in the thermal power sector this year by controlling new builds and cancelling projects in regions with the biggest capacity surpluses, the notice said, citing administration head Nur Bekri.

Utilization rates in the power sector last year fell to their lowest since 1978, with demand failing to keep up with the rapid expansion in capacity.

As part of its power market reforms, China will further promote a scheme allowing suppliers to enter into direct power sales agreements with consumers, and also work to reduce power prices this year, it said.

2. Evolvement and Prospects for Chinese Coal Industry

2.1 Summary

China is the biggest country of coal production and coal consumption in the world (IEA). In 1998, China produced 1250 Mt of raw coal, accounting for 27.5% of total coal production in the world, and holding 71.9% of primary energy in China (SSB). Coal provides 77% of the energy for power generation, 65% of chemical raw material, and more than 50%of commercial civilian energy. The coal industry and relative sectors offer a lot of job opportunities. The economic development and social life in China are based on domestic energy production. Coal occupies more than 90% of proven reserves of nationally conventional energy (SETC). Therefore, the coal industry will still play a dominant role in national economy and social development in a quite long period in the future.

The Chinese coal industry is a large sector set up according to the model of the former Soviet Union, which includes geologic prospecting, coal mine construction, equipment manufacture, coal mine exploitation, coal preparation, products distribution, education, scientific research, design, information service, and non-coal industry.

At the present time, the coal mines in China are divided by the ownership into three kinds: state-owned key coal mines, state-owned local coal mines, and town and village coal mines. In 1998, there were about 72,000 coal mines in the country, including 593 state-owned key coal mines, 1,640 state-owned local coal mines, and 70,000 town and village coal mines. The coal industry has 6.6 million employees, including 4.1 million people in state-owned coal mines. The state-owned key coal mines have 204 billion yuan of originally fixed assets, and the total production value of national coal mines is 146.36 billion yuan, including 89.37 billion yuan in state-owned key coal mines. There are 233 coal preparation plants in state-owned key coal mines with annual production capacity of 346.6 Mt, 36 coal mechanism plants, 25 geologic prospecting teams, 124 coal research institutes and 29 coal design institutes, totaling 10,000 people (SCIB).

The coal supply and demand in China have changed dramatically since 1997, and the coal production dropped from 1397 Mt in 1996 to 1045 Mt in 1999.

The coal industry in China is suffering reform travails and is confronted with a serious predicament. 80% of the state-owned key coal mines had losses of about 3.7 billion yuan in 1999. Coal oversupplied and prices fell. The coal payment in arrears by users had amounted to 33.1 billion yuan by the end of 1999, and 73 coal mines defaulted their staff salaries of 7.5 billion yuan, concerning millions of their employees (Pan, 2000).

At the moment, coal industry is deepening further reform and quick reshuffling, and a favorable turn has appeared recently. From a long view, coal will still be a main engine in economic growth in China, and it will become a competitive, clean and high-efficient energy.

2.2 Coal Resources (SETC, SCIB, SDPC)

The main coal-forming periods in China are different between the North and the South. The coal-forming period of the North was in the late Carboniferous-early Permian Epoch, early-middle Jurassic Epoch, and late Jurassic-early Cretaceous Epoch, while the South's was in the late Permian Epoch. The E'er'duo'si coal mine, which crosses the four provinces of Shanxi, Shaanxi, Inner Mongolia, and Ningxia, is the largest one in the world with more than 100 Gt of coal reserves.

According to the third coal resources prediction and evaluation in the country in 1997, there were 5.57×1012 tons of coal resources within a depth of 2000 m, 2.86×1012 tons within 1000 m were 1.007×1012 tons of coal reserves were proven in different degrees by geologists in 1998, 30% of which were equivalent with the proven amount in place defined by the World Energy Commission, and the rest of exploitable coal reserves 2 were 114.5×109 tons.

Of the coal reserves, soft coal makes up 75%, anthracite holds 12%, and lignite constitutes 13%. 25% of coal is suitable as raw materials for coking and producing gas, 75% for power stations. The average sulphur and ash contents of coal reserves for power stations are 1.15% and 16.84%, respectively (Dai, 1997), as shown in Table 1 and Table 2.

Coal reserves in China are distributed broadly but unevenly. All provinces except Shanghai have coal resources. 90% of national coal resources are distributed to the north of Qinling and Dabieshan, while

91% are distributed to the south of the line of Daxing'an'ling and Xuefengshan. Of total coal reserves Shanxi possesses 25.9%, Inner Mongolia 22.4%, Shaanxi 16.1%, Xinjiang 9.4%, Guizhou 5.2%, Ningxia 3.1% and Anhui 2.4%. The seven provinces and autonomous regions amount to 84.5% of the total.

Of coal reserves in 1998 there are 30% with coal seams less than 300 m deep , 40% with coal seams between 300-600 m, and 20% with coal seams of 600 m-1000 m. The condition of excavating coal is very bad in China. The reserves suitable for open-cast mining are very few, only occupying 7% of the total reserves, and 70% of strip mines are lignite. For the moment, thin seams with thickness less than 1.3 m and seams thicker than 3.5 m have 8% and 43% of the total output, respectively. Coal seams with an inclination of more than 12 degrees have an output of 44% of the total, and 46% of mines are gassy mines (with more than 10 m3/t/d of gas emission). The Ordovician limestone in North China threatens the excavation of its upper coal seams.

2.3 Coal Production

2.3.1 Coal Output and Its Mix

Raw coal output in China was 620.0 Mt in 1980, which leaped to 1116.4 Mt in 1992, ranking first in the world by overwhelming the U.S.A. The output reached the highest of 1397.0 Mt in 1996, and it appeared to increase negatively with output dropping greatly in 1997. The output in 1999 went down to 1045.0 Mt while it was predicted to descend further to 870.0 Mt in 2000.

Owing to closing down a lot of illegal small-scale coal mines, the output of town and village coal mines deceased by 250.0 Mt to 320.2 Mt in 1999, with their proportion of national total coal output falling from 43.1% to 30.6%. The output of state-owned key coal mines dropped by 16.5 Mt to 512.7 Mt, with the proportion rising from 39.9% to 49.1%, while the output of state-owned local coal mines dropped by 16.5 Mt to 512.7 Mt, with the proportion ascending from 17.0% to 20.3% compared with 1997, as shown in Table 3.

Of the raw coal output of 1232.5 Mt in 1998, 44.9% was for coking, and 32.4% for power stations; 18.6% was classified as anthracite and 4.1% was lignite, as shown in Table 4.

Coal can be produced by all the 31 provinces, cities directly under the jurisdiction of the central government, and autonomous regions in the Chinese mainland, except Shanghai and Tianjin. In 1998, the coal output of nine provinces and autonomous regions exceeded 50 Mt, of which Shanxin has an output of 307.2 Mt, Shandong 89.77 Mt, Henan 86.91 Mt, Inner Mongolia 77.23 Mt, Heilongjiang 70.90 Mt, Guizhou 65.61 Mt, Sichuan 56.96 Mt, Liaoning 56.44 Mt, Hebei 56.37 Mt. The outputs of the nine provinces make up 70.4% of the national total. Please see Table 5. In comparison with the highest output in 1996, the output of Shanxi, Sichuan, and Henan dropped greatly in 1998, falling 42.3 Mt, 38.7 Mt, and 20.9 Mt, respectively. This mainly resulted from a lot of small-scale coal mines closing down, the quality of coal, and other factors which also affect the competitiveness.

There were 17 coal mines with output above 10 Mt in 1998, such as Datong in Shanxin; Xishan, Yangquan, Luan, Pingshuo, Jincheng, and Kailuan in Hebei; Pingdingshan in Henan; Yanzhou and Xinwen in Shandong; Hegang in Heilongjiang; Tiefa, Fuxin, and Qitaihe in Liaoning; Huaibei and Huainan in Anhui; as well as Xuzhou in Jiangsu. The output of coal mines leaped; the first five are Datong with 28.65 Mt, Yanzhou with 21.79 Mt, Kailuan with 18.65 Mt, Pingdingshan with 18.47 Mt, and Xishan with 16.12 Mt. Please see Table 6. The main indexes of the Chinese coal industry between 1981 and 1998 can be seen in Table 7.

2.3.2 Coal Mine Extraction

Most Chinese coal mines are excavated with mine development methods whose outputs in 1998 accounted for 96.7% of the national total.

In 1998, there were 593 state-owned key coal mines, 227 of which have annual capacities above 900 kt and constitute 73.7% of the total output, 163 of which fall between 900-300 kt and hold 18.1%, and 203 of which produce less than 300 kt and make up 8.2%. China owns a batch of large-scale coal wells with high advanced mechanization, and there are 11 coal mines with annual output above 4 Mt, of which Dongtan coal mine in Yanzhou and Daliuta coal mine of Shendong Coal Company have outputs exceeding 5 Mt. The Daliuta Coal Mine set up in 1996 adopted coal-cutting equipment from the Joy Company in the U.S.A. In 1999, Daliuta produced about 5.107 Mt of raw coal with a production of 41.5 t per employee. Their target in 2000 is to reach an annual output of 8.4 Mt with 365 employees, producing 83 t per employee, thus getting to the most advanced level in the world (CIRI, 2000(1)).

Almost all state-owned key coal mines employ the long wall mining method. The coal faces mined by the long wall method account for 96% of total mining output. China has possessed the capacity to design and manufacture by itself sets of fully-mechanized long walling equipment suitable for geological conditions with multiple coal seams. In 1998, the mechanization of coal cutting in state-owned coal mines amounted to 73.6%, while full mechanization reached 49.3%. Fully-mechanized mining technology with top-coal-caving for thick seams, created solely by China, has reached the world advanced level. In 1999, there were 23 coal mining teams adopting this technology with annual outputs exceeding 1 Mt. A coal cutting team in the Dongtan coal mine in Yanzhou has created a new record of producing about 5,057,861 tons of raw coal annually (CIRI, 2000(2)).

Most of the local state-owned coal mines adopt mining technologies with partial mechanization. The town and village coal mines usually are extracted manually, and almost half of them employ primal production patterns.

2.3.3 Open-cut Working

At the early period of the 80s, China began to speed up developing open-cast mines, introducing foreign capital and technologies, building up large-scale open-cut mines, including the Antaibao open-cast mine of Pingshuo in Shanxi with an annual designed capacity of about 15 Mt and an investment of $0.64 billion U.S. The Antaibao mine was set up in

1987 in cooperation with the Daoxi Coal Mine Company, a subordinate of the West Oil Company in the U.S.A. In 1991, the West Oil Company retreated from the cooperation.

In 1998, China had 70 open-cast mines with annual capacity of 52.4 Mt and an output of 40.5 Mt, constituting 3.3% of the total raw coal output (Yan et al., 2000). Of these, there were 15 state-owned key coal mines with annual production capacities of 40.8 Mt, an output of 30.8 Mt, and an average stripping ratio of 4.3. The largest open-cast mine is the Antaibao coal mine in Pingshuo, which has an output of 11.81 Mt, 6612 employees, and produced 12.81 t per employee in 1998.

Chinese open-cut mines adopt multiple extraction processes. At the moment, $10m^3$ power shovels with and 108t self-dumping cars can be manufactured by ourselves. $16m^3$and $23m^3$ electric excavators , 154 t selfunloading trucks, and 3100 m3/h buckwheel excavators can be produced in cooperation with foreign companies, with which an open-cast mine with an annual output of 5-10 Mt can be equipped.

In comparison with developing pits, there are some advantages to exploiting opencast mines in China:

-The investment ratio of coal tonnage in a new open-cast mine is 20%-30% lower, and its construction period is 1/4-1/3 shorter than a new open-cast mine;

-The production cost is 1/7 lower;

-Production is one time higher;

-The conditions for safe production are good;

-Coal recovery can reach as much as 95%, compared with about

50% in large-scale mines.

There are 58 Gt of unmined coal reserves and 30 Gt of prospected lignite reserves suitable to open-cast working. These coal resources are mainly located in Inner Mongolia, Shanxi, Yunnan and Xinjiang. During 1996 and 2000, the construction of national open-cut mines reached 27.9 Mt/y, accounting for 25% of national state-owned key mines under construction. It is predicted that the annual output of open-cut mines in China can come up to 80 Mt in the early 21st century and 150 Mt in 2010 (He et al., 1998).

2.3.4 Productivity

The coal industry is one of the departments whose staff is largest. In 1998, the employees in the coal system amounted to about 6.6 million, of which the state-owned key coal mines have 2.64 million people, local state-owned key coal mines 1.46 million and coal mines belonged to TVEs estimated at 2.5 million (Yan etal., 2000).

The working productivities of Chinese coal mines are very low. The coal production only reached an average value of 187 t per capita in 1998;the state-owned key coal mines value was 191 t. The figures amount to 11,890 t in America and 10,800 t in Australia (IEA, 1999). It weakens greatly the comparative advantages of cheap labor and abundant coal reserves.

2. 3.5 Safety in Coal Mines

In the last twenty years, the coal mines in China have improved greatly their safety conditions; however, the mortality rates for accidents in coal mines are the highest in the world.

Between 1980 and 1999, the mortality rates for accidents in coal mines in China descended greatly from 8.17 to 4.54 people/Mt, of which the state-owned coal mines decreased from 4.53 to 0.966 people/Mt as shown in Table 8. But the fatal accidents in town and village coal mines are very serious. In 1999, the figure is up to 10.99 people/Mt, and there are up to 334 accidents with more than 3 deaths per accident and the total death of 2174 people. Of all the accidents gas explosions headed the list with 2075 deaths, accounting for 60% of total accidental deaths (Pan, 2000). The main reasons are that execution of the laws is not strict; small coal mines without basic safety conditions have not been closed down; some accidents have not been disposed of legitimately; safety management is weak; most fatal accidents result from violating regulations in operation; workers in town and village coal mines seldom receive training; and the educational achievement of coal mine workers is low, 50% of whom are illiterate or semiliterate.

On Nov. 7 1992, China enacted "Safety Laws in Mines," which has been in effect since May 1, 1993. The law regulates some issues pertaining to the security guaranties of mines' construction and operation, the safety management, safety supervision and accident disposal, as well as relative law duties in mines' enterprises. Based on it, the coal industry revised "Safety Laws and Regulations in Coal Mines." The State Coal Mine Safety Supervision Bureau, subordinate to the SETC, was established in Jan. 2000 in order to strengthen safety supervision in coal mines. The State Coal Mine Safety Supervision Bureau has set up 19 provincial supervision bureaus, and 68 offices in large-and medium-scale mines, forming a perpendicular management system.

2.3.6 Coal-related Diversified Economic Enterprises

During the mid 1980s, coal mines started to make great efforts to develop diversified economic enterprises in order to improve the economic efficiency and allocate laid-off employees. The government has extended credit of 2 billion yuan with discounted interest for supporting coal-related diversified economic enterprises since 1993. In 1998, the total turnover of coal-related diversified economic enterprises got to 53.8 billion yuan, and their employees amounted to 1.637 million people, including 43.15 billion yuan and 1.414 million people for state-owned key coal mines.

2.4 Coal Preparation (CPUA, Ye, 2000)

Typically only coal for coking and power generation for export was processed before the 90s. China's coal processing capacity has increased considerably, but the ratio of raw-to-processed coal is stagnant. The development of coal preparation has been improved by a competitive coal market and more stringent laws, regulations, and standards in air environmental protection in the recent ten years.

In 1985, the country had 105 coal preparation plants with annual disposal capacity of 144.2 Mt. At the end of 1998, there were 1581 coal preparation plants with a total annual disposal capacity above 494.3 Mt and an

annual disposal capacity above 30 Mt each, including 1492 plants for coking with an annual disposal capacity of 337.1 Mt and 101 plants for power stations with an annual disposal capacity of 157.2 Mt. Of these, there were 233 state-owned key coal preparation plants with an annual disposal capacity of 346.6 Mt, and 1348 local state-owned and town and village coal preparation plants with annual disposal capacity of 147.8 Mt. 3/4 of these plants have been set up since 1995, and most of them are small-scale coking coal preparation plants.

In 1998, there were 310 Mt of raw coal processed, occupying 25.2% of raw coal output, of which 210 Mt were coal for coking, and the cleaned coal output was 140 Mt, exceeding market needs; 100 Mt of coal for power plants was processed, and its share of raw coal was 15%. The coal preparation plants for coking and power plants collectively utilized 2/3 of their capacity. The coal preparation output and share of raw coal of the state-owned key coal preparation plants as shown in Table 9. The raw coal preparation output in 2000 is predicted to be 386 Mt with a share of raw coal of more than 40%.

At the moment, 80% of cleaned coking coal is provided to the metallurgy industry, while the rest is destined for the chemical industry, city gasification, foundries, and for export. The cleaned power coals can mainly be offered for gasification, blast furnace, generation, and export.

With the development of coal preparation, commercial coal quality has been improved enormously. Compared with 1995, the average ash and sulphur contents of cleaned coking coal decreased from 10.03% to 9.85% and from 0.85% to 0.74%, respectively; the average ash and sulphur contents of processed coal for power stations respectively dropped from 12.38% to 12.10% and from 0.74% to 0.64%; and the average ash and sulphur contents of coal for power generation descended respectively from 28% to 26%, and from 1.30% to 1.02% in 1998.

The coal preparation technologies in China have also made obvious progress. In 1998, there were 32 largescale coal preparation plants with annual disposal capacity above 3 Mt and their total capacity of 138.6 Mt.

The coal preparation plants located in Fan Ge Zhuang and Qian Jia Ying in Kailuan and Baodian in Yanzhou are the largest ones for coking with an annual disposal capacity of 4 Mt each. The largest coal preparation plant for power stations is the Antaibao plant in Pingshuo with an annual capacity of 15 Mt.

The main coal preparation method in China is jigging. 59% of coal mines use jigging, 23% employ heavy medium separation of coal, 14% adopt coal floatation, and 4% use other methods. China has had the ability to design and manufacture sets of equipment with annual disposal capacity of 4 Mt for coal preparation plants. At present, the investment cost of new-built coal preparation plants has an annual disposal capacity of 50 yuan per ton.

The share of raw coal washed in China is still on the low side. The main obstacles hindering the development of coal preparation are:

-Lack of incentive policies for coal preparation for power plants;

-The washability of raw coal in China is rather bad; moreover, the coal preparation technology falls behind, so the processed coal output ratio is low (the cleaned coking coal output ratio is 57.8%), its ash content is high, and its sale prices are much higher than raw coal.

-The comparative prices of commercial coal are irrational;

-Some time is still needed to implement rigorously the laws and regulations of air protection and emissions standards.

2.5 Coal Mines' Construction

China has undertaken the largest aggregate coal mine construction project in the world during the last 20 years to meet its increased need for coal. 786 coal mines with a total annual output of 344.5 Mt and each with an annual output of more than 30 kt, were built and put into operation between 1981 and 1998. By the end of 1998, there were 277 coal mines under extended construction, with total annual production capacity of 172.5 Mt. During the same period there were 92 coal preparation plants being set up with a total annual production capacity of 156.0 Mt.

Between 1981 and 1998, the total investment in coal mine construction amounted to 154.95 billion yuan. The investment composition has changed greatly, with more sources of capital. The state investment ratio fell from 69.4% between 1981 and 1985 to 14.3% between 1996 and 1998, while domestic loans went up from 6.1% to 67.8%.

In 1997, the investment per ton of the new coal mines was 500 yuan calculated from construction to put in operation. The coal industry is the one of the most important fields introducing foreign capital into China.

The accumulative foreign capital introduced into Chinese coal mine construction reached $4.18 billion U.S., 78.6% of which are from foreign government loans. There are 23 projects utilizing foreign capital with annual production capacity of 96.4 Mt.

18 key projects in China's coal industry are under construction: five coal mines with a total annual production capacity of 17.2 Mt located in Gujiao, Yangquan, Jincheng, and Liliu in Shanxi; open-cast mines of 12.0 Mt and 5.0 Mt in Zhun'ge'er in Inner Mongolia and Pingzhuang Yuanbaoshan, respectively; three coal mines with 11.1 Mt in Yanzhou and Zhaoteng in Shandong; three mines with 8.8 Mt in Huainan and Huaibei in Anhui; five mines with 7.5 Mt in Pingdingshan, Yongxia and Zhenzhou in Henan; two mines with 2.4 Mt in Shuangyashan and Qitaihe in Heilongjiang; three mines with 3.0 Mt, 1.65 Mt and 1.8 Mt located in Huating in Gansu, Lingwu in Ningxia, and Weixia in Hebei, respectively.

The mine construction technologies in China have made great progress. The freeze sinking, shaft drilling, smooth blasting, bolting, and shotcreting have reached the advanced-world level. Large shaft drilling machines especially for coal mines have been designed by China and have equipped 47 wells with a maximum diameter of 9.3 m and the longest depth of 508 m (CST, 1997).

2.6 Coal Consumption

2.6.1 Coal Demand

With the high-speed development of the economy since the 80s, the coal demand dramatically has gone up. The domestic coal consumption in

1980 amounted to 601.1 Mt, which reached a peak of 1345.9 Mt in 1996 (according to the survey of SPDC and former Coal Industry Department). The figure started to fall to 1310 Mt in 1997. In 1999, it is about 1150 Mt.

The reasons for this large decrease in coal demand are:

-The economic growth speed slowed down. It was 9.6% in 1996; however, in 1999 it descended to 7.1%

-The structure of industry departments, including sectors, enterprises and products has changed. The energy consumption per unit of output value of industry went down an annual average of 6.3%, while the energy consumption per unit of GDP declined 4.5% on average.

-The coal quality improved. According to the survey, the thermo-value of national coal for power stations rose 300 kcal/kg on an average, which cut down the coal need above 70 Mt.

-Imported oil has proliferated. The net imported oil in 1996 was 13.93 Mt, however, it grew to 43.81 Mt in 1999.

-Closing down the small enterprises with high-energy consumption. A batch of small enterprises with high-energy consumption and heavy pollution in the sectors of power, metallurgy, construction materials, petrochemicals, etc. The power industry plans to close down small-scale coal power plants with installed capacity of 30 GW that will be replaced by new large units. It is estimated that the coal can be retrenched 40 Mt yearly.

-The end-users changed to use clean and high-efficiency energy. From 1996 to 1998, the power consumption per capita for living of inhabitants grew from 93.0 kWh to 111.2 kWh, the number of inhabitants in cities and towns using gas increased from 0.138 billion people to 0.16 billion people, and the construction area provided with district heating grew from 734mm2 to 862mm$_2$.

2.6.2 Consumption Mix

The coal consumption mix has made great change. The proportion of coal consumed for power generation in the total coal consumption went up greatly, rising from 18.0% in 1980 to 37.4% in 1997. The coal for transportation dropped from 3.2% to 1.1% because the railway department is increasingly switching from internal-combustion to electric locomotives. The energy use in civil and commercial departments changed to high-quality energy, such as power, gas and heat, directly decreasing coal combustion; their coal consumption fell from 21.5% to 10.6% of the total coal consumed. Please see Table 1-0.

Table 1-0 IEA Breakdown of coal consumption (million short tons)

Use	Anthracite	Coking Coal	Other Bituminous
Residential	0	0	71.7
Industry	24.6	16.3	342.1
Electricity Plants	0	0.2	1305.2
Heat Plants	0	0.19	153.7
Other Transformation[24]	0	359.2	84.0

2.6.3 Coal Trade

In 1998, the inter-provinces trade volume of domestic coal was 847.8 Mt. There are six provinces 7 (autonomous regions) with net output exceeding 10 Mt: 277.55 Mt for Shanxi, 26.85 Mt for Inner Mongolia, 16.46 Mt for Henan, 14.97 Mt for Guizhou, and 10.30 Mt for Heilongjiang and Shaanxi. 10 provinces and cities directly under the jurisdiction of the central government and autonomous regions have more than 10 Mt of net input: 44.31 Mt for Jiangsu, 34.04 Mt for Zhejiang, 31.72 Mt for Liaoning, 30.44 Mt for Shanghai, 29.39 Mt for Hebei, 25.05 Mt for Hubei, 20.75 Mt for Tianjin, 18.20 Mt for Guangdong, 13.31 Mt for Shandong, and 12.57 Mt for Beijing. For the regional distribution of China coal consumption and production see Table 11; for coal transportation see Table 12.

The coal export by China has increased greatly since the middle 1980s (please see Table 13). The export in 1985 was 7.77 Mt, and it grew to 37.41 Mt in 1999. The coal is mainly exported to Japan, South Korea, Hongkong, and Taiwan. Little coal is imported, and only 1.58 Mt of coal in 1998 were from Australia, Russia, and South Africa. Please see Table 11.

The China National Industry Import and Export Corporation is the main agency for coal export in China, and there are other companies which can deal with export, such as the China Mines Import and Export Co., the Shenghua Group Co., and the Coal Import and Export Co. in Shanxi province.

2.7 Coal and Environment

The production and utilization of coal deteriorate the environment, which has become the main concern in China.

2.7.1 The Effect of Coal Production and Utilization on Health and the Environment

The effects of by coal production include:

Subsidence. The subsidence of land is about 30 ha whenever mining one million tons of coal. Up to now, the total subsidence acreage exceeds 600,000 ha, 50% of which is fertile land. At the moment, the reclamation ratio of state-owned coal mines is 13%, and the ratio for mined-out area of opencast mines is 10%.

Coal Refuse. About 130 Mt of gangue will be discharged, piling up to 3300 Mt, and occupying the lands area of 17,000 ha. Of more than 1500 gangue mountains, 125 are in spontaneous combustion. At the present, the national utilization of gangue is 300 Mt, 30% of which is for power generation, 25% for construction materials, 20% for constructing roads, and 23% for filling materials of mines.

Methane from Coal Seams. In 1998, the methane emissions from national coal mines totaled about 8 billion cubic meters. The effects on the environment made by coal utilization:

The hazards of indoor pollution to health. In 1998, 78% of Chinese inhabitants still used coal and biomass for cooking and heating, which leads to indoor air pollution and undermines people's health. Its hazards can be mentioned in the same breath with smoking. In villages, air pollution indoors brings about a high proportion of diseases in the respiratory system. In 1995, the mortality rate of village inhabitants caused by respiratory disease was as high as 169.4 people in every 100,000, the leading cause of death.

Air pollution in cities. Urban pollution in China is typically caused by soot. In 1995, the national SO_2 emissions reached 23.70 Mt, and it reduced to 20.90 Mt in 1998, 85% of which were from coal combustion. SO_2 emissions dropped further to 18.58 Mt in 1999. The national area covered by acid rain has burgeoned to over 1/3 of the state's lands. The economic losses caused by acid rain reach 110 billion yuan annually.

CO_2 emissions. China has become the second largest country of CO_2 emission in the world. 85% of CO_2 comes from coal combustion. In 1996, CO_2 emission from coal combustion in China occupied 29% of the world total. In the last years, coal consumption in China abated greatly, subsequently, CO_2 emission lessened. The CO_2 emission from coal combustion in 1999 is estimated to fall to 120 Mt-C compared with 1996, which contributed to reduced emissions of GHGs.

2.7.2 Environmental Laws and Regulations

The environmental regulations concerning coal in China mainly are: Air Pollution Control (1987, revised in 1995, 2000), Water Pollution Control (1984), Solid Rubbish Environment Control (1995), Land Management Law (1986, revised in 1988, 1998), Mineral Resources

Laws (1986, revised in 1996), Mines' Security Laws (1992), Regulations of Land Reclamation (1988). Of these, the most effective law on coal industry is the air pollution control law. For the emissions standards of coal power plants see Table 14. In 1998, pollution control methods in acid rain-and SO_2-control areas in China started to be executed:

New mines with sulphur content above 3% are forbidden; the exiting mines are restricted to produce and requested to close down.

The sulphur content of coal used in cities must comply with government regulations. Beijing has stipulated that the cities and their suburbs are prohibited from using coal with sulphur content above 0.5% and gas content exceeding 10% (except coal for the chemical industry, metallurgy, and power generation) since Aug. 1998.

New coal power plants are prohibited in large and medium cities and their suburbs, except IGCC plants that produce power by heat.

New and rebuilt power plants with sulphur contents exceeding 1% must be equipped with

desulphuration facilities. On April 29, 2000, China promulgated the second revised version of Air Pollution Control, which has been put in practice since Sep.1, 2000. The Law stipulates:

Carrying out the total control. Confirming the control area of air pollutant emissions and key cities carrying out air pollution control. Checking and ratifying the air pollutant emissions of enterprises and institutions in the control area, and granting emission permits.

Carrying out levying fees for air pollutant emissions.Restricting exploitation of coal mines with high sulphur and gas content.

Encouraging the development and promotion of CCTs. The new and rebuilt power plants and other large and medium enterprises with SO_2 emissions above the emission standard or the total control indexes must be equipped with desulphuration facilities, or take other control methods.

Implementing the law will change the regional distribution of coal production. Those coal mines producing high-sulphur-content coal will be closed down, while the mines with low-sulphur-coal will increase their production. This will lead to improvements in the development of the clean coal technology, such as coal preparation, etc., to raise the coal utilization, to reduce the coal demand, and to create conditions for applying market tools such as emissions rights trading.

China has started to levy an SO_2 emission fee according to the standards of about 200 yuan per ton of SO_2 emissions in the two provinces of Guangzhou and Guizhou, Chongqing, Yibin, Nanning, Guilin, Liuzhou, Changsha, Hangzhou, Qingdao, and Yichang since 1992. From March 1,2000, the SO_2 emission fee will be charged by 1200 yuan per ton of SO_2 emission. Levying a high SO_2 emission fee is one of the important measures for transferring the environmental costs into internalized costs. It will weaken the competitiveness of coal while strengthening the competitiveness of clean energy.

2.8 Reform and Reshuffle

Like Eastern Europe and Russia, the reform of the Chinese coal industry relatively lags behind other sectors because the coal industry is a typical symbol of a traditional planned economy, which is called "the latest fortress" of the old system. So the reform is very difficult and needs to take great venture.

In comparison with the countries in the period of transformation, the reform moves of the Chinese coal industry shares many common grounds with them in: opening coal prices, gradually abolishing loss subsidies, withdrawing the governmental institutes managing the coal industry, closing down enterprises with losses, pushing forward shareholding reform and reshuffling, etc. The reforms in China distinct from others are (to begin with) encouraging rural collectives and individuals to open mines.

2.8.1 Encouraging the Development of Town and Village Coal Mines

The town and village coal mines in China include those collective and private coal mines opened by towns and villages, the collective ones opened by the state-owned coal mines, and others (such as the ones by light industry).

The town and village coal mines are the combinations of the rural economic reform with our special situations, which mainly result from broad distribution of coal resources, the transfer of large quantities of rural surplus labor, and the strong desire to get rid of poverty.

In April 1983, the State Council stipulated "8 measures speeding up the development of small-scale coal mines," which inspired rural collectives and individuals to open mines. The town and village coal mines have been growing swiftly, their outputs in 1985 reached 283.2 Mt, increasing 113.1 Mt over the output in 1983. The highest level of

637.7 Mt was reached in 1996, which went up 4-fold compared with the output in 1980, occupying 45.6% of the national total raw coal output and amounting to 34.6% of national total output of primary energy. The newly augmenting coal output was totally produced by town and village coal mines during 1991 and 1995.

60% of the coal produced by town and village coal mines offers supply for local consumption and 40% for sale in other places outside of the county, of which 20% was transported outside of the province which amounts to 1/4 of national inter-provinces coal output. The town and village coal mines brought about the development of rural construction materials, power industry, metallurgy, mechanism, chemical industry, food industry, transportation, and services. The output values of these sectors constitute 30% of the national total village industry values, which offer job opportunities for more than 20 million rural surplus laborers, make the remote villages break away from poverty and well-off, and provide a large amount of capital for local agricultural development.

The town and village coal mines have made a great contribution to improving the development of agriculture and social and economic development of the countryside, to alleviating the country's financial burden, to easing up the intensive energy supply, to ameliorating the pattern of coal industry, and to recycling coal reserves abandoned and unable to be exploited by large coal mines (this part of coal reserves almost occupying 30% of the outputs of town and village coal mines). They provide beneficial inspiration for the market economic system set up by the state-owned coal mines.

The main obstacles existing in town and village coal mines are: mining illegally and randomly, weak management, high casualties and mortality, and serious waste of resources. In order to facilitate their sound development and strengthen the sector management, the State Council promulgated "the management ordinances of town and village coal mines" in Dec. 1994.

2.8.2 Coal Price

The reform of coal prices in China has gone through a long and tortuous process. In 1992, the government decided to open the injunctive coal prices of the state-owned key coal mines, meanwhile abolishing the loss subsidies. By July 1994, all prices, except the coal for power generation, had been opened. The government still controls the coal allocation and prices for power generation of the state-owned coal mines. When the coal prices are lower than market prices the government will offer some subsidies.

Opening the prices is one of the important reforms in the Chinese energy department, which plays an important role in pushing the market reform of the coal industry. However, coal prices do not reflect the whole supply cost; together with the market's continuous weakening, the coal selling prices of most stateowned coal mines can not compensate their production cost.

The tax reform in 1994 had a great impact on coal price and coal operation. First of all, a product tax of 3% was changed into a value-added tax of 13% (the standard tax ratio is 17%), which caused coal prices (excluding the taxes) relatively to decrease, and lessened the coal revenue. So the government returns a certain ration to coal mines considering the added taxes levied on coal, and makes up the losses of key stateowned coal mines as a form of subsidies.

Secondly, the reform of the resources tax and compensating royalty. The new resources tax is trying to regulate the incomes produced by different levels of resources, to spur the rational development of resources, and to raise prices. The coal resources tax ratios are 0.3-5.0 yuan/t, the resources compensating royalty is levied at 1% of products' sales. The resources tax is levied according to output. In fact, it does not react on regulating the revenues caused by different levels of resources and heightening the coal resources' recovery rate; in reverse, it will place a heavier burden on coal mines.

The outstanding problem existing in coal prices is the very high expenditure of intermediate links. The various fees and added prices with different items levied by circulating process and local government makes the delivery prices far higher than their ex-factory prices. In June 1996, the ex-factory price of high-quality coal for the power station in Datong in Shanxi was 172 yuan/t, the price arriving at Shanghai Port via Qinghuandao Port amounts to 303 yuan/t, and the delivery price of users is much higher.

The government will also levy the railway construction fund in addition to the coal transporting fee levied by the railway department. In 1998, the fund paid by coal mines reached as high as 11.7 billion yuan, most of which was paid by the state-owned key coal mines in midwest areas.

In Aug. 1998, the average price of high-quality coal for power stations was 267 yuan/t; it dropped to 240 yuan/t in Aug. 1999 and increased again to 250 yuan/t in Feb. 2000.

2.8.3 The Reform of Government Institutions

The Coal Industry Department was withdrawn and reshuffled to the State Coal Industry Bureau under the leadership of SDPC during the reforming of central government institutions in May 1998. The bureau's management functions changed fundamentally: it is no longer in possession of or directly manages the stateowned key coal mines. It mainly takes charge of making the sector's planning, policies, laws and regulations, and implementing the sector's management. The staff was cut by 3/4.

There were 94 state-owned key coal mines and 206 enterprises and institutions wholly handed over to provincial government management from July 24 to Aug. 28 1998.

2.8.4 The Reform of the State-owned Key Coal Mines

The reform of the state-owned key coal mines is a fight of assaulting fortified positions in reforming the Chinese coal industry.

In 1992, "Enterprises Laws" started to be implemented, which elementarily confirms the enterprises' law status.

In 1995, the pilots of the modernized enterprises' system started to be set up. The Yanzhou Mineral Bureau is one of the 100 pilots; others demonstrated by the Coal Department are the Xingtai, Zhengzhou, Panjiang, Pingdingshan, and Pingshuo coal mines.

In 1997, 32 state-owned key coal mines reshuffled and set up companies. The coal mines of Yanzhou, Datong, Pingdingshan and Kainuan demonstrated enterprise groups and shareholding reform and going into the stock market.

In general, the endeavor of setting up a modernized enterprise management system in state-owned key coal mines has just started, and there is still a long way to go.

At the same time, the state-owned key coal mines implement to reduce staff and improve efficiency and strengthen competitiveness. The state-owned key coal mines cut down 1 million people during 1992 and 1999. The laid-off people went to service centers to obtain employment again. They were paid for basic life fees according the local standards, were organized to take part in training preparations for getting jobs again, and sought job opportunities through various channels. The central finance, unemployment insurance, and the enterprises-with-losses accounted for 1/3 of the life fees of laid-off people. If the two latter were not offered, the central finance would represent all the burden.

The state-owned key coal mines started to be bankrupted from 1999. This is a fateful step in the reform and reshuffling of the Chinese coal industry. The Benxi Coal Mine Company in Liaoning, the Longfeng Mine in Fushun, and 4 mines in Jixi in Heilongjiang declared bankruptcy in succession.

Of the state-owned coal mines, there are more than 120 with exhausted resources, serious losses, high sulphur and ash contents, and no market. Their total production capacity is 90 Mt annually. In 1998, they produced 50 Mt of coal with a loss of 3.5 billion yuan, occupying 88% of the total losses. More coal mines will be bankrupted in the next years.

Staff of the enterprises in bankruptcy will be paid 3 times the enterprises' average salaries for the previous half-year in the cities that they live for their rearrangement allowances. The bankruptcy fee will come from the prices of land used, assets sold off, and loss subsidies, and the insufficient parts are assisted by central finance.

2.8.5 Closing Down Illegal Small-scale Coal Mines

Market coal prices started to increase, and the development of the town and village coal mines was uncontrollable after the State Council decided to open the coal prices in 1993. The coal output of town and village coal mines in 1996 went up dramatically 210 Mt over the output in 1992. Coal was seriously oversupplied, and the state-owned coal mines fell into an unprecedented predicament. In Nov. 1998, the State Council decided to close down 25,800 small coal mines with illegal mining and irrational layout until the end of 1999, and the decision has reduced the output by 250 Mt. The coal mines with irrational layout are those that are legally exploited in the scope of the state-owned large coal fields and produce coal with high sulphur and ash content. The country has closed down 33,220 small coal mines, decreasing output by 300 Mt as of May 15, 1995. The number of town and village coal mines was reduced from

70,000 at the beginning of 1998 to 38,000 at the end of 1999. Meanwhile the output abated from 570.4 Mt in 1997 to 320.2 Mt in 1999, and the proportion in the total output declined from 30.6% to 43.1%. 18,900 coal mines are planned to close down, cutting down output by 120 Mt.

Closing down coal mines and cutting down their production have obviously meliorated the industrial structure, and the social stocks of coal decreased by 200 Mt to 154 Mt in May 2000, while coal prices stopped falling and began to ascend again.

On the other hand, some newly appearing problems, which result from implementing administration means, cannot be neglected. The first is the issue of supporting local governments, whose revenues are mainly from these small coal mines; the second is the compensation issues concerning closing down the legal small coal mines; the third is the social issues, such as a lot of people losing their jobs the possible debt entanglements resulting from closing down the mines set up by raising money, etc.

2.9 Prospects

2.9.1 The Challenges Facing with Chinese Industry Coal Industry

Competitiveness. Coal is confronted with challenges from competitive clean energy sources in the domestic market such as hydropower, natural gas, etc. and from imported coal. In international markets, the competitiveness of exporting coal is gradually weakening, and now exporting coal seldom makes earnings and even is in losses.

Pressure from the environment. The environmental laws and

regulations are becoming more and more stringent, which has become the pivotal factor restricting expansion of coal production and utilization.

Reform and reshuffling. There exists a series of hindrances in reforming the state-owned coal mines and closing down the mines with losses. The closed small coal mines may see a revival.

2.9.2 Future Coal Mines

In the predicted future, coal is still the main energy source in China, but its importance will relatively descend. It is newly predicted by experts that national coal demand in 2010 will be about 140 Mt, equivalent with the original planned output in 2000, which is completely unexpected. The coal proportion in primary energy demand will come down to about 60% in 2010. The demand for coal will be about 1800-2000 Mt in 2020, and the proportion in primary energy demand will fall to below 60%.

From a long view, the upper limits of coal supply in China will be 2700 Mt in 2050, and coal will become the clean and highly efficient energy source. 70% of coal can be provided for power generation, and the compound liquid fuels produced by coal will probably exceed 100 Mt.

2.9.3 Clean Coal Technologies

It is unavoidable that coal consumption in China will increase within 20-30 years. Hence, clean coal is the future of Chinese energy. Please see Table 15 about the progress of CCTs in China.

2.9.4 Coal Bed Methane

CBM resources are estimated to be 30-50 trillion cubic meters within the seam depth of 2000 m. The China United Coal Bed Methane Corporation (CUCBM) was established in May 1996 and planned to produce 10 billion cubic meters of CBM. The corporation actively develops international co-operation projects adopting the model of sharing output through different quotients. At the moment, the corporation has signed outputsharing contracts with Texaco, ARCO and Philips in the U.S.A. to exploit resources in Huaibei, in Anhui, and in Shanxi in cooperation with the CBM. The cooperation area totals 11,000 km$_2$ with predicted reserves above 500 billion cubic meters. The CBM in Huaibei has been already tried to extract, and its annual output will amount to 0.5 billion cubic meters. At the same time, CUCBM is prospecting CBM in Qinshui basin in Shanxi and in three rivers and middle parts of Liaoning, etc by themselves.

Table 1-1 The distribution of coal resources with sulphur contents

Coal classifications	Average sulphur content (%)	The proportion of various coal classifications (%)					
		Coal with very low sulphur content (0.5%)	Coal with low sulphur content (0.5%-1.5%)	Coal below the middle sulphur content (1.0%-1.5%)	Coal with middle sulphur content (1.5%-2.0%)	Coal beyond the middle sulphur content (2.0%-3.0%)	Coal with high and very high sulphur content (3.0%)
The national total	1.10	48.60	14.85	9.30	5.91	7.86	8.54
For power station	1.15	39.35	16.46	16.68	9.49	7.65	7.05
For coking	1.03	55.16	13.71	4.18	3.29	8.05	9.62
North China	1.03	42.99	14.40	16.94	10.74	8.88	3.57
Northeast	0.47	51.66	14.04	19.68	1.92	2.05	0.00
East China	1.08	46.67	31.14	3.70	3.20	4.72	9.21
Middle South	1.17	65.20	12.42	7.66	2.34	5.50	6.71
Southwest	2.43	13.22	10.71	7.52	2.68	17.40	43.61
Northwest	1.07	66.23	6.20	2.50	4.01	9.31	9.98

Table 1-2 The distribution of commercial coal with sulphur contents

Coal classifications	Average sulphur content (%)	The proportion of various coal classifications (%)					
		Coal with very low sulphur content	Coal with low sulphur content	Coal below the middle sulphur content	Coal with middle sulphur content	Coal beyond the middle sulphur content	Coal with high and very high sulphur content
The national total	1.08	43.48	18.55	12.80	6.70	6.98	5.82
For power station	1.00	42.13	21.97	15.04	10.30	3.00	4.44
For coking	1.10	45.10	16.63	10.71	3.90	9.69	7.44
North China	0.92	39.14	23.66	19.30	9.85	3.25	1.80
Northeast	0.54	50.68	16.61	3.29	2.15	3.87	0.95
East China	1.12	45.79	20.12	13.37	5.34	5.34	9.89
Middle South	1.18	61.99	11.08	10.07	4.83	7.58	4.44
Southwest	2.13	23.87	10.14	6.77	5.33	14.58	38.66
Northwest	1.42	30.21	12.66	14.22	9.21	25.13	5.75

Table 1-3 The raw coal outputs in enterprise of different ownership in China Unit:Mt

	1979	1980	1985	1990	1995	1996	1997	1998	1999
The national total	635.54	620.13	872.28	1079.88	1292.18	1374.08	1325.25	1232.51	1044.82
The state-owned key coal mines	357.77	344.39	406.26	480.22	482.28	537.25	529.16	503.49	512.71
Local coal mines	277.77	275.74	466.02	599.66	809.90	836.83	790.69	729.02	532.11
Of which:									
Provinces	69.76	66.16	61.95	66.43	57.30	58.81	51.88	48.08	
Special Administrative areas	45.18	42.82	50.92	58.71	62.06	63.81	66.91	62.92	
County	56.52	53.14	69.91	79.95	93.99	99.44	106.88	101.85	
Town and village	106.31	113.62	283.24	346.38	519.63	518.19	486.21	479.23	320.20
Individual				43.31	73.29	96.58	84.21	36.94	
Others				4.88	3.63	-	-	-	

Table 1-4 Raw coal outputs of different varieties Unit: Mt

	Coking coal	Coal for power station	Anthracite	Lignite	The total
1980	308.33	158.53	128.97	24.31	620.15
1985	391.09	266.69	182.28	32.22	872.28
1990	512.77	308.17	212.85	45.51	1079.30
1995	607.49	370.86	264.33	49.50	1292.18
1996	622.77	411.14	285.65	54.52	1374.08
1997	637.56	388.96	241.57	57.17	1325.25
1998	553.87	399.22	228.65	50.17	1232.51

Note: The raw coal outputs published by the State Statistics Bureau are 1361 Mt in1995, 1397 Mt in 1996, 1373 Mt in 1997, and 1250 Mt in 1998.

Source: the State Coal Industry Bureau

Table 1-5 The raw coal output in provinces, the cities directly under theJurisdiction of cen-

tral government, autonomous regions during 1990-1998 Unit: 10,000 tons

	1990	1995	1996	1997	1998
The national total	107930	129218	137408	132525	123251
Beijing	1003	995	1001	980	954
Hebei	6191	7055	7409	6786	5637
Shanxi	28593	33176	34946	33038	30720
Inner Mongolia	4762	6445	7317	7909	7723
Liaoning	5101	5249	6041	5842	5644
Jilin	2610	2379	2576	2410	2123
Heilongjiang	8263	7851	8147	7547	7090
Jiangsu	2408	2549	2606	2478	2481
Zhejiang	137	113	123	115	109
Anhui	3205	4322	4642	4769	4584
Fujian	925	860	1168	782	727
Jiangxi	2027	2333	2438	2064	1981
Shandong	5995	8384	8949	9094	8977
Henan	9080	10181	10780	10028	8691
Hubei	924	1437	1521	1517	1326
Hunan	3371	4953	5093	4023	3811
Guangdong	890	1069	882	840	682
Guangxi	979	1233	1252	1097	997
Hainan	1	1.5	1.6	1.5	
Sichuan	6785	9739	9567	6222	5696
Chongqing				2787	2042
Guizhou	3695	5510	6143	6597	9561
Yunnan	2227	2789	3072	3297	3103
Xizhang	1		1.0	1	
Shaanxi	3327	3957	4613	4958	4447
Gansu	1564	2209	2221	2293	2316
Qinghai	320	228	297	328	323
Ningxia	1443	1447	1616	1699	1583
Xinjiang	2100	2693	2986	3021	2927

Source: the State Coal Industry Bureau

Table 1-6 Large-scare coal mines with output above 10 Mt 1998 in China

No.	Coal Mine	Output (Mt)	The ash content of commercial coal (%)	Staff at the end of the year (thousands of people)	The staff efficiency of raw coal (t/worker)
1	Datong	28.65	11.98	115.81	3.561
2	Yanzhou	21.79	15.89	65.52	8.896
3	Kailuan	18.65	25.00	99.16	2.454
4	Pingdingshan	18.47	24.38	78.48	3.303
5	Shanxi	16.12	15.98	65.26	5.718
6	Huaibei	14.96	21.32	84.44	1.862
7	Tiefa	14.21	30.52	47.53	6.583
8	Huainan	13.15	25.18	95.29	1.744
9	Xuzhou	12.77	21.06	80.21	2.414
10	Hegang	12.49	19.92	67.27	1.289
11	Yangquan	12.30	18.16	55.80	2.993
12	Lu'an	12.19	16.11	26.53	9.163
13	Pingshuo	11.81	17.88	6.61	12.811
14	Xinwen	11.73	19.54	59.64	2.298
15	Fuxin	11.39	22.26	54.03	2.265
16	Jincheng	10.81	15.79	26.73	6.140
17	Qitaihe	10.43	23.41	59.14	1.236

*the state-owned key coal mines
Source: Same as the State Coal Industry Bureau

Table 1-7 The main indexes of Coal industry during 1981-1998 in China

	1981	1990	1995	1996	1997	1998
Raw coal output (Mt)	621.36	1079.88	1292.2	1374.1	1325.2	1232.5
Of which, the state-owned key coal mines	335.05	480.22	482.3	537.3	529.2	503.5
The washed coal output for coking (Mt)	51.45	85.51	81.42	87.79	91.64	80.92
The ash content of commercial coal (%)	21.17	18.96	19.97	20.20	20.49	20.21
The refuse rate of commercial coal (%)	0.46	0.12	0.08	0.10	0.10	0.10
The ash content of washed coal (%)	10.34	10.19	10.03	9.88	9.85	9.75
The mechanized degree of mining coal in state-owned key coal mines (%)	39.77	65.10	71.6	72.0	73.3	73.6
Of which, the full mechanized degree (%)	17.67	33.50	46.7	47.2	48.4	49.3
The staff at the end of year in the coal mines opened by the units above country level (10,000 people)	463.38	546.40	508.82	499.0	487.9	460.9
Of which, the state-owned coal mines	273.12	357.15	330.84	322.3	315.7	262.9
The staff efficiency of raw coal in state-owned coal mines (t/worker)	0.870	1.217	1.780	1.923	2.079	2.18
The pit wood consumption in raw coal production (m³/10,000 tons)	86.80	39.80	30.0	29.4	29.9	27.7
Comprehensive power consumption (kWh/t)	35.68	43.89	54.35	53.47	54.88	56.18

Note: The raw coal outputs published by the State Statistics Bureau are 1361 Mt in1995, 1397 Mt in 1996, 1373 Mt in 1997, and 1250 Mt in 1998.
Source: the State Coal Industry Bureau

Table 1-8 The mortality rate in coal mines accidents in China during 1980-1999 Unit: people/Mt

	1970	1980	1990	1992	1995	1996	1997	1998	1999
The total	8.20	8.17	6.76	5.25	4.85	4.55	4.68	4.67	4.54
State-owned key coal mines	7.11	4.53	1.43	1.01	1.18	1.17	1.448	1.022	0.966
State-owned local coal mines	10.50	10.19	9.06	4.22	4.89	4.02	4.015	3.760	3.458
Town and village coal mines	9.03	16.88	12.07	10.50	8.45	7.70	7.935	8.602	10.990

Table 1-9 The coal preparation output and share of raw coal washed in state-owned key coal preparation plants Unit: Mt

	1980	1985	1990	1995	1996	1997	1998
The total							
Raw coal washed	114.2	142.9	190.9	201.7	212.9	223.4	216.4
Share of raw coal washed (%)	18.4	16.4	17.7	15.61	15.50	16.86	17.56
Coking coal							
Raw coal washed	90.4	107.2	126.8	131.0	135.5	138.1	129.4
Washed coal output	50.8	58.2	67.4	76.4	76.9	80.9	74.9
Productivity (%)	56.16	54.31	53.19	58.33	56.75	58.56	57.83
Coal for power stations							
Raw coal washed	23.40	35.8	64.1	70.7	77.4	85.3	87.0
Washed coal output	20.50	15.7	24.8	55.0	63.0	67.4	66.1
Productivity (%)	85.90	43.81	38.71	77.84	81.31	79.04	76.05

Table 1-10 Coal Consumption in different departments

	1980	1985	1990	1995	1996	1997
Power generation (Mt)	109.7	164.4	272.0	444.4	488.1	489.8
%	18.0	20.1	25.8	34.2	36.3	37.8
Providing heat for power stations (Mt)	16.8	14.6	30.0	58.9	63.7	62.5
%	2.8	1.8	2.8	4.5	4.7	4.7
Coking (Mt)	66.8	73.0	107.0	184.0	184.6	193.0
%	10.9	8.9	10.1	14.2	13.7	14.7
Agriculture (Mt)	15.5	22.1	21.0	18.6	19.2	19.3
%	2.5	2.7	2.0	1.4	1.4	1.4
Industry (Mt)	250.8	340.2	406.2	415.2	405.4	393.4
%	41.1	41.7	38.5	32.0	30.1	30.0
Transportation (Mt)	19.3	23.1	21.6	13.1	11.8	14.3
%	3.2	2.8	2.0	1.0	0.9	1.1
Civil and commercial use or other uses (Mt)	131.2	179.4	197.4	165.0	173.1	138.4
%	21.5	22.0	18.7	12.7	12.9	10.6
The total (Mt)	610.1	816.0	1055.2	1299.2	1354.9	1310.7
%	100.0	100.0	100.0	100.0	100.0	100.0

Note: 1. The total coal consumption during 1995 to 1997 uses the data in the report of the survey and predicted research about national coal consumption written by a research group of SDPC and Coal Industry Department.
2. The coking coal consumption in 1995 is the data surveyed in 1995, which is relatively real. The statistic data before did not include or failed to report coal consumption used by coking in indigenous methods which brought about the data low.
3. Civil coal consumption is low, and it was 135 Mt in 1995. The yearly consumption exceeds 200 Mt according to the report of Economy Daily in 4 July, 1996.
Source: the State Statistics Bureau, the report of the survey and predicted research about national coal consumption written by a research group of SDPC and Coal Industry Department in 1999.

Table 1-11 The regional distribution of coal consumption and production in China in 1998

	Consumption	Production
The total (Mt)	1180.0	1232.5
Regional distribution (%)		
North China	21.9	35.6
East China	14.2	12.1
Mid-south	25.3	15.3
South-west	18.4	12.6
North-west	7.6	9.4

Table 1-12 Coal transportation in China during 1990-1998

	1990	1995	1996	1997	1998
Railway transportation					
Coal transportation volume (Mt)	628.7	637.6	720.6	703.45	640.81
The proportion in total goods transportation volume (%)	43.0	42.3	44.6	43.5	41.8
Coal turnover (Mt km)	344640	377718	404847	389365	354208
The proportion in total goods turnover (%)	32.5	29.4	31.3	29.8	28.9
The average transportation distance (km)	548	561	562	554	553
The water carriage directly under the leadership of Transportation Department					
Coal transportation volume (Mt)	78.4	90.7	92.9	85.73	81.19
The proportion in total goods transportation volume (%)	31.2	27.2	27.8	24.7	24.0
Coal turnover (Mt km)	159325	274678	250339	262670	287655
The proportion in total goods turnover (%)	15.1	18.2	17.0	16.2	17.5
The average transportation distance (km)	2032	3028	2696	3064	3543

Table 1-13 The import and export volumes of coal in China during 1980-1999 Unit: Mt

	Export	Import
1980	6.32	1.99
1985	7.77	2.31
1990	17.29	2.00
1995	28.62	1.20
1996	29.03	3.20
1997	30.72	2.00
1998	32.29	1.58
1999	37.41	

Table 1-14 The emission standards of air pollution for coal power plants in China

The names of pollutants	The upper limits (mg/m^3)
TSP	
Town and village	200
Suburbs	500
The old units with rest lift-span above 10 years	600
SO$_2$	
The sulphur content of coal 1.0	2100
The sulphur content of coal 1.0	1200
NO$_x$	
The boiler capacity combusting coal 100t/h	
Releasing sediment in liquid state	1000
Releasing sediment in solid state	650

Note: No requirements for boilers with capacity below 1000 t/h (that is, the units below 300 MW) for the moment.

(The aboves are according to the 3rd National Coal Mines Forecast Files)

3. Coal Mining Condition in China

3.1 China Coal Reserve

As of the end of 2014, China had 62 billion tons of anthracite and 52 billion tons of lignite quality coal. China ranks third in the world in terms of total coal reserves behind the United States and Russia. Most coal reserves are located in the north and north-west of the country, which poses a large logistical problem for supplying electricity to the more heavily populated coastal areas. At current levels of production, China has 30 years worth of reserves. However, others suggest that China has enough coal to sustain its economic growth for a century or more.

3.2 Coal Mine Fires

It is estimated that coal mine fires in China burn about 200 million kg of coal each year. Small illegal fires are frequent in the northern region of Shanxi. Local miners may use abandoned mines for shelter and intentionally set such fires. One study estimates that this translates into 360 million metric tons of carbon dioxide emissions per year, which is not included in the previous emissions figures.

North China's Inner Mongolia Autonomous Region has announced plans to extinguish fires in the region by 2012. Most of these fires were caused by bad mining practices combined with bad weather. 200 million yuan (29.3 million USD) has been budgeted to this effect.

3.3 China Coal Mine Gas[4]

These results in Chinese coal mines being extended to deeper levels. The eastern Chinese, more economical developed, regions have a long history of coal mining and many coal mines have now started deep mining at a depth from 800 to 1500 m. This increase in mining depth, geostresses, pressures, and gas content of the coal seam complicates geologic construction conditions. Lower permeability and softer coal contribute to increasing numbers of coal and gas outburst, and gas explosion, disasters.

More than 95% of the coal mined in China originates from underground operations and some 300 of the Key State-owned coal mines are classified as gassy or prone to outbursts. Outbursts are near instantaneous emissions of gas or sudden movements of coal or rock which can occur unexpectedly when mining. By 2002 there were 193 coal mines with methane drainage systems draining about 1.15 billion m3 of gas of which only 0.5 billion m3 is used. Chinese mines liberated an estimated 14 billion m3 of methane in 2002 from a coal production of 1.39Bt. If, on average, 30% of the gas could be captured in drainage systems, some 4.6 billion m3 of gas is theoretically available each year and hence an additional methane utilisation and mitigation potential of 4.1 billion m3 . The growth potential for CMM utilisation schemes is therefore large. China is the world's largest CMM source awaiting commercial exploitation. Coal production is expected to rise steadily, 1.6Bt being mined in 2004 with a corresponding increase in gas emission.

The coal sector in China has undergone substantial reform to improve efficiency, safety and price stability. Large numbers of small illegal and irrational mines have been closed and returns-to-scale are being achieved by larger mining enterprises formed by merger and acquisition. Initial estimations indicate that CMM emissions could have increased by more than 1 billion m3 as a result of replacing small mine capacity with large longwall operations. This is due to the greater extent of strata disturbance and hence gas release around a longwall compared with the room-andpillar method employed in most small mines. CMM drainage technologies only capture a proportion of the gas released into mine workings. Captures achieved in individual mining panels can typically range from 30 to 80% depending on the drainage technology used, the geology and the mining conditions. Technologies also exist for removing the diluted methane from mine ventilation air (Ventilation

Air Methane or VAM) but these are not yet commercially viable. The potentially drainable CMM resource in China achievable using tried and tested technology is currently so large that treatment of mine ventilation air is not yet warranted. Gas capture and use could be enhanced significantly through improvements in the management of existing technologies and control practices. There is a danger that diversion of attention to attempt commercial use of methane 7 in ventilation air will reduce the drive on improving the capture and control of gas in the mine to ensure safer working conditions.

Part 2 Market Guide for Coal Preparation Engineering in China

1. The Significance of Coal Process (Preparation) for China Coal Industry

1.1 The Coal Preparation and Coal Industry in China

As the biggest coal produce country in the world, China yield 37% coal of the total capacity annual. Coal is the important energy in China, the significance will last for a long time and China energy structure will base on coal at least 50 years. Along with China government and Chinese people pay more and more attention on its environment, the transform of economic growth for its coal industry, spread of the purpose for its coal, the clean coal and other deep process are also achieving better development. Coal preparation industry is the primary base for coal deep process technology, certainly, has achieved great improvement. Please have a look at table 1-1, it's a simple information about the development of China coal preparation industry from 1980s to 2005.

Unit MTA (million tons annual)

Table 1-1 The change of coal preparation quantity in China

	Designed Capacity	Actual Capacity	Percentage of R.O.M Coal
Early in 1980s	111 MTA	117 MTA	18.95%
End of 2005	812 MTA	837MTA	33%

From 2000, the new constructed coal preparation plant (CPP) those capacities above 2.4MTA almost adopted the whole dense medium separation technology. At the end of 2005, the proportion of the coal preparation technologies had changed a lot. The chart 1-1 has given the data.

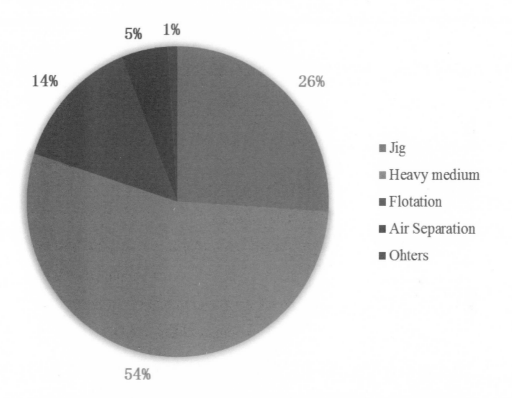

Chart 1-1 The Proportion of Coal Preparation Technologies in China (2005)

The new constructed CPP are also the heavy fabricated steel structure besides the centralized control system. The operation and management efficiency have improved much better.

1.2 The Macro Environment of China Coal Preparation Industry

PEST (Political–Law, Economic, Social, Technological) analysis

for the macro environment of China preparation projects and engineering

services.

Table 1-2 PEST Analysis for China Coal Preparation Industry

Political — Law	Economic	Social	Technological
• In China government, every related ministries and commissions have already issued for enforcement and development plan those related coal preparation industry. *The eleventh five years development plan for coal industry* has pointed out, 'China should do deep process, research clean coal technology, develop coal preparation industry'. • China requires the coal resources to be combined, the small-middle size coal mine should unite together, and construct new coal handling and preparation plants (CHPP) for the new mines. • National and many local governments will invest to set up some new companies those focus on equipments innovation for coal preparation technology. • There are also many advanced policy for high-tech coal preparation companies such as low tax, provide a loan with low interest rate. • Saving energy and reducing pollutant are the most important policy in China now. The coal preparation technology meets the fresh opportunity and challenge in China. • And the new middle-big sized coal mines should have its matched CHPPs by the national policy for coal industry.	• Government supports more R&D funds and many kinds of awards to accelerate the innovation. China is planning to achieve more with coal preparation equipments. • In China, the washed is only 33% of R.O.M Coal. Compares to 60% in USA, 95% in Germany and 75% in Australia, there is still a big gap. High ash and high sulphur coal are the crucial problems those lead the high consumption of energy and awful pollutant. Most of the CHPPs are small capacity, and the byproduct of CHPP has a low usage. • So far there are many old jigging + flotation CHPPs in China. The low efficiency is wasting much clean coal, and the operation cost is still very high besides difficult management and maintenance.	• More investment for coal preparation industry in China, China had already spent 57 billion RMB on coal preparation in the past 'tenth five years'. 'The eleventh five years' plans to wash 50% R.O.M coal. Thus, many local companies are investing more and more to CHPPs. • There are many old CHPPS need to be upgrade every year in China. • 'The eleventh five years' plans to construct many new coal mines those capacity will be 200 million tons totally. During this period, the investment for new construct CHPP is about 16.5 billion RMB. • Many investment companies, power companies and other non-conventional coal companies become coal miners.	• China Government proposed to structure the harmonious society. And the philosophy of respecting human life and health is becoming the main stream social value. Thus, the "Energy Saving & Emission Reduction" of coal industry is getting more and more urgent. • China government is advocating to establish the economy society, and encourage to consume resources in cycle and reasonable way. • The community and plebs are getting more and more comprehension of the negative impact those caused by coal industry such as health and environment. Therefore, to develop the coal preparation for using coal in high efficiency and reasonable way besides upgrading the transportation system are becoming more and more important and being focused.
Political — Law	Economic	Social	Technological

Overall, evidently the coal preparation will be one of the key developing tasks of China coal industry.

2. Simple Analysis for the Whole Prospective Market

2.1 The Whole Market Capacity and Projects Distributing in Five Years

From 2003 to 2006, there average investment for new construction CPP was RMB 3.5 billion annually in China, and the investment doesn't include the upgrades. In 2007, the new construction CPP projects cut down sharply due to the coal resources' development stage and mining projects' pipeline. But according to the market survey, there will be a fresh outburst of new CPP construction projects from 2008 to 2012. Now we had known that there was already near 10 billion investments for new and upgrade CPP projects opened for bidding in 2008, and the investment is stable and follows up their schedules at present. Thus, the financial crisis has little and limited negative inflation impact on China coal preparation industry. Basis on "The China Eleventh Five Yeas Plan for Coal Industry", there will be about 18 billion investments for new CPP projects in five years. And most of them will open for bidding and construction in 2008, 2009 and 2010, some of them prepare to construct between 2011 and 2012. There will be 110 new CPP projects at least, and most of them are planning to have huge capacity that will be above 5 million ton annual even above 10 million annual, the huge CPPs take up about 35% of all the new CPPs.

Among all the programming CPP projects, the capacity and location are in accordance with the coal resources' distributing. Most of the programming CPPs located in the main coal industry bases, such as Inner Mongolia, Shanxi, Shaanxi (the north of Shaanxi), Ningxia, Anhui Province, etc. And most of the new construction and programming CPPs' capacity are 5Mt/a plus, even 10Mt/a plus and 15Mt/a plus. All the places above occupy about 80% of total investments in China.

Additionally, the coal reserves in the Southwest of China (Yunnan, Guizhou, Sichuan and Chongqing) are also abundant. But it is difficult to develop big coal mines here due to its geological and mining conditions. Thus, all the coal mine CPPs' capacity are restricted by those reasons above. Such as the Junlian Mining Zone which across the Luzhou and Yibin City in Sichuan Province, all of this zone's capacity is 15Mt/a, but this mining zone have been divided into several small-middle coal mines due to its mining condition and the not so good relationship of the local investors. Therefore, the new programming CPPs' capacity has been restricted by the coal mines. So far, the biggest programming CPP in this mining zone is 1.8Mt/a. certainly, the coal reserves in Xinjiang and Qinghai are also very abundant, but the mining development is somewhat lag in this stage due to the bad traffic condition.

2.2 Simple Market Prospect for Up-grade Coal Preparation Plants

Because almost all the up-grade CPP projects should be report to every mining group's HQ and apply for investments at the end of every

Chinese traditional year from the CPP, and those programming upgrade projects should get agreement from its HQ, then those projects could be in the queue of the coming new year's investment plan. Thus, it's much difficult to account how many up-grade CPP projects in the coming years. Without doubt, the market foreground of up-grades is the same huge as the new construction CPP market, very good. Firstly, most of the small-middle size CPP those finished before 1995 have meet many operation and maintenance problem now such as the low yield and high ash clean coal due to outdated jigging + flotation technics besides serious environment problem. Secondly, some new CPP those adopted the fabricated steel structure with completed dense medium process and constructed in these years have their unique problem now. Because some wash equipments those imported abroad are not meet the operation conditions and somewhat not suitable for China R.O.M coal's quality, and some of the CPP have the theory problem from designing and engineering stages, therefore, most of the new constructed CPP also need up-grade or reconstruction. Consequently, there will be a huge investment for up-grade CPP in every mining group annually. According to the market data of 2007, the investment for up-grade CPP is about 9 billion RMB in this year. (*And this data doesn't include the up-grade CPP projects those hadn't opened for bidding.*)

2.3 Capacity Analysis for Operation Services Market

The fabricated steel structure CPP is still considered fangle in China. And the coal mining companies are total lack of management and operation ability in this stage, so it's difficult for them to manage and maintenance the new CPP. Thus, the professional operation service providers come and fast expand their business in this field. They service to coal mining companies with excellent operation and maintenance besides their experiences. Additionally, in recent years, some of HK and mainland companies those are not the conventional coal enterprises invest huge money on middle-big coal mines and the related deep process industries. Due to total lack of the professionals and little experiences, they'd like to invite some professional operation provider to help them manage their coal mines and CPP. So we could see the potential huge market in this field. If you were the professional operation provider, are you ready?

According to the data from three professional operation providers in China, the gross profit of the ten CPP those operated by them had broken RMB 470 million plus only in 2007. It means that almost every CPP could bring about RMB 47 million plus gross profits annually. Do you know how many people work for each CPP? Only 2~4 people is enough for one CPP's daily operation. And they only recruit several professionals in the HQ office such as Beijing, and attract some middle level engineers for CPP operation and the CPP management. It's very huge and easy-earning profit.

Remark: The operation service is a very new business mode in China coal preparation industry. This business mode is only about 3 years' history from the first attempt. There are only 3 foreign companies and 1 domestic company who provide the operations service in mainland. Both the abundant CPP operations experiences and the engineering background are very important and essential, additionally, all the players should know the washing equipments and spare parts well. All the experiences and skills could be equal to the operations demand. So this business mode has its relative high entry rampart. Generally, there are only six companies could provide the CPP operations services in China. It's very hopeful for this fast growing business mode.

3. Simple Guide of the Buyers' Behavior

This is the typical industrial group buyers' market. The potential target clients are all the mining groups or related enterprises. Their purchasing behavior is well known as below.

• Almost every project needs huge investment, and also need the approval from related local governments even should forward the application to national government.

• It's the group decision-making mode, many people and departments will participate in the procedures. It's difficult to handling the networking.

• Of course, almost every key people who in charge of the final decision has his or her unique proper personal purpose. For example, if the CPP project finished and could have very good operations performances, his authority would be enriched very well in his group. As we known, the commission is also very important in China business, but how to deal with it without law problem is the most important task which the foreign companies should learn how to do it in China.

• The engineering and technical services' abilities are the same important as the companies' reputation.

• Back with the CPP EPCM projects, the clients pay equal attention to the advantages of engineering and the integrated bidding price. It's neither the technical oriented nor price oriented market. But most of clients give priority to engineering, and consider the price as secondary standards while they are evaluating the bidding suppliers.

• And during the construction procedures, the players should take environment protection and social benefit into account.

4. Simple Micro Market Environment---the Main EPC/EPCM Players

In recent years, the EPC (Turn-Key Project) construction mode is getting more and more popular in China and it also widely accepted by major clients. And some upgraded CHPP is delivered by EPCM mode. The basic status of the CPP EPCM market is somewhat leaded by foreign engineering companies. Four magnates almost occupied all the middle-big size new CPP EPCM projects, and all of the projects have huge investment and great profit. Most of the domestic engineering companies are playing in relative small and low-end market.

The Disadvantages of This Status:

For foreign companies

Although the foreign companies have successfully introduced

the advanced CPP design, engineering and construction's experience to China, all of them have their fixed and unique mode with special advantages and disadvantages. The competition is the mainstream in this market, thus, they are lack of communication, and the way for learning from others' strong points to offset their own weakness is also closed. Additionally, when the main EPCM and engineering providers collocate or purchase the process equipment, they always rely on their own-manufacture equipment or only buy some import equipment those produced by their partners abroad due to their dealers' contract. But while those import equipment is operating in China CPP, some of them cannot achieve the designed work efficiency, and it restrict to meet the system optimization due to some of the import equipment doesn't match the R.O.M coal quality in China and the limited skills of the CPP workers. All things above have some negative effects on the yielding target and operations management. Finally, the users' benefits have been decreased.

For domestic companies

The local EPCM providers in China mainly came from the local coal related design institutes. And all of them knew little of the advanced design and construction experiences due to total lack of communication and cooperation with foreign companies. And other coal preparation engineering services related fields are similar to EPCM market.

5. Hypothetic Leaders of the Middle-advanced Market in Future

If any company wanted to become the future leaders who provide the engineering and technical services in China coal preparation industry especially in the middle-advanced market, they should adopt the new and practical service mode for China coal industry. And the key engineers should have the experience both in local design institutes and the international engineering service experiences in foreign EPCM companies. Those engineers could understand the local users much better and could communicate with foreign DI and equipments producers much better. Thus, basis on their advanced coal process engineering, technology, projects management experiences and excellent equipments, those future leaders could provide the world-class engineering services the China clients. The future leaders should have some traits as below.

World-class advanced design and engineering services;

More precise and effective project management;

Better quality-price ratio of integrated process system and equipments, the equipments could integrated into the process system with high efficiency and stable operation performances, could help clients to increase their profits;

Excellent services philosophy, much better than the main providers at present. Consider more for clients;

Systematical and timely after sales services, could have the solution for clients while the meet with some operations problem.

This market is crying for the leaders in China, and who will be the future leaders in China? We look forward to see the incoming kings.

Part 3 Practice Papers of China Coal Mining & Coal Preparation Technologies

1. Application of Electrical Haulage Shearer on Working Face of Steeply Inclined & Ultra-low Coal Seam

Abstract: The paper introduced application range , mechanical part , electrical control part , main functions and actual application of MG110/130-TPD model electrical haulage in-web shearer on a working face of ultra-thin coal seam with large inclination .The application showed that the shearer runs stably with good mining effect and improves safety level and efficiency of production of working face .But there are still problems of channeling gangue and irregular running track caused by chain haulage for further research.

Introduction

Sichuan Dazhu Coal Electricity (Group) Co., Ltd., Xiaohezui mine is a ultra-low coal seam. Most of the coal seam thickness is 0.5-0.8m; the angle is 0°-45°. For a long time, the coal mining by blasting, collapse method roof control, retreat to long wall mining, scraper transport, single hydraulic prop, so low degree of mechanization that mining efficiency is not good. In 2006, the mine used MG100-TP type single drum coal shearer and improve the efficiency of coal mining. However, there are some problems in the operation of this type of shearer:

1. With the increase of coal hardness and coal seam inclination, the

shearer will be difficult to work and loading effect becomes poor.

2. No safety brake device that the threat to the safety of production.

3. Have to carry out the machine operation, which is not conducive to the safety of the coal mining machine driver.

In view of these, Sichuan Dazhu Coal Electricity (Group) Co., Ltd. and Liaoyuan Coal Mine Machinery Manufacturing Co., Ltd. developed a new type of MG110/130-TPD model electrical haulage in-web shearer jointly. The application showed that the shearer runs stably with good mining effect and improves safety level and efficiency of production of Xiaohezui coal mine.

1.1 MG110/130-TPD Model Electrical Haulage in-web Shearer

1.1.1 Scope of Application

MG110/130-TPD model electrical haulage in-web shearer can working with scraper conveyor, single hydraulic prop, metal friction prop, roof master, to achieve coal mining and coal loading in the working face of long wall mining. This machine is suitable for coal seams which dip angle is below 35 degrees, the coal seam thickness is 0.52~0.8 m, the length of the inclined longwall working face is about 120 m. And some requirements like coal hardness f ≤3, moderately stable roof, the floor undulation should not be too large, coal seam without hard inclusions. In addition, all electrical coal mining machines are explosion-proof requirements, working environments of methane, coal dust, hydrogen sulfide; carbon dioxide concentration does not exceed the content of.

1.1.2 Mechanical Part

The coal shearer make-up of the host body, coal loading part, composed of bottom bracket and spray cooling system. The traction part, the cutting part, the transportation-transmission device, the electric control box and the rocker arm, are all arranged on the whole casing. The traction part realizes the walking function of the shearer on the traction chain, which is mainly composed of the motor, the three stage planetary gear reducer, the guide chain wheel shaft group and the hydraulic braking system, and the max speed is 5.84m/min. The cutting part is a speed reducing mechanism between the motor and the roller, and the cutting part is provided with a torque clutch mechanism to prevent the motor from being damaged due to overload. The electric control box and the host body are welded into a whole structure to reduce the butt joint surface and improve the rigidity of the whole machine. Spray cooling system of shearer is within the inside and outside spray, the electrical components of cooling water, water hose, combined with water valve and valve and valve assembly.

Coal shearer work will have a lot of dust, and the main components (such as motor rocker, etc.) will produce high heat, therefore coal shearer set up a spray cooling system for dust and cooling to ensure the normal work.

1.1.3 Electronic Control System

MG110/130-TPD model electrical haulage in-web shearer is equipped with KXJ24-130/1140(660) C type mine explosion proof and intrinsically safe electric control box. The electric control box adopts advanced PWM frequency conversion technology, PLC control technology and industrial computer control display technology. It has a wide range of speed regulation, large traction, non-slip ability, strong adaptability to the working face, so the operation control of coal mining machine is more convenient and reliable.

1.1.4 Main Functional Features

MG110/130-TPD model electrical haulage in-web shearer is driven by single rocker arm double motors which cutting power is large. The integral casing structure, the cutting reaction force and the pulling force are all the main body of the structure, and the reliability is high. Using AC frequency conversion technology, to achieve the traction stepless speed regulation, high electric traction efficiency, high traction and reverse speed. Wide speed range (0-5.84m/s) according to the specific situation of the working face for speed control. Remote control mode to achieve traction and main stop function, shearer driver can be off the machine operation. The screen can be displayed on the warning, gas and other information, real-time display of operating conditions of coal shearer. With the fault inspection procedures to facilitate the analysis of equipment failure, maintenance. Adapting to different dip working face to make less floating coal. Internal and external dust spray has a cooling effect on the cutting teeth. Emergency brake device of hydraulic traction sprocket in special situations such as power failure emergency braking, to prevent the decline of coal shearer. The unit can realize the exchange of the left and right working faces, and save the cost of the unit. High climbing ability, the maximum operating angle of 45 degrees.

1.2 Field Application

MG110/130-TPD model electrical haulage in-web shearer was used in Xiaohezui Coal mine 4026(22) working face in 2009. The thickness of coal seam is 0.46 to 0.77m, with an average thickness of 0.61m, strike 22°~ 25, dip 112°~115°, dip angle of coal seam is 13°~ 43°with an average angle of 28°. The hardness of coal seam is 1-3 and the hardness of surrounding rock is 6-8. Coal seam stability is medium and 1/3 is coking coal. The mining height is 0.75m, which needs to cut partial roof, the direction length is 550m, and the inclined length is 112m. Field application at the beginning due to the performance of the mining machine is not familiar with coal mining machine,, the effect is poor even can't be used. After research, it is determined that the use of excessive dust water (inside, outside the spray are used) and lead to the roller cannot produce coal. After reducing the water discharge of dust, the effect of coal mining was initially revealed.

It was found that although the overall operating efficiency of the coal mining machine is good, but there are some problems in the experiment.

(1) Coal shearer transport ministry of transport capacity is poor,

there is a large number of floating coals transporting in increased working surface floating coal.

(2) In operation, the two ends of both ends of the bottom plate of the unit are straight and flat, and the phenomenon of the bite is appeared, which makes the load.

(3) Traction chain appears scar easily broken chain.

(4) The chain wheel adopts the full closed protection device so that protection effect is good, but at the same time it increases the difficulty of the field treatment of the fault of the traction chain.

(5) Leakage phenomenon occurred in the inner spray seal, and then water enters the gear box and leads to the deterioration of lubricating oil.

In view of the above problems, take the following measures:

(1) Redesign and replacement of the department of transportation, increased width, solve the problem of shearer transportation capacity is not enough, improve the speed of transportation, thoroughly improve the unit transportation effect.

(2) The reform of the boat shaped floor to prevent the phenomenon of cutting the bottom.

(3) Redesign of the spray sealing device to prevent the spray water seepage into the reducer.

By using the above measures to improve the shearer, the operation effect of the shearer has been improved significantly, and various technical indicators have reached the requirements of the coal mining machine operation.

1.3 Epilogue

The effects of product and mist cooling of this type coal shearer in ultra-low coal seam is good. And the emergency brake device can prevent wounding accident efficient when the coal shearer breakdown and start to slipping. That's conducive to keep safe production of the working face. In the Xiaohezui coal mine, the level of mechanization increase substantially after used this coal shearer. The average daily output up to 390 T, has created a very good economic benefits.

The shearer has the following problems in the course of operation:

(1) It's easy to channeling gangue when mining in the large dip angle working face which will threat machine operator's safety and cannot do the parallel operation, also the production efficiency is not high.

(2) Unit using chain traction which relative to the scraper conveyor is a free body and move irregularly, there is the possibility of a broken chain down. The next step will be to further study the above issues.

2. Goodbye! The World's HOT Potato of Low Coal Seam Mining Technology

Have you ever heard about the pseudo inclined fell steeply inclined low coal seam comprehensive mechanized mining technology? Here are the details.

"Steeply inclined" refers to "the angle is more than 45 degrees".

"Low coal seam" means "the coal seam which the thickness less than 1.3 meters.

Nowadays, there are several countries doing research and test about steeply inclined low coal seam mining technology, but the result is not ideal. Fortunately, this problem was resolved by Chongqing Energy Group recently.

In the past few days, it was published that the project result about "pseudo inclined fell steeply inclined low coal seam comprehensive mechanized mining technology research and application" passed the authentication. This project was leaded by Chongqing Songzao coal and electric Co. Ltd, Beijing HOT Mining Technology Co. Ltd, Alpha Industrial Technology Pty Ltd (Australia), and Sichuan Aerospace electric hydraulic control company also participated in this project.

Figure 2.1 coal mining machine is running

Picture, Courtesy by HOT Mining

Authentication team thinks that the core technology about this project has following advantages, the mining technology is reasonable, the equipments are reliable, and it is cost-efficient. It made a significant contribution to the development of our coal mining mechanization for our country. And it reached the international leading level.

At present, as for the steeply inclined low coal seam, blasting and pneumatic pick are the most common methods. The coal companies in Ukraine, France, Spain, and Sichuan province in China have continued to carry out the steeply inclined low coal seam fully mechanized study and test. But the results are not good.

However, this project mentioned just now has resolved some problems as below that perplex several coal mining countries.

1, Shear and hydraulic support glide down along working face which has a big gradient.

2, In the process of production, the machines sink, even topple over, and unable to work.

3, coal in production and the caving coal gangue splash around, it hurts people and machines.

4, In the process of machines' maintenance and repairment, mechanics have a big risk of falling down along steep working face.

Not only that, this project also has an innovative breakthrough on the key problems in automatic control system. The test coal mine is FENGCHUN Coal Mine under Songzao coal and electric Co. Ltd. The mine coal seam dip angle is 55 degrees – 75 degrees. Thickness is 0.8m-1.3m. The rock in floor and roof is broken and loose. It is unable to use blast-winning technology and fully mechanized mining technology, and they have no choice but to use pneumatic pick, and it is inefficient and has a big number of labour used.

In the test of experiment in this mine, because they used a new mining method and technology, at the end, the amount of labour used decreased half, monthly production of working face doubled and no accident.

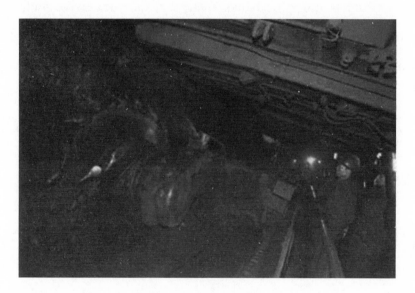

Figure 2.2 coal mining machine is running
Courtesy by HOT Mining

Zhongfu Li, the general manager of Songzao coal and electric Co. Ltd said, "pseudo inclined fell steeply inclined low coal seam comprehensive mechanized mining technology research and application" project started in April 2014. It mainly aimed at low coal seam which dip angle is 55 degrees-75 degrees, and the thickness is only 0.8m-1.3m. It mainly researched comprehensive mechanized mining technology and process as well as the corresponding coal winning machine and accessory device, hydraulic support, guide conveyor, etc. Finally, they developed the relevant technology and complete sets of equipment successfully. They Created a set of optimized "man, machine, material, environment, method" factors, and achieved a safe and effective coordination of technology and production management system.

Zhengqi Song, an academician of Chinese academy of sciences thinks, under the background that the subversive methods of coal mining such as coal seam gasification are difficult to generalize and use, this breakthrough is a remarkable achievement.

3. Optimized Solution of Improving Coal Loading Capability of Low-Seam Shearer

Abstract: Currently, in view of the poor loading effect of shearer at low coal seam, the four main technique improvement methods have been proposed, such as setting curved block coal plates, using leaf inclination roller, using high-power small-size planet head and compact chain conveyor. The details of the implementation have been introduced. These methods can provide technique support for improving coal loading effect.

Keywords: *shearer; low seam; coal loading effect*

Introduction

In recent years, China attaches great importance to the improvement of mining technology of low coal seam, it shows that there are large reserves of low coal seam on the one hand (about 20% of total reserves), it also shows the coal quality of low coal seam is very high on the other hand, for meeting the requirement of resource development is also one of the reasons. For example, when doing mining of coal and gas outburst coal seam, the low coal seam is mined as the protective coal seam. The shearer is widely used because it has the advantages of adapting to the variation of coal seam thickness, strong adaptability to the fluctuation of roof and floor. However, the shearer used now for low coal seam still has many problems, such as the coal loading effect is not good, poor adaptability to the floor, poor reliability, and the poor coal loading effect is an important factor of restricting the development of low coal seam shearer. In order to improve the coal loading effect, I try to explore some ways to improve the coal loading effect of shearer from the following aspects.

3.1 Curved Block Coal Plates

The curved block coal plates is set inside the helical drum, put the remaining coal into the scraper conveyor to improve the coal loading effect, reduce the quantity of floating coal and coal dust. At present, the most common structures are as Figure 1 and Figure 2, the pin wheel on the reversing frame is external meshing type, external diameter is larger than that of drum hoop, and the height of drum vane of the shearer is about 150mm~250mm, external diameter of reversing frame is far larger than that of drum hoop, when the coal cut down reach the root of reversing frame driven by the vanes will be blocked by the reversing frame which will seriously affect the coal loading effect.

Figure 3.1 External gearing driving model spillplate

Picture, Courtesy by HOT Mining

Figure 3.2 Structure chart of external gearing driving model spillplate

Picture, Courtesy by HOT Mining

The method to solve the problem above is by adopting the external gearing driving model spillplate, namely overturning with the annular gear of whirling stand, as illustrated in Figure 3. Internal gearing consists of two half rings, the diameter of whirling stand installing the rocker arm is quite small, as illustrated in Figure 4, after installation, the diameter of whirling stand is equal or bigger than the diameter of low coal seam drum ring. With this structure, the coal could enter the AFC smoothly under the push of vane, and gets better coal loading performance.

Figure 3.3 Internal gearing driving model spillplate

Picture, Courtesy by HOT Mining

Figure 3.4 Rocker arm

Picture, Courtesy by HOT Mining

3.2 Inclined Vane Model Drum

The vane and barrel of the low coal seam coal shearer drum is arranged vertically basically, for low coal seam coal shearer, the rotation speed is quite high, and the lead of vane is small, which leads to big twisting angle on the barrel, the coal would not be pushed out along with the axial direction by vane easily. Furthermore, the centrifugal force of drum rotation is big, appreciable quantity coal would be cast out along with the drum tangential direction, and be detained on the machine road, which leads to poor coal loading performance. In order to solve the shortcomings of the existing structure, we can make the angle of loading vane at the edge of drum larger than the friction angle between coal and steel, as shown in Figure 5, it can effectively inhibit the coal in the vane groove from getting out from the tangential direction of drum. What's more, increase the lift angle of 1/4 circle range of loading vane tail, as shown in Figure 6a. Making $\Delta \alpha$ larger than the friction angle between steel and coal or making the tail part (in the range of $\psi = 45°$) into bending shape (as shown in Figure 6b) can larger $\Delta \alpha$. This structure can turn up the coal which is under the height of scraper conveyor trough and push them to scraper conveyor in the way of accelerated movement in order to improve the coal loading effect.

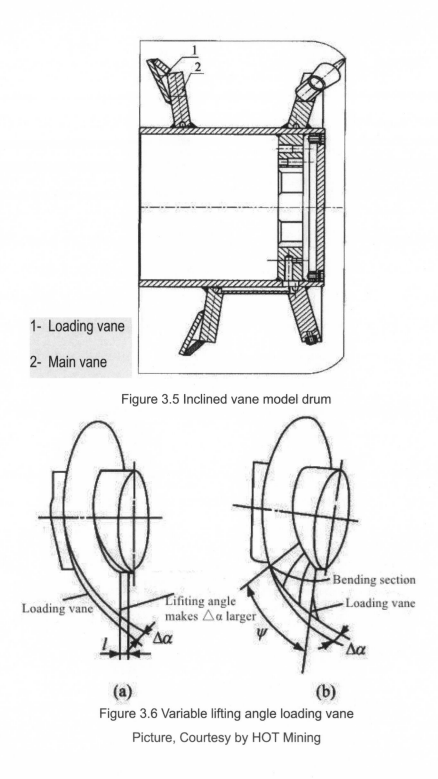

1- Loading vane

2- Main vane

Figure 3.5 Inclined vane model drum

(a)   (b)

Figure 3.6 Variable lifting angle loading vane

Picture, Courtesy by HOT Mining

3.3 High-power Small-size Planet Head

Because planetary gear transmission has motion characteristics of power split and dynamic axis, each center wheel composes coaxial transmission and reasonable application of inner gearing, so the structure can achieve a higher reduction ratio in a very compact space. It is because of planetary transmission characteristics of compactness, level at the end of the rocker arm of coal mining machine widely used in the structure to improve the effect of low seam coal mining machine, we can adopt the method of increasing vane height. In the case of definite roller diameter, minimize cylinder collar diameter, that is to say, as far as possible compression wilow the planetary gear transmission gear ring diameter. In order to ensure the planet wheel and planetary shaft strength and stiffness requirements, the choice of planets wheel support bearings becomes the key of design.

At present, commonly used planetary wheel bearing under the condition of space allows arrangement often choose short cylindrical roller bearings or spherical roller bearings. The arrangement can be divided into bearing installed wilow the planet wheel and packed in planets shelves. When compressed inner gear ring diameter, Due to large radial dimensions of the planet wheel bearing, to meet the high lifetime under the condition of strong shock and heavy load bearing. It is difficult to achieve the goal of compressing inner gear ring diameter.

In order to ensure the rationality of the planetary gear transmission, meet the requirements of reliability and size, using outer ring structure design is using multiple row short cylindrical roller. This structure is called one-piece planet wheel bearing components, as shown in Figure 3.7. Short cylindrical roller installed between the planet wheel inner hole and planetary shaft, use planetary wheel inner hole as bearing outer ring, and use planetary shaft as The bearing inner ring. Using a spacer ring between row and row in the axial direction is to prevent interference between row and row. Make a short cylindrical roller, planetary gear, planetary shaft and spacer ring to form an integral planet gear bearing components. Figure 3.8 is the practical application. It greatly reduces the diameter of the radial head size, it solved the high-power small-size planetary reduction design technology of contradictions.

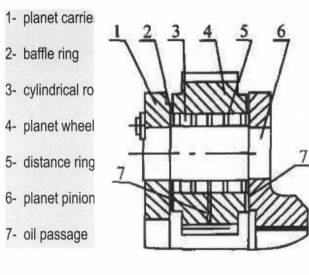

1- planet carrie
2- baffle ring
3- cylindrical ro
4- planet wheel
5- distance ring
6- planet pinion
7- oil passage

Figure3.7 Integrated planet wheel bearing assembly

Picture, Courtesy by HOT Mining

83

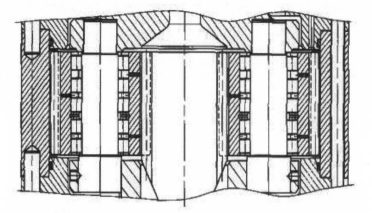

Figure 3.8 Rocker arm planet deceleration structure diagram

Picture, Courtesy by HOT Mining

3.4 Adopting Compact Flat Chain Conveyor

As shown in Figure 3.9, the coal by drum cutting in the promotion of the rotating vanes were thrown into the conveyor chutes, in this process, the chutes conveyor trough will block most below the conveyor trough height of the coal into the chute. For low coal seam shearer, vane height is small, the chutes conveyor trough will block a considerable number of coal into the chute. Therefore, lower chutes conveyor trough height will effectively improve the loading effect of shearer.

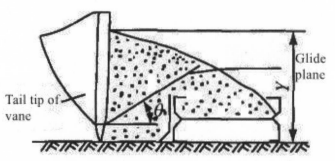

Figure 3.9 Interact relation between coal, vane and conveyor trough

Picture, Courtesy by HOT Mining

At present, the vertical chain of the scraper conveyor which used in the low coal seam is most of round-link chain, leading to high height of the scraper which will limit chutes conveyor trough height's reduction. Under the premise of ensuring the strength, using flat chain for vertical chain is the most effective way to lower the height of conveyor trough. As shown in Figure 10, using flat chain for vertical chain, the height of middle trough could be lower about 40mm, for the low coal seam shearer, this will improve coal loading effect. In addition, using this structure, you can greatly reduce the shearer machine face height, increase coal space and improve the coal shearer's adaptability to coal seam fluctuations.

Figure 3.10 Vertical chain of scraper chain adopts flat chain
Picture, Courtesy by HOT Mining

The above 4 kinds of technical measures can effectively improve loading effect of shearer at low coal seam so as to provide technical support for the design of low coal seam shearer.

Author, Ms. Serena Ling Fu, Mining Engineer

Email: serena.fu@hot-mining.com

WhatsApp: +86 15108333341

Paper Supervisor, Mr. NengJun Yu, Professor Mining Engineer, Corporate Supervisor of HOT.

4. Longwall Method Applied To Steeply Inclined Coal Seam Successfully

4.1 Introduction of Steeply Inclined Seam Longwall Mining Projects

Figure 4.1 Steeply Inclined Seam Longwall Mining machine

Picture, Courtesy by HOT Mining

According to the angle size, Chinese coal industry could be divided into the following stype: nearly-horizontal coal seam if the dip angle <12°, gentally-inclined coal seam if the dip angle is between 12°~25°, inclined coal seam if the dip angle is between 25°~45°, steeply-inclined coal seam if the dip angle >45°(among which if the dip angle is between 35°~55°, it's called large inclination coal seam). Large inclination coal seam and steeply-inclined coal seam are widely scattered in many coal mines in China, which takes about 21% among the explored reserve, and many of the coal seams are scarce and protectively-developed coal resources. The large inclination coal seams are complicated and hard to exploit coal seam recognized all over the world. Improving the standard of safety assurance and recovery rate is the most important strategical issue for Chinese coal resources and energy.

The big angle and steep inclination of the longwall mining working face and the condition of roof and floor makes it hard to ensure the stability of the equipment. Except for some studies about this field in Former Soviet Union and Poland in 1970s~1980s, there's few study, and no achievement in recent years, thus, no breakthrough has been made about the longwall mining equipment.

HOT Mining has get many achievements in the study of longwall mining technology and equipment of large inclination coal seam in recent years. HOT Mining's strategic partner, Sichuan Coal Group, and other units to solve the problem of large inclination coal seam mechanization mining, and conducted mechanization mining successfully in the working face with average coal seam angle 38°. After more than 10 years research, it has developed the hydraulic support applied in the steeply-inclined coal seam, with maximum dip angle of 50°.

At present, the standard of large inclination longwall mining technology of Sichuan Coal Group could represent the most advanced technology in the world. But according to recent years' practice, it has the best performance when the longwall mining equipment is applied in the coal seam angle which is small than the coal gangue angle around 40°, and the annual outcome could reach 0.6MT. However, when the working face coal seam dip angle is larger than the coal gangue angle, the coal shearer couldn't cut coal in two ways, and there'll be more breakdown, the output decreases and the safety couldn't be ensured.

4.2 The nececissity of the large inclination longwall mining projects

The steeply-inclined coal seam is common in Chinese coal mines, which takes about 21% among the explored reserve, and many of the coal seams are scarce and protectively-developed coal resources. How to exploit it safely and high efficiently has become a series strategic problem for state resource sustainable.

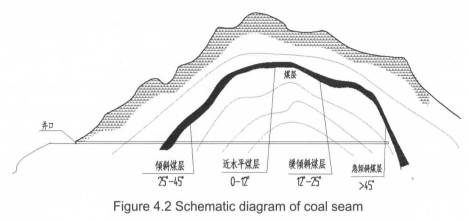

Figure 4.2 Schematic diagram of coal seam

Picture, Courtesy by HOT Mining

There're 3 critical defects if the steeply-inclined coal seam is exploited with non-mechanized method by tool pillar, stage, flexible shield support and manual blasting:

1) The first one is frequent security incidents, the MT death rate is more than 6.0;

2) The second one is low recovery ratio, only about 30%~40%, which leads to waste of great coal resources;

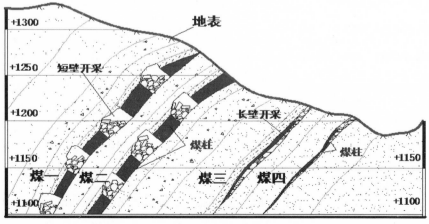

Figure 4.3 S Schematic diagram of coal seam mining

Picture, Courtesy by HOT Mining

3) The third one is bad working environment and high working intensity, and the average working face output is 60,000-150,000ton/year.

To overcome the problems above, the only solution is mechanization mining method.

There's still no important breakthrough in the world in the field of large inclination and steeply-inclined coal seam mechanization mining, the coal shearer is the critical equipment, however, the biggest applied angle of coal shearer is only about 45°in the world.

4.3 Introduction of Large Inclination Longwall Mining Support

According to the investigation of Chinese main coal mines, many coal mines of the provinces and cities that produce coal have coal seams not less than 40°large dip angle, most of them are between 40°~60°, such as Chongqing Nantong Coal Mine, Chongqing Tianfu Coal Mine, Xinjiang Urumchi Coal Mine, Xinnjiang Construction Crops Coal Mine, Xinjiang Ewirgol Coal Mine, Gansu huating Coal Mine, Gansu Jingyuan Coal Mine, most of the coal mines in Guizhou Province, Heilongjiang Shuangyashan Coal Mine, Heilongjiang Qitaihe Coal Mine, Heilongjiang Hegang Coal Mine and etc. Generally speaking, these coal mines don't use longwall mining method for the coal mines with dip angle is more than 40°, some of the coal mines don't exploit coal seam with this kind of angle, and some of the coal mines use conventional mining method to exploit, which leads to the result of low productivity, high labor working intensity and bad safety. Some of the coal mines use large inclination longwall mining method to exploit coal seams with dip angle below 40°, and they don't exploit the coal seams with dip angle above 45°with longwall mining method. According to information research, there's no report about medium-thick coal seam with dip angle above 45°using one-way longwall mining method. It indicates that many Chinese coal mines need to use the one-way longwall mining method which could adapt to the coal seam dip angle >45°.

At present, with the decurrence of exploiting standard, some coal mines of Sihuan Coal Group Guangneng Company such as Lvshuidong Coal Mine, Liziya South Coal Mine have the coal seam dip angle>40°in the recoverable reserve, and most of them are between 45°~60°. These coal resources need a suitable longwall mining equipment which could adapts to the large inclination well.

According to the analysis, it suggests that it's hard to exploit coal seam with dip angle>60°by longwall mining method, and there's mature technology by using pseudo inclined flexible shield support; and there's no mature mining method for exploiting coal seam with dip angle between 45°~60°, in order to extend the working life of the coal mine and ensure the safety and efficiency, many coal mines need to make achievement in this field. Among the longwall mining equipment applied in the large inclination coal mines, the existing conveyor could meet the demands, the first critical problem for large inclination coal seam longwall mining is the working face hydraulic support couldn't meet the requirements, and the second critical problem is to invent the face-end supports which could meet the safety protection requirement.

Longwall mining equipment consists of hydraulic support, coal shearer and conveyor. As the main equipment for mechanization mining, the one-time investment of hydraulic support holds more than 70% of the whole longwall mining equipment investment budget, which is the key of realizing longwall working face safety and high efficient production. The roof and floor of the hydraulic support must fit the underground coal mining environment, and could provide power source for mining and conveying equipment. After decades of years research and development, we have made great achievement in design and manufacture of hydraulic support, and developed many kinds of hydraulic supports which could adapt to various geological condition and different coal seam thickness.

4.3.1 Coal Shearer

Four technical problems of large dip angle seam coal shearer as follow: 1.it is difficult to move for hauling the shearer when up going cutting. 2.the coal shearer will slide down and runaway. 3.tube cables will damage the equipment and hurt people. 4. operating staff will be easily injured by the flying gangue. Coal shearer is composed of hauling moving unit, cutting unit, electric control box and attached tube cables etc.

(1) The maximum seam inclination of coal shearer is smaller than 45° in the world. No drum shearer's seam inclination is bigger than 45°.

(2) The stress of coal shearer will be changed along with the coal seam dip angle start to change. When the coal seam dip angle is bigger than 40°,many faults of traction walking system come out like the

walking gear is broken down of coal shearer, guide foot is breakdown and traction box internal gear is fractured. Failure rate of airborne inverter is high because of the cutting vibrating.

(3) Now coal shearers domestic and overseas only have one stage braking that is hydraulic brake. Coal shearer will be runaway when the hydraulic system is broken down or the moving gear is raptured or the axis of motor is raptured. It will cause serious effect.

(4) When the shearer is operating, the cables, dustproof pipes and cold water pipes are moving closed behind shearer in the cable groove from side to side. It will cause tube cables broken off, endanger men's safety, even cause gas explosion if tube cables overlap and sharp decline suddenly when the coal shearer goes down.

(5) The men working space and the operation space of the coal shearer is completely closed and isolated. The display of original coal shearer is designed in shearer's body. In the process of coal mining, in order to observe the working condition and parameters of coal shearer workers need to open the Isolated protection device. Shearer drivers and workers are easily hurt by gangue because of the large dig angle and flying gangue.

(6) When the coal shearer is working in coal seam angle >40°, it could only go down cutting and go up operate the reamers in vain, which can not play the ability of mechanized equipment enough. Because the problems of no enough up traction and antiskid are not resolved.

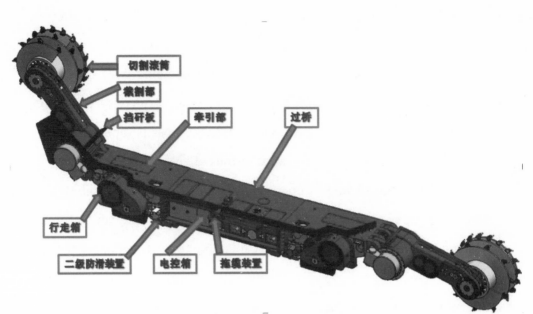

Figure 4.4 Coal mining machine

Picture, Courtesy by HOT Mining

4.3.2 Hydraulic Support

(1) Suitable seam inclination is smaller than 60°.

(2) The push jacks of hydraulic support are easily hurt without shell.

(3) The hydraulic control of gangue plates might be elevated up to the support beam to damage the tube cables.

(4) The automatic moving function should be improved of hydraulic support.

(5) The automatic tilting prevention and antiskid function of hydraulic support should be improved.

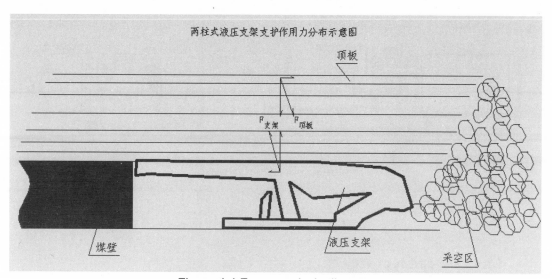

Figure 4.4 Force analysis diagram

Picture, Courtesy by HOT Mining

4.3.3 Scraper Conveyor

Selection of face scraper conveyor in fully-mechanized coal mining should be suited to production capacity of face coal shearer .Most of us choose the heavy scraper conveyor, to meet the requirements of the coal shearer's production capacity etc; The structural form and the components of the working face scraper conveyor must be able to match the structure of the coal shearer. For example, selecting the width of the scraper conveyor trough according to the width of the coal shearer's travel unit to ,selecting the length of the scraper conveyor according to the length of the working face, meanwhile, it should also be support matched with support advancing ram ,connection unit spacing and structure.

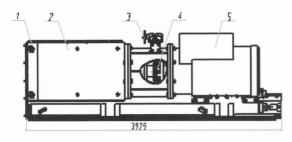 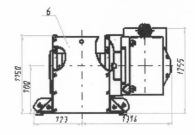

Figure 4.5 Scraper Conveyor

Picture, Courtesy by HOT Mining

4.3.4 Face-end support

Face-end support, especially for steeply inclined coal seams, is an important part of full-mechanized coal mining. The face-end support for the lower party of steeply inclined coal seams' working face controls the roof of connection part between working faces and wood roadways, it is also a pusher jack of stage loaders. The support for the upper side of face-ends can use single hydraulic props with steel I-beams' framed timber supporting, because of the conveyor, which the sample working face is using, has a overhead drive head and a transverse motor. So we are going to mainly analyze the support for the lower part of working face.

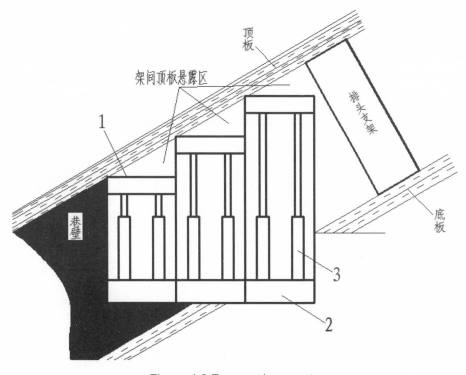

顶板

架间顶板悬露区

排头支架

1

巷壁

底板

3

2

Figure 4.6 Face-end support

Picture, Courtesy by HOT Mining

4.4 Large Dip Angle Fully Mechanized Coal Mining Project

4.4.1 General Situation of Working Face

Parameters of working face: the length of coal seam strike is 700m, the length of inclined is about 88-160m, dip angle of coal seam is 0°-49°, average dip angle is 34°, inclined area is 74873.72m2.

Geological Structure: This working face is a monocline, it is located the West Wing of the Daluowan Anticline 561 mining area. There is a oblique working face formed by anticline and syncline of two axial N31~E because the working face is affected by the tectonic stress of

N59°W. Ventilating roadway of working face is less affected by the fold, dip angle is between 36°~38°, the affected part is the north of ventilating roadway. Mechanical roadway is affected greatly by the fold, the dip angle varies between 0°~49°. Geological profile of working face is shown in Figure 1.

The working face mainly formed by reverse fault (number 01, 03, 11) of N50°W inclination because of the effect of fold, the throw is 0.7m~3.5m, it is in parallel with the fold. Specific location is: 5616-01# strike reverse fault, H=0.7m, 27.8m away from the south of mechanical roadway 61872 point; 5616-03# strike reverse fault, H=3.5m, 16m away from the south of mechanical roadway 61878 point; 5616-11# strike reverse fault, H=1.1m, located 3# exploration entry 61877 point of working face. Ventilating roadway developed fault without the effect of fold, there is a strike reverse fault at the point of ventilating roadway 61770, H=0.90m.

Roof and Floor of Coal Seam: The false roof of coal seam is a layer of clay stone, the thickness is about 0.2m, and immediate roof is carbonaceous mudstone, the thickness is about 8m. The main roof is carbonaceous mudstone and sandstone. There is a thin layer of limestone containing flint above the main roof, commonly known as "small iron plate" which is the marker bed. Direct floor is carbonaceous mudstone, and the thickness is about 0.7m. The hard floor is mudstone, sandstone and shale, the thickness is 1.0m~12.2m, average number is 6.60m. Under the hard floor is bauxite and fracture bauxite rock. We can see from the data that the roof is relatively complete, but there are some small faults and fracture. The roof of coal seam belongs to class two.

4.4.2 Equipment selection

Because of the geological structure of the 260m section of the working face approaching to the open-off cut is very complicated. Strike of the upper segment of the working face 90m to more than 200m, meanwhile, when construction of the roadway , strike of the conveyor roadway from the negative slope 7°suddenly become positive slope 12°, dip direction is also from-10°become the positive slope gradually to 39°, Dip of the working face is basically normal and becomes more uniform at 40°; Coal Seam of the working face with dirt band 2 to 4 layer, is a complex structure of coal seam, coal thickness 0.6m~3.18m, most stable at around 2.5m.

Combined with the existing level of technology, the research group decided to adopt the steeply inclined fully-mechanized mining technology for mining, on the first after alignment of upper segment and lower segment, connected together and then integrated propulsion, working face equipment according to characteristic working face of the steeply inclined make the following requirements:

(1) Coal shearer

Fully Mechanized Coal Mining Face in Steeply Dipping used of coal shearer as chainless haulage, using of coal shearer large inclination angle fully mechanized mining face the chainless traction, use shearer traction driving gear box and travel gear box with rows of pins and mounted on a conveyor engaging, on the other side on ramp plate of conveyor by coal wall side use roller to keep machine balance, coal shearer set with hydraulic brake system, In the case of ensuring the failure of a brake, it can also meet the operation and braking of the coal shearer, not because of a brake and coal shearer appeared to down.

It uses cutting coal downlink, uplink collect floating coal, mainly considering the traction shearer and down of shearer whether can be controlled, With the accumulation of mining experience, at present, the large dip and working face of steeply inclined fully-mechanized mining technology, cutting coal downlink are feasible, a disadvantage is that the uplink cutting coal easy appear channeling gangue. After frame the front door of gangue, problem of channeling gangue is solved.

(2) Conveyor

Scraper conveyor is the key to ensure the stable operation of coal shearer. The conveyor is controlled by the hydraulic support of the working face and the rigid connection of the conveyor, support has a large capacity to limit down of the conveyor. Support must ensure that not to fall, the conveyor will not fall.

(3) Hydraulic support

Hydraulic chock-shield support is used in the working face, which absorbs the advantages of the shield support, and can be used for the working face of 60°, which increased a walkway and field operating space.

In order to prevent support working face dumping to the lower side of working face, the first, manage the end support, not to let down the end support, support of big dip fully-mechanized mining technology the roof beams and the bedplate can be connected into a whole, by jack and related facilities prevent dumping and slipping down. The second, when support moving height of support-dropping is not more than 2/3 of height of side protective plate, the third, control sequence of support-moving; the fourth, appropriate take oblique to regulate.

(4) End support

End support in the lower part of the working face not only to solve roof control on working face and connection region of conveyor roadway, but also face support thrust gear of conveyor roadway type reversed loader, and form a strong closed space to ensure that safety of men in and out of the end support, into the working face. Therefor we choose three horizontal layout type end support, this have proprietary intellectual property rights, and have better effect. For end support of the working face, because of horizontal layout the use of the conveyor on the end and horizontal layout by reducing mechanism, using the individual hydraulic prop with dip shed support of steel-beam.

4.4.3 Safety Protection of Working Face

Due to the large angle of coal seam, in the production process of fully mechanized mining, there is channeling gangue between the supports; side rolling in the working surface; Coal wall spalling, or coal rolling during the process of cutting coal, etc.

Gangue (coals) in the working face solution of safety protection is set the gangue blocking device before frame and between frame.

1) Gangue Blocking Device Before Frame

In each section of central groove on the conveyor frame (cable groove side) is provided with a lifting jack using gangue blocking plate. The machine road and the working surface (personnel walking and working space) are separated, so that the coal mining machine cut coal and coal wall piece cannot be rushed into the working surface wounding. When observation and treatment of coal mining machine, conveyor, scaffold moving, one or a few pieces of corresponding gangue blocking plate, and then make it raises.

2) Gangue Blocking Device Between Frame

In the section layout of the hydraulic support of top beam set an upper can lift up and down, and can control the switch of door in the gangue. The door closed, under the rolling down the coal gangue, make the personnel work and walking below from harm, when people pass, open the door. The door goes up and down with the hydraulic support, around the switch with a jack as a driving force.

4.4.4 Safety protection for export under working face

When the coal seam dip in the working face is more than the slope of the coal, the mining of coal(gangue) accelerated rolling down, arrived at bottom of the working face achieve the fastest speed, largest impact, it is difficult to ensure export under the traffic and the safety of staff maintenance of pillar, prop drawer, and tail of reprint machine, etc.

After repeated research, based on using three horizontal type end support, plate on the end support set plate of blocking the gangue, ensure personnel safety between the support column and rear linkage.

4.4.5 Organized measures

In order to ensure the smooth implementation of project research work, established a field test research group, members of the senior engineering and technical personnel and management personnel with many years of practical experience. Set up three professional teams in the research group: Field implementation group, technical research group, production coordination and security group. The main responsibilities of each group are as follows:

1) Field implementation group: In strict accordance with the development of safety technical measures and operation procedures set by the arrangement work, and in a timely manner the problems appeared in the production safety in time to report back to the operation department and technical research group.

2) Technical research group: According to the actual situation, formulate reasonable equipment installation, retreat technical safety measures and operation procedures in working face.

3) Production coordination and security group: Equipment and spare parts preparation, standby, maintenance; The management of coal and the supply of water and electricity; equipment maintenance and repair; liaison work between production and management department.

5. Rock failure Process Analysis Method for Modeling Coal Strata Movement

Author: ChunAn Tang, Chief Scientist of Mechsoft (Dalian) Co., Ltd., Professor at DUT, Vice President of CSRME

The extraction and use of coal resources remarkably benefits human being but also causes a series of adverse impacts on the environment that challenge all of the coal mining countries. Coal extraction commonly causes strata movement and land subsidence that then leads to mining hazards such as ground water in-rush, rock burst and damages to buildings or structures on the surface, as well as pollution of the environment. After advance of the face the roof located behind the support becomes unsupported, loose and even caved. In longwall mining, the primary objective is to design coal pillars that are left in place to control mine stability and surface subsidence and, hence, to prevent damage to surface or near-surface structures such as buildings, railways, highways, rivers and pipelines. Poor knowledge of the characteristics of strata movement due to longwall mining can create very serious ground hazards, potentially jeopardizing the safety and lives of mine personnel, as well as affecting the productivity and efficiency of a mining operation. For decades, extensive effort has been paid to study the strata movement and stress distribution law induced by mining excavation and obtain comprehensive understanding of the permeability evolution of coal seam performed an empirical study of the sub-surface deformation caused by retreating longwall mining and monitored the strata movement over a longwall panel and indicated that the three-joint-arch structure formed by the broken key roof stratum is monotonically unstable structure and its limit value is determined by the breaking convergence value. Moreover, the mechanism of the main roof breaking at shallow depth is due to the bifurcation instability of the roof structure. Though extensive effort has been paid to understand the rupture and collapse of overburden strata and the abutment stress redistribution patterns above coal face and key strata and around coal pillar, there remains unclear about the dynamic mechanical state of a coal pillar and the nonlinear behavior associated with mining-related rock mechanics problems during the extraction of a longwall mining panel. A thorough understanding of in situ stress environment is essential for effective ground control during underground mining. In particular, understanding the stress field around a longwall panel and overburden strata movement law is one of the key components that enables mining engineers to predict potential failures. Herein, the progressive damage, fracture and collapse process of rock strata, from the initiation and propagation of cracks firstly in the two heads and the middle part of strata to rupture and collapse of strata, viz., weighting, is simulated by Rock Failure Process Analysis (RFPA) to investigate the characteristics of strata movement, surface subsidence and abutment stress distribution above coal face and key layers as mining. The work described here has attempted to investigate the rupture and collapse characteristics of overburden strata and the redistribution of abutment stress patterns above coal face and key strata during the underground mining based on the geological condition of a typical longwall panel from a coal mine.

5.1 Essences of RFPA Method

Nonlinear and discontinuous numerical methods have become an important tool in modeling mining engineering processes for the analysis of stresses and deformations in mining. Although many numerical methods, such as finite element method, boundary element method, finite-difference method, and discrete element method, can do well in simulating nonlinear behavior in rock deformation, most of them are not a physical modeling of the nonlinear behavior of brittle rock. Though these methods have gained a sufficient degree of functionality, and may also incorporate compaction features, they may not always help in our understanding of why rock material demonstrates nonlinear behavior. It also prevents us from approaching seismicity problems since the seismicity-prone material is by no means homogeneous.

One of the most important factors affecting the progressive failure is heterogeneity. When rock is subjected to a stress field, cracks may nucleate, propagate, interact, and coalesce. During fracturing, the heterogeneity plays a marked influence in determining the fracture paths and the resulting fracture patterns. The influence of heterogeneity is pronounced on the progressive failure process. Therefore, a more reasonable numerical model for the rock or rock mass should be able to demonstrate the progressive failure due to heterogeneity, which results in nonlinear behavior. This may only succeed via a statistical approach. Thus, a new numerical method, Rock Failure Process Analysis Code (RFPA), to modeling progressive failure of rock is developed by Professor Chunan Tang and further extended to model the observed evolution of damage and induced seismicity due to the progressive failure leading to collapse in brittle rock or rock mass.

RFPA is based on element stress analysis and it fully considers the nonlinearity, non-homogeneity and the anisotropic properties of rocks in its analysis. It accounts for material heterogeneity to obtain a collective macroscopic behavior different from those of the elements through a stochastic local failure stress field. There are four features distinguishing it from other numerical models:

1) By introducing heterogeneity of rock properties into the model, it can simulate non-linear deformation of a quasi-brittle behavior with an ideal brittle constitutive law for the local material;

2) By introducing degradation of material parameters after element failure, it can simulate strain-softening behavior;

3) By recording the event accounts and event rates of failed elements, the associated seismicity with the progressive failure in rock can be simulated;

4) By the setting of step caving, the advancing of mining face can be simulated.

When it comes to the application of RFPA code, it can be used to study:

1) Rock deformation process and energy released (acoustic emission) under loads and deformation.

2) Sinking of the ground surface and rock mass movement

3) Fluid-rock interaction of civil and hydraulic engineering.

4) Gas-rock and heat-rock interaction of Geotechnical Engineering.

5) Simulation failure of rock mass.

6) Slope stability analysis.

5.2 Numerical Model setup

In this section, RFPA method is used to investigate the characteristics of deformation and fracturing of overburden strata during the extraction of coal seam. The main mineable coal seam of the coal mine is 6 m thick on average and is nearly horizontal. The panel is mined using the longwall retreat mining method with natural roof caving. The immediate roof of the panel is composed of sandy mudstone and is approximately 2 m thick. The average depth of coal seam below surface is approximately 84 m. Coal has been produced by means of longwall retreat method with 5 m mining height. The model domain for the study area is 100 m high and 300 m long. The numerical model is discretized into 30,000 elements (1003300) and contains a total of 12 strata based on the site-specific geological conditions as shown in Figure 1. Considering the effect of bedding and weak planes on the failure of rock mass, it is necessary to embed some bedding planes between two contiguous strata in the model. The mining length of coal seam in the model is 115 m, with 23 steps in total, i.e., 5 m each step of mining. According to the site-specific mining conditions, it is assumed that the time interval of each step is a half day, i.e., the extraction of coal seam lasts 11 days and a half day in the model simulation.

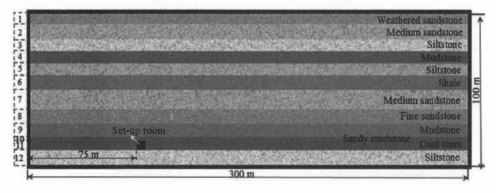

Figure 5.1 Model for simulation of overburden movement

In the simulation, the elements in the numerical model are characterized by the Young's modulus I, uniaxial compressive strength, tensile strength, and Poisson's ratio. It is crucial to properly assess the properties of the surrounding rocks to obtain acceptable results for numerical modeling. Therefore, the physical and mechanical properties of each geological unit must be determined. In general, the properties of the surrounding rocks are determined by laboratory testing. Samples of the surrounding rock described above were obtained from exploration drilling cores and rock blocks taken directly from the coal mine. Uniaxial compression tests were used to determine the uniaxial compressive strength, Young's modulus, and Poisson's ratio. The cohesion and friction angle of the surrounding rocks were obtained by triaxial compression tests. Based on the results of these tests, the panel stratigraphy and other important geotechnical parameters of the coal seam, roof, and floor strata adopted in the simulation for the numerical model are listed in Table 1. The boundary conditions of the numerical model are that the both sides of the model are restricted by displacement in the horizontal direction, the upper boundary of the model is free and the bottom of the model is fixed by displacement. In the simulations, coal mining in 23 steps by 5 m/step was consecutively carried out to simulate the progressive coal extraction process.

Table 5-1 Physical and mechanical properties of coal and surrounding rocks

No	Formation	Young's modulus (Gpa)	UCS (Mpa)	Density (×10³kg/m³)	Thickness (m)
1	Weathered sandstone	6	50	2.48	7
2	Medium sandstone	8	60	2.65	10
3	Siltstone	10	60	2.56	8
4	Mudstone	2	36	2.56	8
5	Siltstone	8	50	2.56	8
6	Shale	4	45	2.6	10
7	Medium sandstone	8	30	2.5	12
8	Fine sandstone	6	20	2.5	10
9	Mudstone	4	20	2.6	9
10	Sandy mudstone	1.5	5	2.5	2
11	Coal seam	1	33	1.4	6
12	Siltstone	10	100	2.5	10

5.3 Overburden Movement Process

The typical sequences of overburden strata movement and caving as the face advances are presented in Figure 2. As the face advances some distance of 20 m from the set up room, layer 10 of sandy mudstone bends under the gravity, cracks initiate at mid span of lower side and at both ends of the upper side of layer 10 as shown in Figure 2A1. When the span is beyond the limit characteristics of layer 10, the cracks will propagate and coalesce near the end of coal face, and at last lead to the caving of layer 10 with a caving thickness of 2 m, as shown in Figure 2A2.Later on, layer 10 continuously caves as the face advances 35 m as shown in

Figure 2B.

Layer 9 bends under the gravity with the continuous advance of the face. When the face has advanced to 45 m, fractures initiates and propagates along the bedding planes between layer 8 and layer 9 over layer 10, and tensile fractures also initiate at mid span of lower side and at both ends of the upper side of layer 9, as shown in Figure 2C. As the face advances to 50 m, the caving of layer 9 occurs and cuts and caves along the coal face, as shown in Figure 2D. As the face advances to 60 m,bed separation and cracking in layer 8 can be observed as shown in Figure 2E. As the face continuously advances to 70 m, the adjacent upper strata close to the face begins to fracture, rotate and cave as shown in Figure 2F. As the face advances to 75 m, the caving of the layer 8 occurs in Figure 2G. As the face continues to advance to 85 m, layer 10 over coal face shortly caves, bed separation along the bedding planes (such as between layers 6 and 7, between layers 3 and 4), and cracking above the strata of layer 7 occurs. The adjacent thick upper strong main roof (layer 7) tends to cantilever over the goaf. It gradually bends and finally ruptures at the ends as shown in Figure 2H1 and H2. As the face advances to 105 m, cracking occurs in the layer 6 and bed separation can be observed along the bedding planes in the upper strata as shown in Figure 2I. Thereafter, the overburden rock strata caves in periodically as the face advances as shown in Figure 2J.

It follows that the typical sequences of overburden strata movement and caving with the advancing of the face can be summarized as follows: A set-up room is made in the coal seam, the intact stress is disturbed and the pressure redistributes itself. As the face advances away from set-up room, the roof beds above the excavation bend downwards from over the coal across the coal face. As the span across the coal face reaches to a certain limit, the roof bed above the excavation ruptures and caves. The roof beds above goaf will again bend and cause the beds to sag away from each other. The bending of roof beds causes the formation of bed separation in the overburden, and even the rupturing and caving of the roof bed adjacent to the goaf. Thereafter, the overburden roof beds caves in periodically as the coal face gradually advances.

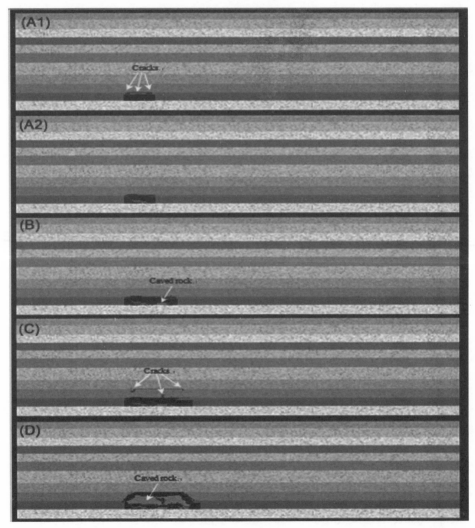

Figure 5.2 Sequence of overburden strata movement and caving as the face advances.

(A1 and A2) Coal face advances 20 m, (B) coal face advances 35 m, (C) coal face advances 45 m, (D) coal face dvances 50 m, I coal face advances 60 m, (F) coal face advances 70 m, (G) coal face advances 75 m, (H1 and H2) coal face advances 85 m, (I) coal face advances 105 m, and (J) coal face advances 115 m.

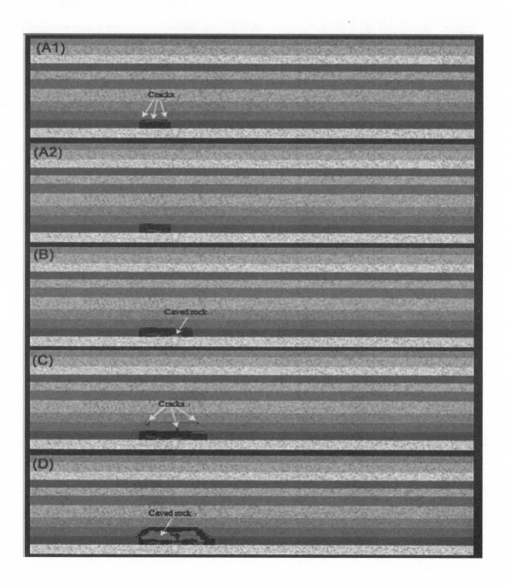

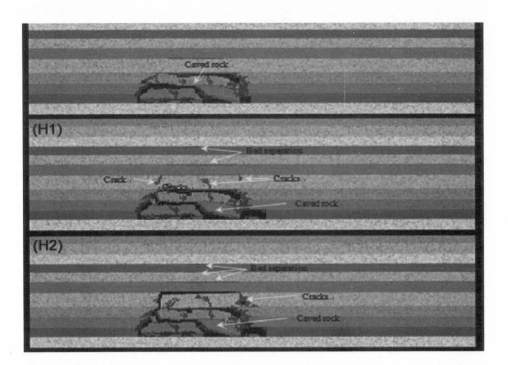

Figure 5.2 (Continued)

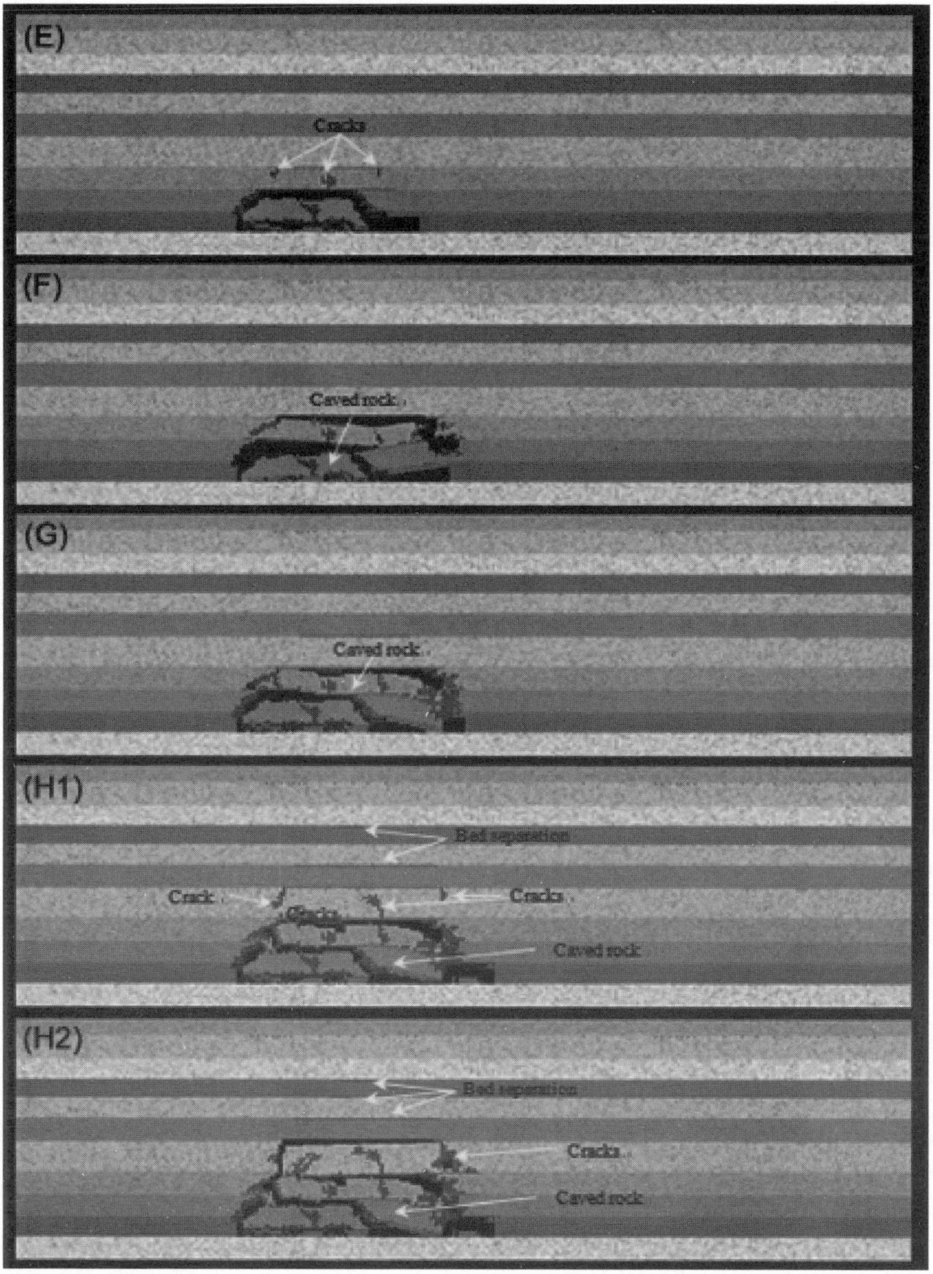

(E)

Cracks

(F)

Caved rock

(G)

Caved rock

(H1)

Bed separation

Crack   Cracks

Cracks

Caved rock

(H2)

Bed separation

Cracks

Caved rock

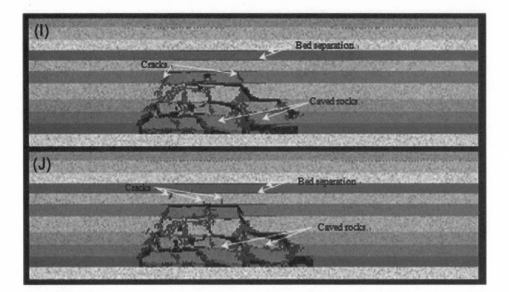

Figure 5.2 (Continued)

5.4 Associated Stress in Overburden and Weighting Characteristics

Figure 5.3 presents the associated stress field in the overburden in panel mining. As the face advances, bed separation first occurs in layer 10, and high tensile stress concentrates at mid span of lower side and at both ends of the upper side of layer 10. Cracks initiate at mid span of lower side and at both ends of the upper side of layer 10 when the mining-induced tensile stress is beyond the tensile strength of layer 10 as shown in Figure 5.3A1. It follows that the fracturing of layer 10 is induced by high tensile stress. Later on, layer 10 shortly caves with the advancing of the face, as shown in Figure 5.3A2 and B. As the face advances to 45 m, bed separation occurs in the middle of layer 9. Meanwhile, the high tensile stress induces cracks at mid span of lower side and at both ends of the upper side of layer 9 as shown in Figure 5.3C.

As the face goes on, layer 9 near the goaf always undergoes the effect of the mining-induced tensile stress and thus is severely damaged, while the maximum stress zone in layer 9 near the face progressively moves forward and correspondingly the mining-induced damage zone also moves forward. Finally layer 9 unsymmetrically ruptures and caves as shown in Figure 5.3D. Thereafter, as the face advances, the overburden strata caves in periodically under the mining-induced high tensile stress, as shown in Figure 5.3E-I.

As the face advances to 20 m, the layer 10 caves with a caving height of 2 m as shown in Figure 5.3A1. Then layer 10 shortly caves with the face advancing and the caved zone gradually expands upwards. As the face advances to 50 m, the caving of layer 9 occurs and the height of caved zone goes up to about 11 m, as shown in Figure 5.3D. As the face advances to 75 m, the first periodic weight of main roof with an interval of 25 m occurs and the height of caved zone reaches to 21 m as shown in Figure 5.3F. As the face advances to 105 m, the second periodic weight of main roof with an interval of 30 m occurs and the height of caved zone reaches to 43 m as shown in Figure 5.3H. Thereafter, overburdened caves in periodically and periodic weighting of main roof occur as the face advances. It can be seen from numerical simulations that RFPA model well reproduces the overburden movement process, reveal the rupturing mechanism of overburden strata and captures periodic weighting of the roof even though there is not any pre-existing cracks or fractures in the model.

Figure 5.3 Stress distribution in overburden strata as the face advances.

(A1 and A2) Coal face advances 20 m, (B) coal face advances 35 m, (C) coal face advances 45 m, (D) coal face advances 50 m, I coal face advances 60 m, (F) coal face advances 75 m, (G) coal face advances 85 m, (H) coal face advances 105 m, and (I) coal face advances 115 m

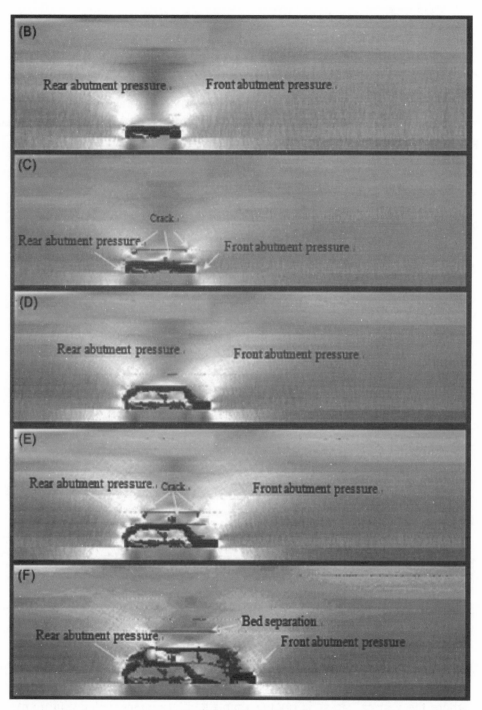

Figure 5.3 (Continued)

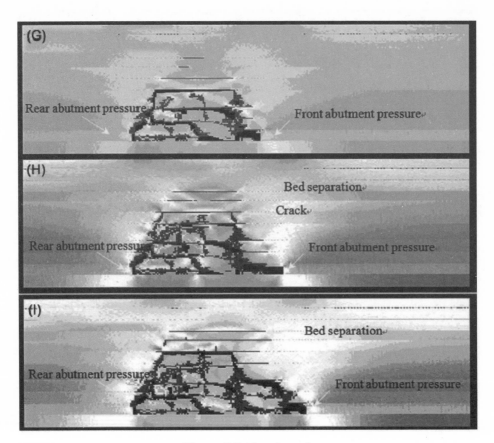

Figure 5.3 (Continued)

5.5 Abutment Pressures With the Face Advancing

When an opening is created in the coal seam, the stress that was present before the opening was created is redistributed to the adjacent coal pillars that are left. When an opening is created in the coal seam, the stress that was present before the opening was created is redistributed to the adjacent coal pillars that are left. The areas within the remaining coal where the vertical stress is greater than the average are called abutments and hence the stresses in those areas are called abutment pressures. The abutment pressures over coal face gradually increase as the face advances, and Figure 5.4 shows the distribution and evolution of abutment pressures over coal face with the face advancing. As the face advances to 20 m, stress concentration forms around coal wall and the distribution of abutment pressures exhibits a monotonic curve with a maximum pressure around the coal face as shown in Figure 5.4A. As the face advances to 25 m, the abutment pressures over the face decrease drastically due to the first immediate roof weighting, as shown in Figure 5.4B. Later on, the abutment pressures over coal face gradually increase with the face advancing, as shown in Figure 5.4C and D. As the face advances to 50 m, the abutment pressures over the face again decrease drastically due to the first main roof weighting, as shown in Figure 4E. The main roof strata caves in the goaf and takes the dead weight of the caved strata as waste rock, as shown in Figure 5.4E—K, in which the stress in the goaf is that of the waste rock withstands the caved strata. As the face goes on advancing, the abutment pressures over coal face gradually increase again, as shown in Figure 5.4F and G. As the face advances to 75 m, the first periodic weighting of main roof occurs and abutment pressures over the face again decrease drastically, as shown in Figure 5.4H. Thereafter, abutment pressures over the face change periodically as the face advances as shown in Figure 5.4H—K. It is noted that the front abutment pressures over coal face are higher than back abutment pressures over coal face due to the continuous effect of mining excavation from coal face.

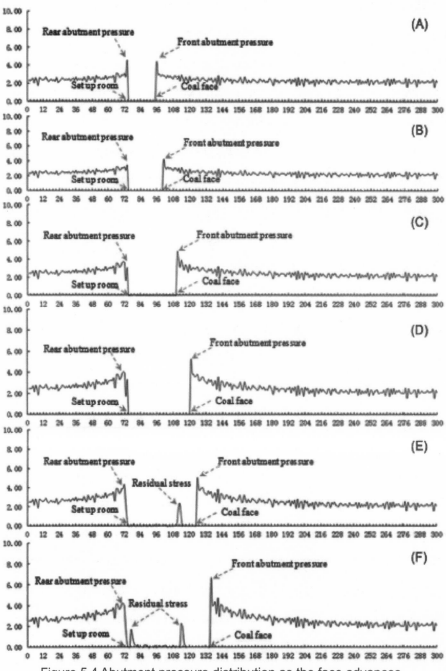

Figure 5.4 Abutment pressure distribution as the face advances.

(A) Coal face advances 20 m, (B) coal face advances 25 m, (C) coal face advances 35 m, (D) coal face advances 45 m, I coal face advances 50 m, (F) coal face advances 60 m, (G) coal face advances 70 m, (H) coal face advances 75 m, (I) coal face advances 85 m, (J) coal face advances 105 m, and (K) coal face advances 115m.

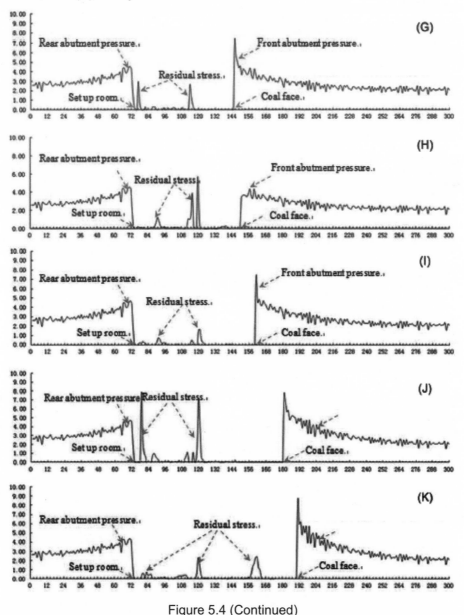

Figure 5.4 (Continued)

5.6 conclusion

RFPA method was used to simulate the deformation and fracture characteristics of overburden strata, in which stress, damage, and seepage coupling are taken into account. The case study on fracturing and caving of overburden strata induced by longwall mining was performed to study the overburden movement and associated abutment pressures distribution over coal face using RFPA code, which considers the heterogeneity and nonlinear characteristics of overburden rock strata. Numerical results show that as the face advances, bed separation and the bending occur in the adjacent upper strata, cracks initiates at mid span of lower side and at both ends of the upper side of the upper roof. The upper stratum ruptures and caves when the span reaches to a certain limit. The overburden movement gradually propagates from the goaf to the upper strata. Generally the immediate roof shortly caves with the advancing of the face. The main roof ruptures and caves when the face advances to a certain distance and the first weighting occurs. Thereafter, the overburden rock strata caves in periodically as the face advances. Meanwhile, numerical simulations show that the equilibrium of stress in overburden is disturbed due to coal mining and that the abutment pressure over coal face is redistributed. The abutment pressure over coal face is characterized with low stress zone, high stress zone, and in situ stress zone along the mining direction. The front abutment pressures over coal face are higher than back abutment pressures over coal face due to the continuous effect of mining excavation from coal face. Numerical simulations show that RFPA model well reproduces the overburden movement process, reveal the rupturing mechanism of overburden strata and captures periodic weighting of the roof even though there is not any preexisting cracks or fractures in the model. It is concluded that RFPA method is of significant help in better understanding of coal strata movement characteristics in both theory and practice.

6. Application of Microseismic Monitoring Technique on Overlying Strata Movement

Author: ChunAn Tang, Chief Scientist of Mechsoft (Dalian) Co., Ltd., Professor at DUT, Vice President of CSRME

As a three-dimensional space monitoring technology for monitoring rock mass micro-fracturing, microseismic monitoring technology has achieved rapid development. The microseismic monitoring technology mainly monitors time, space and intensity as well as related microseismic source parameters of micro-fracturing rovides in brittle rock mass under external force. With constant development and improvement of monitoring hardware and software, the microseismic monitoring technology has now been widely used in mines subjected to high ground stress both nationally and internationally, and has become an important means for ground pressure research and management in deep mines.

This section introduced two applications of microseismic technique on overlying strata movement. The first case is that a multichannel ESG microseismic monitoring system was established to monitor real-time and continuous microrupture of overlying strata by the advanced mining dynamic disaster monitoring equipment at the working face 62114(C14) in the Xinzhuangzi mine. In this case, a large number of monitoring data under the conditions of working face mining process are obtained. The relationship among 3D microseismic location event clusters, fracture zone and structure collapse regularity can be analyzed. The layout plan of methane extraction drainage boreholes are finally determined based on the different methane rich zones. The second case is microseismic monitoring technique is adopted to investigate the distribution regularity of microseismic events released by the coal mining-induced roof rock mass along the vertical and horizontal directions in combination with mine geological data. In this case, a zoning method is first established for the roof strata movement in the vertical and horizontal directions on the basis of the quantity and energy distributions of the microseismic eventsrecorded using the microseismic monitoring technique. The vertically zoning method is then applied to analyze the microseismic monitoring results obtained in the Dongjiahe Coal Mine, which divides rock mass into six zones along the vertical direction, i.e. the caved zone, the block zone, the vertical fracture through-going zone, the vertical fracture zone, the separation zone and the continuous zone. The horizontally zoning model divides the roof strata movement into three zones, i.e. the calm zone, the generation zone impacted by working face and the historical generation zone. After that, based on the horizontally zoning model, a method is developed to determine the displacement angle using the microseismic monitoring data, which has been verified in the Dongjiahe Coal Mine.

6.1 Microseismic Monitoring Technique

Development and application of modern high-precision microseismic monitoring technique originates from the South African gold mining activities in the mid-1980s. The objective was to solve plenty of rockburst and rock destruction problems induced by deep gold mining (more than 1000 m) at the Welkom area in South Africa and thus to avoid operational personnel and equipment damage. The principle of this technique consists of four aspects as given in the following: (1) using sensors to acquire seismic signals caused by rock fracture along with rock mass in the redistribution of stress; (2) determining the spatial location and magnitude of microseismic events through analysis and processing of seismic wave information; (3) estimating the development of non-linear strain region induced by microseismic activity according to the relationship between the cumulative number of microseismic events and energy release; and (4) judging the stability of rock mass.

Plenty of researches show that rock will inevitably release energy in the form of acoustic or seismic signals before its irreversible damage. Each seismic signal contains abundant information about the internal changes of rock mass. The signals recorded by microseismic monitoring system (MMS) are processed. The time, location, energy release and scalar seismic moment magnitude of each microseismic event can be routinely estimated from associated seismograms. These results depend on sensor sensitivity, dynamic range, frequency response, three-dimensional coverage of the sensor array, etc. Having recorded and processed a number of seismic events within a given volume of interest over time, one can then quantify the changes in the strain and stress regimes of the rock mass deformation associated with the microseismicity.

During the rock damage process, with collapses of voids or propagation of microcracks, the strain energy stored in the rock mass is released rapidly in the form of elastic wave i.e. microseismic phenomena. The microseismic monitoring technique for overlying strata movement is a technique to monitor the micro-cracking and stability of overlying strata by utilizing the elastic waves emitted due to excavation or mining.

6.2 Principle and Characteristics of Roof Collapse

The movement rule of surrounding rock structure and fracture development shows that the overlying coal and rock mass must generate the deformation and failure on the effects of the protective seam mining. The continuous destroy is in coordinate in the bottom of the key strata after mining, in other words, different distributing fractures will occur in the form of tensile stress or pressure stress. Generally speaking, there exits three zones in roof strata above the goaf after a key stratum is mined, namely 'caving zone', 'fracture zone' and 'bedding separation fracture zone', as shown in Figure 6.1.

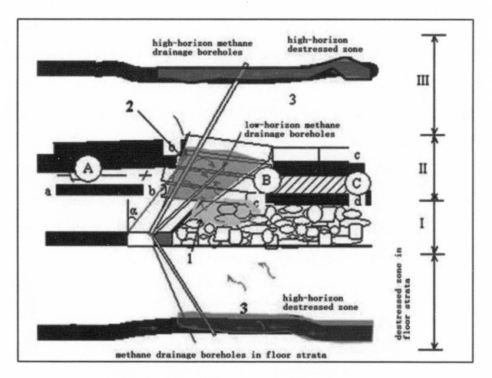

Figure 6.1 Zoning model of mining induced fractures.

Note: I, caving zone; II, fracture zone; III, bending zone; A, coal wall supporting zone; B, separating zone; C,re-compacting zone; 1, top void zone in upper goaf; 2, vertical fracture zone in fracture zone; 3, remote distressing seam void zone

Along the working face trend direction, the rock mass of caving zone will accumulate showed irregular state since mining stress influence, and the fracture distribution is in the condition of 'O' type in the goaf, the goaf methane is easy to enrich in the caving zone of the retained goaf side roadway because the methane is very light and the gas float upward, as shown in Figure. 6.1(1); bedding separation fractures are dominant in continuous deformation zone. Seam permeability within this zone can be significantly enlarged. Coal seam within the fracture zone provides good passage for methane drainage, as shown in Figure 6.1(3). The roof rock of regular caving zone and vertical fracture zone will distress and expand, and developing vertical fracture and bedding separated fissures, linking horizontal and vertical fracture with irregular caving zone, as a result, providing a favourable storage place for distressed gas in distressed coal seam and accumulated gas in the goaf as shown in Figure 6.1(2). In general, the methane of caving zone and bedding separation zone is easy to be drained. However, it is very difficult to define the methane rich zone of the fracture zone for the layout of methane boreholes.

6.3 Case Studies

6.3.1 Analysis of structure collapse regularity for overlying strata in stope

The hydrogeology tectonic background of 62114 face working in Xinzhuangzi coal mine is considerably complicated. The main lithology is siltstone, Feld spathic sandstone, detritus sandstone, siltstone and fine-grained sandstone and other rocks. The fractures and joints are relatively developed and friable. Pointing to conditions, Xinzhuangzi mine uses C14 coal seam as a protective seam to protect C13 seam. The C15 seam will not be mined for it is thin seam, so the C14 seam is a first mining seam. Moreover, the distance between C13 seam and C14 seam is just about 12 m, the horizontal bedding separated fissures will form when the C14 seam is mined. The boreholes can be arranged, and the methane in the C13 seam can be drained, so its outburst risk can be eliminated, finally, it can safely mine.

Since the April 6, 2009, the microseismic system has been working. It is composed of a seismic monitoring system, a visualization system and a remote intelligent wireless transmission GPRS system. Then three parts of microseismic monitoring system are uniaxial or triaxial sensors, acquisition unit and host analyzing data computer. This microseismic monitoring system is ESG system by Engineering Seismology Group of Canada.

The system of Xinzhuangzi mine has 30 uniaxial sensors. Each acquisition unit consisted of six uniaxial sensors, so there are five acquisition units for host computer, as shown in Figure 2. All signals are transmitted by copper twist cables to the acquisition unit underground, and then transmitted by an optical cable to the host analyzing data computer on the ground surface as well as the safety and production monitoring offices of the mine. Currently, the zone of monitoring is the first stage mining zone that has two face working and several roadways, C13 and C14 seam, especially C14 seam. The sensors are installed in the 2662 m, 2730 m bottom road, the gateway of C14 seam and other roadway which include the exploration zone and the surrounding rock mass. The monitoring zone will be extended the entire C13, C14, C15 seam mining zone, nearly 62114 face working.

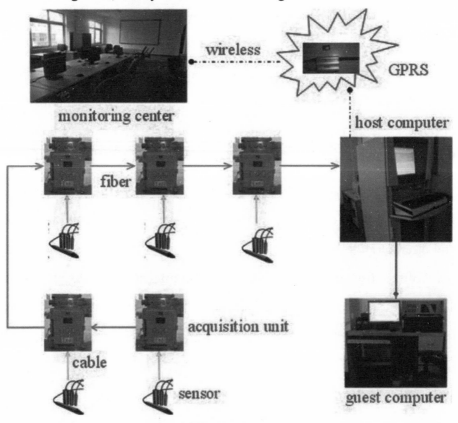

Figure 6.2 Network graph of monitoring system

In spatial volume and time period, seismic events are plotted in 3D with coordinates of hypocentres of events. The change of the spatial clusters can be analyzed by comparing the spatial distribution of events during different time periods. This result can show the high stress zone or abutment stress zone with the microseismic monitoring system. Under the influence of mining, the stress in rock strata re-distributes. Based on the principle that rock fractures occur in the zone of high stress differentials, the fracture zone is close to the high stress zone, and in combination with the microseismic monitoring system, the high stress and high tress differential zones can be rapidly located, hence finding out the fracture zones.

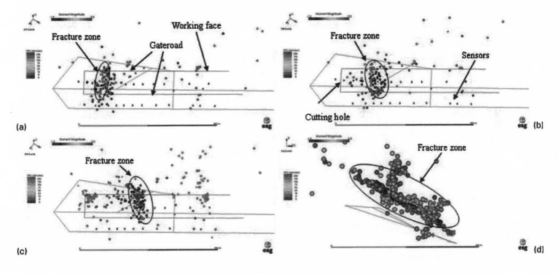

Figure 6.3 Fracture zone in goaf of different months.

Note:(a) face direction of April; (b) face direction of July; (c) face direction of October; (d) trend direction of April to December

Now the results of the microseismic monitoring and the fracture and methane rich zones in the goaf of the panel 62114 in three typical months (April, July and October) are shown in Figure 6.3. It is seen that the monitored results from April 6 to 30 when the working face was between the 2# and 3# geophones installed at the gateroad about 80 to 100 m away from the cutting hole. A large number of location events were generated along the whole 62114 working face, and as a word, microfractures were well developed in this region, as shown in Figure 6.3a.

With the working face moving forward, microfractures were also movable and well developed next to the down gateroad along the face direction, and extending into the goaf from July 1 to 31 when the working face was close to 9# geophone about 240 to 260 m away from the cutting hole, as shown in Figure 6.3b. However, the microfractures transferred gradually to the upper gateroad along the face direction from October 1 to 31 when the working face was close to 14# geophone about 490 to 510 m away from the cutting hole, as shown in Figure 6.3c. Therefore, it can be seen that the microfractures of overlying strata presented various distribution characteristics. Figure 3d shows the combined monitoring results of the nine months from April 6 to December 10. The results indicate that a fracture zone exists in the overlying strata which depth is ~47 m. At the same time, the zone provides a space for gas to move in and accumulate, forming methane rich zone, if methane drainage boreholes are drilled into this zone, methane can be effectively drained.

In addition, along the distance in the face direction, the agglomeration degree of microseismic events is remarkably different, as shown in Figure 6.4. The picture indicates that he microseismic events in A and B zone is obviously more than other zones, both the zones are located at the inside gateroad. The width of A zone is ~50 m, the number of A zone is 60–105; and the width of B zone is ~40 m, the number of B zone is 35–55, but the microseismic events are very few at the middle of face direction, namely compacted zone, and the number of this zone is ~20.

Therefore, the location events inside the gateroad is more, and the microfracture is rovideson, becoming the fracture zone, especially, the vertical fracture inside the retained roadway is significant, the A zone is greater than B zone from the number of location events or the dimension of fracture development zone. Following with the 62114 face mining, the fracture zone will appeared constantly above and near the return gateroad; as a result, different dimension methane rich zones can be defined until from April to August. From a cross-sectional view, the combined results of the monitoring along the face direction from April to August are fairly obvious.

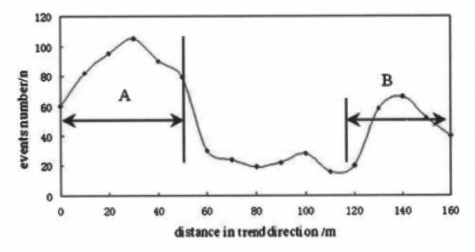

Figure 6.4 Distribution of microseismic events in trend direction

According to the statistics from April to August, the fractures in the roof were well developed. The fractures were concentrated near the gateroad, in particular near the return gateroad. As the face advances, the length of the zone would increase; however, the width of the zone would not vary too much. Between the gateroad, the zone width was within 50m and the height of the zone in the roof was within 41m. Therefore, the results reveal that the fracture zone is an irregular cylinder in the overlying strata of coal and rock seams.

In summary, as the face advances, the fractured area in the goaf is formed. Those located inside the gateroad are defined as the fracture zones. The height and width of the zones very continuously with the face advance rate. Moreover, the microseismic monitoring system can monitor the fracture zones and methane rich zones in real time, thus providing scientific basis for rovideson of gas drainage design. Finally, the designed borehole parameters and layout can be established based on the results of the microseismic monitoring system.

6.3.2 A zoning model for coal mining-induced strata movement

Dongjiahe Coal Mine is located in northwestern China and the No.22517 working face is one of the typical mining advancing faces of the mine at this moment. As shown in Figure 5a, the ground surface corresponding to the middle of the working face slopes gently while that corresponding to the western and eastern ends of the working face is full of ravines and gullies. There is a river flowing through the eastern surface of the working face. As shown in Figure 5b, the length of the coal mining face is 1217 m and the width is 185 m, and the thickness of the coal seam is from 2.5 to 4.1 m with an average of 3.3 m. Overall, the coal seam dips towards the north-east direction and belongs to No. 5 coal seam. The boreholes X13, X17 and X19 are located within the mining working face. It is found from these boreholes that there is a mudstone of about 0.6 m thickness in parts of the western region of the working face, which may form a false roof when the coal seam is mined. Above the mudstone, there is No.4 seam of 0.05 m thickness. The working face is advancing from east to west. Thus, the open-cut is located at 1217m (pitch distance), and the mining stop-line is located at 100m (pitch distance). The maximum height differences along the west-east and north-south directions are 50m and 20m, respectively. Thus, the inclination angle of the working face is about 3° and the working face is almost horizontal.

As shown in Figure 5a, the rock mass strata around the working face are as follows according to their formation ages from old to new: intermediate Ordovician System Fengfeng Formationin, upper Carboniferous System Taiyuan Formationin, lower Permian System Shanxi Formationin, lower Permian System Xiashihezi Formationin and Quaternary System overburden soil. As shown in Figure 5b, two faults were exposed in the shafts of the working face. One is located at 150 m (pitch distance) in the haulage roadway, whose strike is 5° south by west, dip is 30° and spacing distance is 2.9 m. The other lies at the open-cut with the strike of 70° south by west, the dip of 40°, and the spacing of 1.6 m. Moreover, there is an anticline from 480 m to 720 m (pitch distance), and the maximum height difference between the core of the anticline and its two wings is 4 m. Besides, there are thin seam zone from 530 m to 840 m (pitch distance) in orbital roadway, and those from 500 m to 810 m in the haulage roadway. The advancing schedule of the No. 22517 working face is shown in Table 6.1.

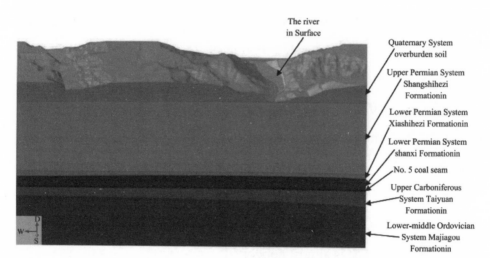

Figure a Geological situation of the No. 22517 working face.

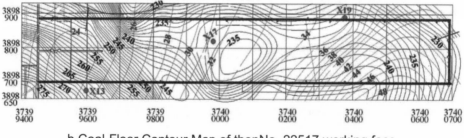

b Coal-Floor Contour Map of thenNo. 22517 working face.

Figure 6.5 General geological situation of the No. 22517 working face in in the Dongjiahe Coal Mine.

Table 6.1 Advancing schedule of the No. 22517 working face in Dongjiahe Coal Mine

Date (YYYY/MM/DD)	The mining face (Pitch distance)	Date (YYYY/MM/DD)	The mining face (Pitch distance)	Date (YYYY/MM/DD)	The mining face (Pitch distance)
2014/12/23	1005 m	2015/04/09	714 m	2015/07/18	677 m
2015/01/09	981 m	2015/04/18	700 m	2015/07/30	665 m
2015/01/19	942 m	2015/04/29	694 m	2015/08/08	657 m
2015/01/30	917 m	2015/05/08	688 m	2015/08/15	648 m
2015/02/09	885 m	2015/05/19	681 m	2015/08/19	642 m
2015/02/15	856 m	2015/05/30	750 m	2015/08/30	628 m
2015/02/27	847 m	2015/06/09	745 m	2015/09/08	615 m
2015/03/09	803 m	2015/06/19	736 m	2015/09/19	603 m
2015/03/19	779 m	2015/06/29	730 m	2015/09/29	592 m
2015/03/30	760 m	2015/07/09	720 m	2015/10/09	578 m

The sensors placement scheme for microseismic monitoring can be determined based on the monitoring purpose and the geological conditions in the No.22517 working face. The layout of the microseismic monitoring sensors in the No.22517 working face is depicted in Figure 6a. The network topology of the microseismic monitoring system is shown in Figure 6b. The monitored data are transmitted by a cable from the microseismic sensors installed around the working face to an underground workstation located within the mining stop line. The data then transmitted to the data storage and processing center in the grouting station on the surface via an optical fiber that runs along the underground roadway. After being processed in the data storage and processing center, the data are finally sent to research institutes for further analysis and to the mining management committee for decision-making.

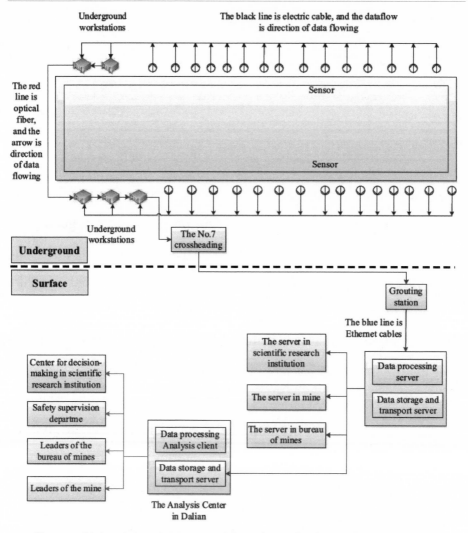

Figure a Network topology map of the microseismic monitoring system.

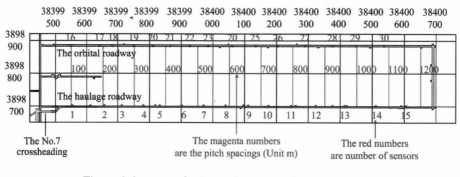

Figure b Layout of microseismic monitoring sensors
(The black numbers are the coordinates, unit m).

Figure 6.6 Microseismic monitoring scheme in the Dongjiahe Coal Mine

The No. 22517 working face has been in production since 5th October 2014. The microseismic monitoring was carried out in the working face from 25th November 2014 to 10th October 2015 and the spatial distributions of the overall monitoring results are shown in Figure 7a and b. The microseismic events mainly concentrated in two zones: The first microseismic event concentration zone lies close to the stop line of the No. 22517 working face, where a buried fault exists. Thus, the microseismic event concentrated zone is mainly impacted by the geological structure, whose center lies in the orbital roadway of the No. 22517 working face (Figure 7a) and whose side view presents a skew distribution (as shown in Figure 7b). The second microseismic event concentration zone is close to the working face, which is closely related to the coal mining in the working face. Thus, this microseismic event concentrated zone is mainly impacted by the coal mining. The coal mining – induced microseismic event concentration zone displays an elliptical distribution in the plane view (as shown in Figure 7a), which is consistent with the so-called "O" ring proposed by Liu, and displays an inverted trapezoid distribution in the side view (as shown in Figure 7b).

It can be seen from Figure 7c that the energies the microseismic events near the working face vary from several joules to hundreds of thousands joules, whose distribution near the working face complies with the bimodal distribution model put forward by Kijko & Dessokey. The first peak of the energy distribution of appears within the range from 5J to 100J while the second peak appears within the range from 100J to 50000J. As shown in Figure 7c, the microseismic events were distributed mainly in the range of the first peak before April 2015. The microseismic events in the range of the second peak increased rapidly and were dominant gradually after April 2015, which may be caused by the switch from the fully-mechanized mining to the blasting mining.

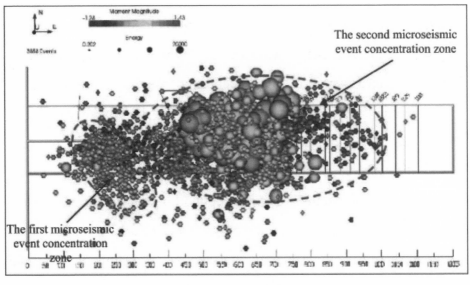

Figure a Top view

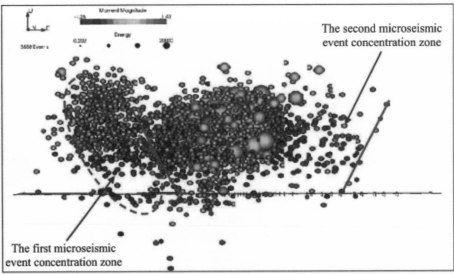

Figure b Vertical view

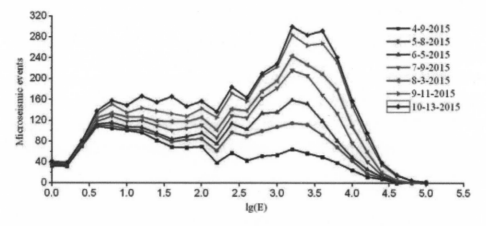

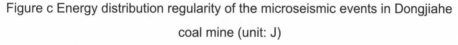

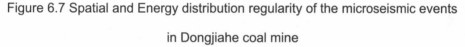

Figure c Energy distribution regularity of the microseismic events in Dongjiahe coal mine (unit: J)

Figure 6.7 Spatial and Energy distribution regularity of the microseismic events in Dongjiahe coal mine

The microseismic events (3140 in all) in the concentration zone induced by the coal mining are selected for statistical analysis, the distribution of the number and energy of microseismic events vs the depth can be obtained (as shown in Figure 8). The average elevation of the working face is EL 250 m. The following features points are identified according to the distribution of the microseismic events along the depth (Figure 8a): the points A (EL 260 m), B (EL 300 m), C (EL 360 m), D (EL 460 m) and E (EL 520 m). Among them, the point A corresponds to the lowest point where the microseismic events are monitored above the coal seam, the point B corresponds to the location where the number of the microseismic events start to increase rapidly above the coal seam, the point C is an abnormal point between the locations where the number of the microseismic events has been rapidly increasing, the point D is the location with the maximum number of the microseismic events, and the point E corresponds to the abnormal points between the locations where the number of the microseismic events has been rapidly decreasing. Similar phenomena can be observed from Figure 8b, also.

The following key strata can be positioned if the feature points identified according to the distribution regularity of the microseismic events along the depth is combined with the log of the borehole No.17 as depicted in Figure 9: the No. 50 stratum of fine siltstone with a thickness of 3.3 m, the No. 38 stratum of fine siltstone with a thickness of 14.9 m, the No.29 stratum of fine siltstone with a thickness of 14.7 m, the No.17 stratum of fine siltstone with a thickness of 20.1 m and the No.10 stratum of medium grained siltstone with a thickness of 11.1 m. Based on the key strata theory, the roof rock mass of the Dongjiahe Coal Mine is divided into 6 zones along the vertical direction, which are the caved zone, the block zone, the vertical fracture through-going zone, the vertical fracture zone, the horizontally separated zone and the continuous zone from the coal seam to the ground surface (Figure 9).

The horizontal distribution of the microseismic events in the roof rock mass includes the concentration zone induced by the advancing working face and the historical concentration zone impacted by the historical structure plane. According to the horizontally zoning model, the microseismic events in the coal mining induced concentration zone should display an inverted trapezoid zone in the side view, which coincides with the monitoring results in the No.22517 working face, as depicted in Figure 7b. With mining face being advanced, the new microseismic events added monthly were from 30 m behind the mining face to 220 m in front of the mining face (as shown in Table 2). The microseismic events in the coal mining – induced concentrated zone are selected for statistical analysis. According to the log of the No.17 borehole shown in Fig.12, the thickness of the overlying strata can be determined (not including the rovides ground cover), and the displacement angle of the roof rock mass movement can then be calculated, as summarized in Table 3. According to Table 3, the average displacement angle in the No. 22517 working face is 67°.

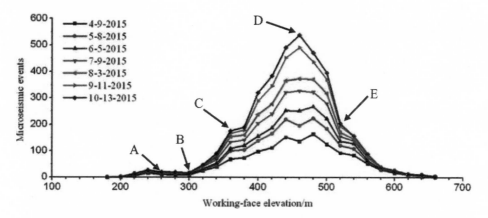

Figure a Number of the microseismic events along the vertical direction

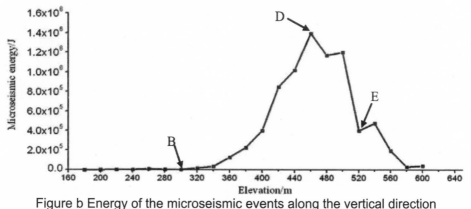

Figure b Energy of the microseismic events along the vertical direction

Figure 6.8 Distribution regularity of the microseismic events along the depth

Table 6.2 Relationship between the mining face and the distribution regularity of the microseismic events in Dongjiahe caol mine (from 2015/4/9 to 2015/10/10)

Date (YYYY/MM/DD)	The mining face (Pitch distance)	The range of the new microseismic events added monthly (Pitch distance)	The range of the new microseismic events added monthly (takeing the mining face as the reference)	The peak position of the cumulative microseismic events (takeing the mining face as the reference)
2015/04/09	750 m			
2015/05/08	730 m	750–500 m	20 m behind of the mining face to 230 m in front of the mining face	30 m in front of the
2015/06/04	707 m	750–500 m	43 m behind of the mining face to 207 m in front of the	57 m in front of the
2015/07/09	681 m	700–450 m	19 m behind of the mining face to 231 m in front of the	31 m in front of the
2015/08/03	661 m	700–450 m	39 m behind of the mining face to 211 m in front of the	61 m in front of the
2015/09/11	612 m	650–400 m	38 m behind of the mining face to 212 m in front of the	62 m in front of the
2015/10/10	577 m	600–350 m	23 m behind of the mining face to 227 m in front of the	27 m in front of the

Table 6.3 Displacement angle of strata movement in the No.22517 working face

	April 9	May 8	June 5	July 9	August 3	September 11	October 10
Working face position (pitch distance, unit: m)	750	730	700	681	657	615	578
Advanced impact position (pitch distance, unit: m)	600	550	530	500	485	460	452
Advanced impact distance (unit: m)	150	180	170	181	172	155	126
Strata thickness (unit: m)	386	386	386	386	386	386	386
Strata inter displacement angle (unit: Degree)	69	65	66	65	66	68	72

Stratigraphic unit	No.	Elevation unit: m	Thickness unit: m	Lithology	Note	Zone
Cenozoic	1	695.43	77.00	masking layer		
The Upper Permian System	2	618.43	7.40	coarse grained sandstone		Continuous zone
	3	611.03	3.30	fine siltstone		
	4	607.73	10.00	medium grained sandstone		
	5	597.73	2.70	fine siltstone		
	6	595.03	3.00	fine sandstone		
	7	592.03	11.70	fine siltstone		
	8	580.33	2.10	fine sandstone		
	9	578.23	58.00	fine siltstone		
The Upper Shihezi Formation in Upper Permian System (P2s)	10	520.23	11.10	medium grained sandstone	key strata	Horizontally separated zone
	11	509.13	4.20	fine siltstone		
	12	504.93	8.80	medium grained sandstone		
	13	496.13	8.80	fine siltstone		
	14	487.33	1.20	fine sandstone		
	15	486.13	28.50	fine siltstone		
	16	457.63	1.20	medium grained sandstone		
	17	456.43	20.10	fine siltstone	key strata	
	18	436.33	1.30	medium grained sandstone		Vertical fracture zone
	19	435.03	10.40	fine siltstone		
	20	424.63	5.70	medium grained sandstone		
	21	418.93	10.20	fine siltstone		
	22	408.73	3.00	fine sandstone		
	23	405.73	35.30	fine siltstone		
	24	370.43	1.80	medium grained sandstone		
	25	368.63	5.20	fine siltstone		
	26	363.43	0.80	medium grained sandstone		
	27	362.63	2.00	fine siltstone		
	28	360.63	2.00	medium grained sandstone		
	29	358.63	14.70	fine siltstone	key strata	Vertical fracture through-going zone
	30	343.93	4.00	medium grained sandstone		
	31	339.93	1.10	fine siltstone		
	32	338.83	4.80	medium grained sandstone		
	33	334.03	7.60	fine siltstone		
	34	326.43	3.20	fine sandstone		
	35	323.23	2.60	fine siltstone		
	36	320.63	8.30	medium grained sandstone		
The lower shihezi formation in lower Permian System (P1x)	37	318.33	4.60	fine sandstone		
	38	307.73	14.90	fine siltstone	key strata	Fragmented block zone
	39	292.83	2.70	fine sandstone		
	40	280.13	5.50	fine siltstone		
	41	284.63	1.80	medium grained sandstone		
The Shanxi Formation in lower Permian System (P1s)	42	282.83	1.70	fine siltstone		
	43	281.13	4.20	coarse sandstone		
	44	276.93	3.60	fine siltstone		
	45	273.33	4.60	coarse sandstone		
	46	268.73	4.06	medium grained sandstone		
	47	264.63	0.84	fine siltstone		Caved zone
	48	263.83	0.35	silty mudstone		
	49	263.47	5.60	fine siltstone		
	50	257.87	3.30	fine sandstone	key strata	
	51	254.57	0.86	fine siltstone		
	52	253.71	0.77	no.3 coal seam		
	53	252.95	0.81	fine siltstone		
	54	252.14	0.35	no.3 coal seam		
	55	251.79	1.56	fine siltstone		
	56	250.23	4.33	coarse sandstone		
	57	245.90	5.98	fine sandstone		
	58	239.92	3.00	medium grained sandstone		
	59	236.92	2.79	fine sandstone		
	60	234.13	1.66	coarse sandstone		
	61	232.47	3.19	no.5 coal seam		

Figure 6.9 vertically zoning model based on the microseismic monitoring

147

The Water, Rail and Major Roadway Pillar Leaving and Under Coal Mining Regulations provide the mining parameters and the thickness of loose layer (Table 4) as well as the boundary angle, the displacement angle and the break angle of (Table 5) of the typical work face in history in the Dongjiahe Coal Mine. It can be seen from Table 4 that the geological conditions of the No.22517 working face are similar to those of the No.CW11501 working face although the thickness of the coal seam in the No.22517 working face is smaller, and the size of the working face is larger. The boundary, displacement, and breaking angles of the No.CW11501 working face are 59.9°, 63° and 69.1°, respectively (sa shown in Table 5). Therefore, the displacement angle of 67° obtained based on the microseismic monitoring technology basically coincides with that provided by the underground coal mining regulations.

Table 6.4 Mining elements of the typical work face in history in the Dongjiahe Coal Mine

Area (Layer age)		Observation Station	Mining Elements							Thickness of loose layer (m)
			Mining thickness (m)	Dip angle (°)	Mining depth (m)	Dimension (m)	Progression (m/month)	Mining method	Roof management	
(Carboniferous and Permian)	Chenghe Mining Area	CD1250	2.19	7	285/301	520/125	42	Blasting	Full Caving	106.3
		CR22508	1.93	8	206/201	575/105		Blasting	Full Caving	26.2
		CQ5316	2.1	6	193/166	256/236		Blasting	Full Caving	8–147
		CQ5208	2.15		240	573/282		High-grade	Full Caving	110
		CQ5118	2.1	210	230/256	465/100		High-grade	Full Caving	120
		CW11501	5.7	2	210/239	158/158		Full-mechanized	Full Caving	175.5

Table 6.5 Angle parameters of the typical work face in history in the Dongjiahe Coal Mine

Area (Layer age)		Observation station	Angle parameters										
			Boundary angle				Displacement angle				angle of break		
			ā0 (°)	ā0 (°)	ā0 (°)	ø (°)	â (°)	ā (°)	ā (°)	ē(°)	ā0 (°)	ā0 (°)	ā0 (°)
(Carboniferous and Permian)	Chenghe Mining Area	CD1250	60	64	64	42	72	70	77.5		73	74	82
		CR22508	74	75			75.6	74			76	77	
		CQ5316	69.5					74	77.5			78	80
		CQ5208		66					72				74
		CQ5118	54		61		72		71		78		77
		CW11501	59.9				63				69.1		

6.4 Conclusion

This section introduced two applications of microseismic technique on overlying strata movement, which has proved the feasibility of the microseismic monitoring technique to monitor strata movement and associated microseismicity induced by mining. In the case studies, several conclusions can be obtained. First, a complete microseismic monitoring system is established for detecting fracture zones in 62114 face working, the relationships among seismicity, the fracture evolution rule in the roof strata and mining process are found. Second, based on the mechanism theory of overlying strata in the goaf, a conceptual model of finding the methane rich zone is proposed like the conditions of Xinzhuangzi coal mine, which provides a method for drainage boreholes layout and gas controlling. Third, the results indicate that there exists a fracture zone inside the goaf, above and near the retained gateroad, and the methane rich zone is defined. Besides, the relationship between the vertically zoning model, the horizontally zoning model and the distribution regularity of the microseismic events released by the roof rock mass strata movement are investigated. The proposed vertically zoning model, and the horizontally zoning model are applied to analyze the microseismic data monitored in the No. 22517 working face of the Dongjiahe Coal Mine and determine the displacement angle based on the microseismic events. The heights of the fractured zone and vertical fracture through-going zone around the No. 22517 are determined, which are consistent with those predicted using the traditional three-zone model. Moreover, the analysis of the monitored microseismic data shows the average displacement angle around the No. 22517 working face is 67° using the microseismic monitoring data, which is equivalent to the historical measurements obtained from the typical working faces of the Dongjiahe Coal Mine.

7. Underground Coal Gasification: New Trend of Supply-Side Economics of Fossil Fuels

Author: Mao Fei, Sichuan Development Holding Co., Ltd.

Abstract

China has a huge demand for energy. Under the present energy structure of rich coal, lean oil, less gas, limited and low-rising rate renewable energy, discussion focus is now on the high-efficient mining of coal as well as its clean-and-low-carbon use. In view of this, based on an analysis of the problems in the coal chemical industry and the present coal utilization ways such as Integrated Gasification Combined Cycle (IGCC), this paper proposes that underground coal gasification (UCG) technology is a realistic choice. By virtue of its advantages in many aspects such as safety & environment, integrated use of superior resources, economic feasibility, etc. this technology can serve as the front-end support and guarantee for coal chemical industry and IGCC. Under the present situation, the following proposals were presented to promote the development of this technology. First, R&D of technical products should be strengthened, a comprehensive feasibility study assessment system should be established, and the relevant criteria in the industry should be formulated. Second, precise market positioning of UCG products should be made with much concern on the integrated economic indicators of each product's complete flow scheme, following the principle of "Technical Feasibility First, Economic Optimization Followed". Third, a perfect operation and management pattern should be established with strict control over high-efficient, environmentally-friendly, safe, harmonious & compact objectives in the whole industry chain. In conclusion, to realize the large-scale UCG commercial production will strongly promote the optimization and innovation of fossil fuels supply-side economics in China.

Keywords: China; Underground coal gasification (UCG); Supply-side economics; Fossil fuel energy; Coal chemical industry; Integrated gasification combined cycle (IGCC); Energy safety

In 2014, China supplied 19% of the world's energy and consumed 23% of the world's total, with an increase of 8.6% in natural gas consumption and an increase of 3.3% in oil con-sumption. In the year, China imported 3×10^8 t of crude oil and 583×10^8 m^3 of natural gas, and its dependence on foreign oil and gas were 61% and 30%, respectively. Despite a global economic downturn, China still witnessed a further increase in natural gas consumption in 2015 reaching 1800×10^8 m^3, accounting for 5e6% of the world's total consumption. It is projected that China will surpass Russia as the world's second largest natural gas consumer in mid-2020 and surpass the United States as the world's largest oil consumer by around 2030 [1]. By 2030, China's total natural gas consumption will reach 5800×10^8 m^3, accounting for 10% of the world's total, and its per capita annual natural gas consumption will be 450 m^3, three times that at present, which, though basically at the current world average level, is still less than 20% of the US per capital by present. It has become the public consensus to increase the proportion of natural gas utilization, which can be further confirmed from the actual data of China's recent natural gas consumption, imports and increase rate [2], fuel gas consumption and increase rate [3], as well as national planning and guidance report on natural gas [4].

Despite a huge annual energy demand, China has an extremely low reserve-production ratio of conventional fossil energy sources, except for coal which has sufficient production and a high reserve-production ratio. The reserve-production ratio of oil is just 11.9 years and that of natural gas is just 25.7 years, and more seriously, the current rate of new proven oil and gas reserves is significantly below the increase rate of consumption [1]. It is forecast that by 2030, the self-sufficiency rate of clean fossil fuels (hydrocarbon) will be less than 40% in China, showing a serious supply and demand imbalance. Such a huge supply gap of fossil materials cannot be ignored internationally. Historically, what Japan and Europe suffered and what Ukraine is suffering have proven that a too low energy self-sufficiency rate will bring great constraints and a painful experience to the development of a country [5]. If China places too much hope on international supply in fossil fuels, price stability and supply sustainability will not be guaranteed, which will even pose threats to na-tional security. Under the present energy structure of rich coal, lean oil, less gas, limited and low-rising rate renewable energy, discussion focus is now being shifted from the use of coal to the ways to mine and utilize coal in a secure, clean and effi-cient way. In the current situation, underground coal rovid-cation is a realistic choice catering to current needs.

7.1 Underground coal gasification and research status

As one of the technologies for coal development, under-ground coal gasification (UCG) technology is an industrial process which converts coal into product gas through thermal and chemical action of coal for clean development and utili-zation of coal.

7.1.1 Industrial process

7.1.1.1 Research progress at abroad

The concept of underground coal gasification was conceived by Mendeleev in 1888. Since then, a number of countries have done a lot of research work in the field of underground coal gasification. By far, there have been some 33 underground coal gasification projects overseas, mainly in the Soviet Union, the United States, Australia, South Africa, Canada and Europe.

In the 1970s and 1980s in the United States, 38 tests were

carried out on several project bases in the then Lawrence Berkeley National Laboratory and several other research in-stitutions, and "regressive underground coal gasification" technology was developed [5]. The United States positioned this technology as a technical reserve for national energy se-curity, which will be used in times of energy crisis. But no further research has been conducted in the optimization of its economic efficiency.

In the Soviet Union, Skochinsky National Institute of Mining developed underground gasification technology, which has been applied in a great number of mines within the Soviet Union and has been proven technically feasible. By far, six underground coal gasification projects have been implemented in the Soviet Union [6]. Among them, Ergo Exergy [7] in Uzbekistan is the world's only underground coal gasification project currently still under operation.

In partnership with the US companies and by reference to its UCG technology, a Canadian company developed UCG technology [8] through continuous self-development and field experiments. The technology basically represents the main-stream of UCG technology in western countries, and has been applied directly or indirectly in UCG tests in Australia, South Africa, India, China and other countries. The Canadian com-pany declares that it has achieved industrialization of the technology.

Australian underground coal gasification has been based on Canadian technology. By far, Australia has relatively the most complete industrial chain of industrial tests of underground coal gasification. A representative project is Linc's Chinchilla [9] Underground Coal

Gasification Liquefaction Project.

South Africa has launched coal liquefaction projects and has some coal chemical industrial basis. However, its under-ground coal gasification technology is largely introduced directly or indirectly from Canadian UCG technology. During 2006e2012 in South Africa, relevant industrial tests were carried out in Eskom [9] and other areas and more industrial tests on a much larger scale were planned to be implemented. However, no substantive work has been carried out yet.

Currently, countries ready for underground coal gasification technology research include Britain, Pakistan, Bulgaria, Vietnam and Poland; EU, India and other countries and re-gions are focusing on the development of this technology. Britain started its first underground gasification test worldwide in 1912. Recently, it approved the 61274×10^4 m^2 coal mining rights for underground gasification research in the North Sea basin. The Central Mining Institute (CMI in Poland) and Linc (in Australia) worked together to undertake the EU HUGE2 underground gasification project, which is a follow-up research of the HUGE, an EU Project of CBM in Deep Part. The Indian government is drafting underground coal gasification policies, and Pakistan is partnering with China University of Mining and Technology in preliminary tests in the desert 360 km north to its capital.

In terms of implementation effect, the Ergo Exergy Project and the Chinchilla Project can best reflect the overall level of the industry. Established in 1961 and with a production ca-pacity of 100×10^4 m^3/d, the shaftless Ergo underground coal gasification station gasifies brown coal into power coal gas for the Exergy thermal power station and blended heavy oil power generation. Demonstrated in 1999, the project had been fully halted by 2013 due to years of disputes and the inability to demonstrate that the project will exert no environmental impact. Technically, this project features negative pressure

gasification and direct conversion of gasified coal into syn-thetic oil. It is the first representative project in the world to enable coal gasification, gas purification, and synthetic oil all in one.

7.1.1.2 Current research in China

Yu Li [10], Wang Zuotang [11], Liang Jie [12], Yang Lanhe [13], Liu Shuqin [14] from China University of Mining and Technology, and Chai Zhaoxi [15] from the State Adminis-tration of Coal Mine Safety, Li Wenjun from North China

Please cite this article in press as: Mao F, Underground coal gasification (UCG): A new trend of supply-side economics of fossil fuels, Natural Gas Industry B (2017), http://dx.doi. org/10.1016/j.ngib.2016.12.007

Institute of Science & Technology and some other researchers and teams have carried out tests basically on shaft gasification in Xuzhou, Tangshan, Xinwen, Zhongliangshan, Huating, Wulanchabu and other places after introducing and absorbing technologies from the Soviet Union, the United States, Australia and other countries. The most representative one is the underground gasification project under the "863 Program" undertaken by Suncun, Xiezhuang and Ezhuang Coal Mines under the former Xinwen Mining Bureau.

In terms of technical phases, China mainly assimilated the Soviet Union technologies before the 1980s; it began to introduce the US technologies in the 1990s; in the 21st century, it gradually developed theories and technologies repre-sented by long-passage, large cross-section, two-stage, positive and negative direction (abbreviated as "LLTS-UCGP") and reverse combustion gasification based on the assimilation of western and Soviet Union technologies and innovation. As early as the 1950s, China was engaged in underground coal gasification research in Hegang, Fushun, and Southern Anhui, but no significant technological breakthrough had been made until 1985 in Mazhuang Mine and Xinhe Mine in Xuzhou. Through gasification of 80 m-deep residue coal pillars with a thickness of 1.15 m and an inclination of 680, China University of Mining and Technology obtained coal gas with a daily production of 16×104 m3 and a calorific value of 4 MJ/m^3; in the tests in Xinhe, through gasification of steep-inclined seams with a thickness ranging from 2 to 4 m, coal gas was obtained with a daily production of 20×10^4 m^3 and a calorific value of 3.2e5.6 MJ/m^3. In 1995, China University of Mining and Technology established two gasifiers for industrial tests in Liuzhuang Mine in Tangshan and obtained high-yield gas flow. However, these two gasifiers were forced to work under a vapor pressure due to serious gas leakage, and the project was halted as a result of coal depletion four years later. In 1999, Shandong Energy Xinwen Mining Group Co., Ltd. Carried out 13 years of gasification tests in three pairs of physically exploited mines through residue pillars in partner-ship with China University of

Mining and Technology. This project was the first attempt to test in 2.5 m-thick gentlyinclined gas coal. Through continuous exploration of the output, composition, calorific value and other data of injected air and oxygen-enriched vapor, different gasifier types and different gasification lengths and widths were studied to explore the comprehensive utilization of the calorific value of coal gas in ground heating, gas supply and power generation. Because of this project, a wealth of data and experiences in China's underground coal gasification were accumulated and a systematic and scientific basis was provided for the further optimization of subsequent projects. In 2007, Chongqing Zhongliangshan Coal, Electricity and Gas Co., Ltd. Tested the project successfully in the 3.5 m-thick steep-inclined coking coal. Nevertheless, this project was halted as a result of environmental pollution by large amounts of H2S in the coal gas. In 2010, Huating Coal Industry Group Co., Ltd. Sucrovi in pillar tests, and further explored the economics of power generation by oxygen-enriched vapor gasification. An underground coal gasification company established jointly by several entities including ENN and China University of Mining and Technology (Beijing) engaged the chief engineers and workshop directors of underground coal gasification projects from Uzbekistan as chief experts to explore shaftless, sub-horizontal underground coal gasification technologies in China for the first time, with a depth of coal seam of 280 m, a thickness of 6e8 m, and drilling spacing of 30e40 m. In October 2007, successful ignition and stable gas delivery were realized with daily air gas of 30×104 m3, oxygen-enriched gas of 15×10^4 m^3, and gasified coal of 100t. In June 2009, exemplary low-calorific-value power generation was realized with 3 sets of 500 kW generator generating power for 783 days. But in the absence of further planning for coal gas utilization, surplus gas was evacuated. The project was sus-pended after completing its test functions at the end of 2014, and scale research after optimization is being considered. It is planned that 2×10^8 m^3/a LNG will be produced in the first phase. There are totally 7 gasifiers, involving a total invest-ment of about CN 1.5e2.0 billion yuan and daily producing 340×10^4 m^3 synthesis gas; the planned production of the second phase is 5×10^8 m^3/a LNG.

The projects recently implemented in China include: "the Key Technology for UCG Industry" under the "863 Program" just concluded in 2015 and undertaken by ENN Group; the "Integrated Project of Coalbed Gas Extraction and Underground Coal Gasification of Steep Thin Seam Clusters in Zhongliangshan" started in December 2015 by CECEP and Chongqing Zhongliangshan Coal, Electricity and Gas Co., Ltd. The projects ready to be implemented include: the project of underground gasification of Shanjiaoshu coal mine, a major science and technology project of Guizhou Province undertaken jointly by Guizhou Panjiang Refined Coal Co., Ltd. And China University of Mining and Technology; Sanhuisankuang underground gasification project jointly-undertaken by Chongqing Energy Group and Linc Group (Australia). This shows that China is one of the countries with the largest number of underground gasification test sites and the most active research, but further research is needed in key scale technologies and industrial chain extension.

Analysis and trends of representative research projects at home and abroad

A summary of some representative underground coal gasification projects at home and abroad (Table 1) shows foreign projects are mostly shaftless, which have advantages such as flexible mine construction, low costs, and high speeds and disadvantages such as a limited number of coal and low resource utilization efficiency; domestic projects are mostly shaft projects, featuring high shaft construction costs, low subsequent roadway and drilling costs, high resource utilization efficiency, and good adaptability to complex geological conditions. They particularly have advantages in the use of existing facilities, equipment and systems of production mines. At present, the shaft projects implemented in China basically utilize the infrastructures of old mines. With increasingly mature drilling and well control technology and decreasing costs, shaftless underground gasification will be

Table 7.1

Parameters of coal gas products of some representative UCG projects at home and abroad.

Country	Project name	Technique	Agent injected	Gas composition						Q_{net} Calorific value/(MJm^{-3})
				CH_4	H_2	CO	C_mH_n	CO_2	N_2	
Soviet Union	Ergo exergy		Air	1.8e1.9%	17.6e19.7%	4.5e7.5%	0.2e0.3%	17.2e20.0%	42.7e58.0%	3.18e3.56%
	Geer Krumlov	Soviet Union UCG	Air	2.8%	29.4%	19.5%		18.3%	27.8%	6.67%
	Lehizensk	Shaftless	Air	2.38%	15.8%	7.62%	0.19%	32.2%	38.33%	3.67%
	Moscow suburbs		Air	1.9%	35%	15.3%	0.4%	28.1%	16.2%	6.71%
	Maas Mine		Air	6.3%	37%	25.8%		28.8%	1.4%	9.55%
The United States	High Vegas	CRIP	Air	4.1%	24.5%	21.2%	0.3%	47.8%		7.04%
	North Wyoming	Shaftless	Air	4%	20%	10%		16%	50%	3.77e5.44%
Australia	Chinchilla, Queensland	UCG Shaftless	Air	18%	32%	17%				5%
China	Xinhe, Xuzhou		Air	2.91%	23.58%	7.78%			52.25%	5.02%
			Oxygen-enriched vapor	11.05%	59.9%	12.64%			2.84%	13.65%
			Air	2e4%	10e20%	5e25%			40e65%	4.18e5.86%
	Liuzhuang, Hebei	LLTS-UCGP	Oxygen-enriched vapor	7.8e14.1%	40.6e53.1%	11.2e28.1%			5.1e17.9%	13.78%
	Hebi, Henan		Air	2%	13%	20%			59%	4.73%
	Feicheng, Shandong	Shaft	Air	3e5%	15e25%	5e8%			40e65%	3.76e5.02%
	Xiyang, Shanxi		Air	2e4%	15e20%	5e10%			40e65%	4.18e5.02%
			Oxygen-enriched vapor	7e10%	45e55%	10e15%			10e15%	11e13%
			Air	3.04%	24.59%	3.37%			52.81%	4.22%
	Suncun, Xinwen		Oxygen-enriched vapor	9.28%	52.86%	9.32%		17.51%	5.6%	11.36%
			Air	1.51%	16.34%	12.73%	0.25%		51.66%	4.1%
	Huating, Shanxi	Reverse, shaft	Oxygen-enriched vapor	3.52%	36.19%	29.61%	0.49%	25.73%	4.46%	9.27%

Please cite this article in press as: Mao F, Underground coal gasification (UCG): A new trend of supply-side economics of fossil fuels, Natural Gas Industry B (2017), http://dx.doi.org/10.1016/j.ngib.2016.12.007

increasingly used for new and deeply buried coal resources; shaft underground gasification will be increasingly adopted for deep resources or existing coal pillars.

The calorific value of coal gas is mainly linked to the water and oxygen content of the gasification agent injected, regardless of shaft or shaftless projects. Data in Table 1 show a lower calorific value of the coal gas when air is injected ("air gas"), basically between 3 and 7 MJ/m^3, while the calorific value of the coal gas injected with "oxygen-rich vapor" (ox-ygen-rich water gas) is basically between 9 and 14 MJ/m^3. In order to increase the unit calorific value and achieve large-scale gasification, it is suggested to use oxygen-rich water gas in the future in the development of underground coal gasification technology.

In terms of gas composition, useful gases are mainly H_2, CO and a small amount of CH_4 and CmHn. The market need for the H_2/CO ratio can be met through adjustment of the O_2/ H_2O ratio in the injected gases. In addition, CH_4 mining and underground gasification can be combined through process control, just as the Chinchilla Project did. In the future, it is even possible to produce CH_4 as much as possible in a high-pressure environment, just as demonstrated in the EU.

Through research and analysis of the limited projects at home and abroad, underground gasification theories and technologies are feasible, but all the gasification work has been done "just for gasification purposes". There are only individual primary chain cases in the industry, without continuous, scale and economically-viable projects. Recently, a number of countries and regions show a great interest in the technology or carry out relevant research, and many enterprises and research institutes are planning to promote the industrialization of underground coal gasification, due to its great prospects, China's environmental capacity constraints, and European impact by the international relationship.

7.1.2 Problems solved

7.1.2.1 Relevant theoretical basis for coal gasification

Thanks to the development of coal science, coal quality science, coal chemistry, combustion science, mining science and other relevant disciplines, the combustion and chemical synthesis theories of underground coal gasification have been basically verified, a large number of technologies for coal gasification and chemical synthesis have been developed, and a lot of experiences have also been summarized. The United States Department of Energy (DOE) announced that underground coal gasification technologies would be extensively used for the production of coal gas to meet the urgent national needs in case of an energy crisis.

7.1.2.2 Infrastructure facilities for scale production

With the development of geology, mining, chemicals, materials, machinery, credit control and other industries, similar equipment for evaluation, gasification agents, oven building, monitoring and control, and gas gathering required for the implementation of underground gasification projects has been provided for research and improvement, and infrastructure facilities have been provided for further research and development. The successful implementation of underground coal gasification projects best represented by Australia's combined project of underground coal gasification and ground liquefaction has demonstrated the feasibility and availability of underground gasification technical route and process equipment.

7.2 Comparative advantages of underground coal gasification technology

7.2.1 Safety and environmental advantages

Restricted by the existing mining methods and techniques, traditional coal mining can't overcome mashgas, ceiling plates, water damage, fires, blasting, electromechanical, and transport accidents and other occupational diseases such as silicosis. Without changes in mining principles, it will hard to funda-mentally eliminate such accidents. Although remarkable achievements have been made in the reduction of the death rate per million ton (DRPMT) in China (from 3.08 in 2004 to 0.157 in 2015), the rate is still 8e10 times as high as that in the United States. In addition, significant social loss will be caused due to injuries, silicosis, occupational poisoning, hearing loss and other chronic noise. Through converting physical coal mining into chemical coal mining, underground coal gasification significantly reduces the number of personnel required. The limited number of operators basically does not need to be in direct contact with coal, and the coal gas produced is delivered to the ground through pipelines, thus fundamentally avoiding such accidents and occupational diseases.

Coal mining also caused surface subsidence ($30 \times 10^8 m^2$), land occupation and pollution by waste rock ($1.2 \times 10^8 m^2$), soil erosion, destruction of water resources, release of green-house gases like CH_4 and other problems in China. Moreover, in the process of storage, loading and transport, there may be dust pollution and transport accidents, and coal combustion may also cause a lot of coal-burning pollution. Data show that China's CH_4 emissions account for about 60% of the world's total, while dust, CO_2, Nox and SO_2 released by coal com-bustion account for 60%, 71%, 67% and 87% of the world's total [16], respectively. By 2035, China's carbon emissions will account for 30% of the world's total, fully above the level of the OECD countries.

To cover its insufficient environmental carrying capacity, China has approved over 80 relatively environmentally-friendly ground coal gasification projects over the past decade. Currently, China has a capacity of coal gasification (built and under construction) of 114×10^8 m^3/a, and the ca-pacity of projects in the phase of pre-feasibility studies is 680×10^8 m^3/a; the capacity of coal-to-olefins (CTO) projects that have been put into operation is 1136×10^4 t/a, and the capacity of projects under construction is 1439×10^4 t/a; the capacity of coal-to-ethylene glycol projects that have been put into operation is 332×10^4 t/a, the capacity of projects under construction is 245×10^4 t/a, and the capacity of projects in the phase of pre-feasibility studies is 650×10^4 t/a; the above projects involve a total amount of funds of CN 1.3 trillion yuan.

Although the existing ground coal gasification and IGCC have improved over the traditional coal gasification and coalfired power plants, they cannot fundamentally solve the safety and environmental problems caused by such frontend processes as coal mining and processing, transportation, ground gasification, and liquefaction, due to the inability to fundamentally change such processes. This also causes the emergency shutdown of many coal chemical projects and a few IGCC projects during construction (and even operation) and a low operating rate, due to environmental problems like high salt and wastewater.

During underground coal gasification, only gas is brought out of the ground, while large amounts of ash, heavy metal salts and other substances remain, and large amounts of water vapor and residual heat are recycled. Intractable SO_2 and Nox are turned into tractable H_2S, N_2 and Ncontaining compounds. This helps reduce surface subsidence, minimize the disturbance of underground hydrosphere and lithosphere, and save a lot of tailings area. More importantly, CH_4 and H_2S emitted by physical exploitation are fully utilized, and emissions of dust and other harmful substances are reduced due to reduced transportation.

7.2.2 Comprehensive utilization of resources and energy efficiency advantages

As of 2013, the proven coal reserves were 1.48×10^{12} t in China, 8% of them being high-sulfur coal forbidden to be mined by conventional means and over 12% of them being low-grade brown coal hard to use.

Table 7.2

Underground coal gasification material balance.

Output				Input		Efficiency			
Estimated gas production/(10^8 m^3a^{-1})	Calorific value of gas/($MJSm^{-3}$)	Gas production rate/(m^3St^{-1})	Total calorific value/(10^4 $GJSa^{-1}$)	Amount of coal gasified/(10^4 tSa^{-1})	Calorific value of coal/($MJSkg^{-1}$)	Water consumption/(10^4 tSa^{-1})	Oxygen consumption/(10^8 m^3Sa^{-1})	Oxygen consumption per ton of coal/m^3	Water consumption per ton of coal/t
3.78	6.28	2700	237	14	21.77	2.9	0.43	307.19	0.25
15.12	6.28	2700	950	56	21.77	11.6	1.72	307.19	0.25
37.80	6.28	2700	2374	140	21.77	28.9	4.30	307.19	0.25

Statistics in 2013 shows over 300×10^8 t of abandoned coal and about 2.7×10^{12} t of coal with a depth of over 1000m. If large amounts of idle coalrelated investment currently under construction, operation or physical mining are included, the amount of idle coalrelated investment in China will be much larger. At the same time, strategically, the coal industry should figure out ways to make full use of the idle resources with high sulfur, coal and gas which are hard to explore through the existing facilities.

Through underground coal gasification, coal seams that can be mined by conventional means can be developed. In addition, high-sulfur coal, low-grade brown coal and gas, and coal with serious water damage and other coal hard to develop can also be mined in a safe, efficient and environmentally-friendly way. More importantly, coal abandoned by physical mining and unexploited deep coal resources can also be recovered. In the process of underground gasification, water in the mine can be comprehensively recycled and zero emissions can be ensured. Moreover, sulfur and gas heat can also be recycled, and coal tar and other higher-value products can be recovered. This protects the environment while ensuring resource classification and recycling.

In China, coal resources and water resources are reversely distributed, leaving coalrich areas generally short of water. Therefore, the Chinese government basically bases coal production on water resources in its ground coal chemical policy. The use of UCG technology in the frontend of the coal chemical industry to ease the bottlenecks of high water consumption and large amounts of salt wastewater will bring opportunities to the green, sustainable development of the coal chemical industry.

Based on relevant theories and test data (as shown in Table 2), if the annual gasification capacity is 14×10^4 t, 56×10^4 t, and 140×10^4 t respectively, then the coal gas volume of 3.78×10^8, 15.12×10^8, and 37.80×108 m^3 can be obtained respectively.

23.73×10^8, 94.93×10^8 and 237.34×10^8 MJ of heat energy can be finally obtained, and 307m^3 of oxygen and 0.25t of water will be consumed for each ton of coal, as it is calculated by me. These data indicate great advantages in energy efficiency over traditional development means.

While enhancing resource recovery, underground coal gasification can effectively improve the efficiency of energy conversion, given its products are mainly CO and H_2. Table 3 shows that physical mining and conventional power generation of coal deliver only about 23% of aggregate energy efficiency, and the comprehensive energy conversion rate is only 30% even if ultra super-critical techniques are adopted; the use of UCG-IGCC can further enhance the energy efficiency of gas-fired combined cycle power generation (to 50% in theory) while greatly improving mining recovery; if the advantage of C1 chemical engineering is given full play, the comprehensive energy efficiency of UCG-coal chemical can reach 63% in theory, more than twice that of super-critical techniques. It is forecast that 47% of the world's energy will be consumed in the form of electricity over the next 20 years. If environmental pollution is further addressed in the front-end gasification of IGCC and comprehensive energy efficiency is further improved, then IGCC will have a much broader industrial prospect.

The status of the energy supply structure shows that a better way for China is deep processing and utilization of coal. However, coal chemical and IGCC technology is not economically rational, and there are major problems with the environment (especially with water). No rational way has been found in clean coal use. Considering the supply sustainability, energy efficiency, environment, safety, and technical feasibility of all types of resources as well as the existing national industrial base and layout and other major factors, the author considers new coal chemical industry and IGCC as a major supply of fossil fuels in China. Underground coal gasification technology can serve as the front-end support and guarantee for coal chemical industry and IGCC. As one of the ways to supply sustainable fossil raw materials in China, this technology will play an important role in improving the environ-ment and leading industrial upgrading of coal, coal chemical industry and thermal power.

7.2.3 Economic feasibility

Based on the above analysis of energy efficiency, the economic feasibility of underground coal gasification will be further analyzed. Its economy is estimated by the simplest means (product use, e.g. power generation) through field sur-vey and analysis of some projects that have been implemented in China with reference to the construction costs of the existing physically-exploited mines. Just like physical explosion, coal costs are based on conventional exploration costs, while comprehensive thermal efficiency of power generation is 36%, the unit price of the electrical product is CN 0.44 yuan/(kW$h), and the mine construction cost is calculated at the current labor costs. Based on the above three types of scales, the investment costs are CN 3.4 yuan×10^8, CN 9.6 yuan×10^8 and CN 23.1 yuan×10^8, respectively, among which, all types of access construction costs account for 5.41%e12.6%, oxygen equipment construction costs account for 21%e49%, and mine construction costs account for 72.84%e37.86%. Table 4 shows that the total construction cost of coal per ton is between CN 2442 yuan and 1653 (power generation cost: CN 1060 yuan/t). However, when the scale is beyond 56×10^4t/a, the con-struction cost will be lower, indicating that the gasification scale of 150×104t/a is economically reasonable. In terms of operating costs, the power generation costs of coal per ton are CN 203 yuan/t, on the above three scales, the gasification costs are CN 292 yuan/t, CN 224 yuan/t, and

CN 214 yuan/t, respectively, the profits of coal per ton are CN 48 yuan/t, CN 116 yuan/t and CN 126 yuan/t, respectively and the static in-vestment payback periods are approximately 12.2 years, 7.7 years, and 7.2 years, respectively.

Based on the calculation of single items and comparison of the investment, income, resource utilization and development mode of the raw coal sales, power generation, underground gasification generation, and gasified CH_4 synthesis of 100×10^4 t capacity (Table 5), underground gasification

generation has a construction cost of just 50e75% compared to raw coal sales and power generation. Once gasified, CH_4 gasification is equivalent to raw coal sales, but its energy ef-ficiency is significantly superior to raw coal sales and power generation and the advantage of rolling investment can be fully brought into play. In terms of unit investment returns, gasification power generation and CH_4 gasification are significantly superior to raw coal sales or power generation. Macro ROI analysis also further demonstrates good economic prospects of scale underground coal gasification.

In summary, the analysis of material balance, financial analysis of single items and analysis of different ways of

Table 7.3

Comparison of energy conversion efficiency in the subsequent processes of physical coal mining and underground gasification.

171

Energy conversion mode	Coal mining-conventional power generation	Mining-ultra supercritical power generation	UCG-IGCC	UCG-coal chemical industry
Mining recovery	66%	66%	90%	90%
Energy conversion efficiency	35%	45%	55%	70%
Comprehensive energy efficiency	23%	30%	50%	63%

utilization of coal show good economic and social prospects of underground coal gasification technology in case of scale production.

7.3 Current difficulties and recommendations for next development

7.3.1 Current difficulties

Although theoretical research and experimental engineering cases show that underground coal gasification technology is feasible, the current research has not overcome key technologies in scale underground coal gasification, nor has ach-ieved the industrial goal of scale and economically-feasible development. Therefore, this technology is still in the phase of industrial tests, without industrialization or a complete industrial chain formed.

The pilot projects are basically in the phase of industrial tests. Except for the Ergo Exergy project, no project has an annual capacity of over 5×10^4 t for a single well, let alone continuous scale operation. By far,

Table 7.4

ROI analysis of direct power generation through underground coal gasification.

Scale	Gasification and power generation investment (CN 1 million yuan)	Investment per ton of coal of gasification and power generation (CN yuan)	Mine service life (a)	Annual sales income (CN 1 million yuan)	Subtotal annual operating cost (CN 1 million yuan)	Pre-tax annual profit (CN 1 million yuan)	Pre-tax profit per ton of coal (CN yuan)	Static investment payback period (yrs.)
14×10^4 t per year	341	2442	16	75	69	6	48	12.2
56×10^4 t per year	964	1722	16	303	239	64	116	7.71
140×10^4 t per year	2314	1653	16	759	584	175	126	7.22

there has been no verifiable scale project in the world or technical specification or standard for the industry, let alone a complete set of sophisticated underground coal gasification equipment.

Unlike general engineering tests, underground coal rovidcation is an extensive project in terms of resources, technology, capital, talent and market, for which available tests are limited. Therefore, there is insufficient research in gasification scale, the acquisition of industrial indicators, ovenmaking equipment, gathering and transportation equipment, safety, environmental protection, and energy conservation. Practice has proven that the project is "theoretically feasible", but not "technically rational" and "safe or efficient".

7.3.1.1 Technical problems

The most important technical problem is unstable product quality and control. Currently, underground gasification ovens are basically controlled in a state of blind

173

firing, resulting in unstable quality of cokeoven gas. With small-scale gasification, bottlenecks such as a small width of combustion impact and a short length of advance should be overcome to increase gasification output. And the costs of gasification agents are high. The gasification agent that is mainly composed of O_2 and steam is one of the important materials in coal gas products, which has high costs. Therefore, it is necessary to obtain and efficiently use high concentrations of O_2, high-temperature water vapor and other agent materials at a lower price. Currently, a large number of boreholes/roadways results in high costs, while the existing manual techniques for oven-making require high costs, and there is no good technique for mechanical oven-making and high-precision equipment. There is no mature scale gathering system, and no safe and efficient gathering and transportation is considered for high-temperature, high-pressure, highly toxic, flammable, highly-corrosive, long-distance, and large-amount coke-oven gas; insufficient safe and environment-friendly energy reserves and complex components of coal gas products containing large

Table 7.5

Comparison of estimated investment returns on coal in different utilization modes.

Development mode	Investment (In CN 100 million yuan)	Annual revenue (In CN 100 million yuan)	Resource utilization	Way of development
Raw coal sales	20	3.50	50%	One installment
Raw coal power generation	30	7.78	50%	By installments
Gasification power generation	15	4.43e6.15	70%	Rolling development
Gasification, CH4 gasification	20	7.08	70%	By installments

amounts of beneficial and harmful substances, which contain large amounts of thermal energy. Such coke-oven gas and thermal energy are valuable resources if well used and will be a waste and will cause pollution. Therefore, overall planning, fine classification, and separate utilization are required, but no clear research has been done.

7.3.1.2 Product structure and economy

Conventional coal gas chemical systems involve a great amount of investment. Due to unstable yield and quality, which results in the limited high value-added use, the current underground gasification projects treat and use coke-oven gas in an extensive and single way. In the implemented projects, coal gas is basically used directly for heating or for power generation by gas-fired units with a small installed capacity. Due to the constraints of their costs, prices and efficiency, these projects cannot give play to the advantages of a variety of ingredients as high value-added materials or achieve ideal economic benefits, directly leading to a lack of confidence and motivation of enterprises.

The current research and development considers only direct gasification input and output, ignoring basin and field mineral development, mine system safety, reduction of other con-struction costs, reduction of production costs, and environ-mental protection, planning for the extended functions and purposes of high-gas physical exploration and protection layers for protruding coal seams as well as the utilization of other benefits from underground gasification.

7.3.1.3 Organization management

The project involves a great number of disciplines in several sectors, including the mining industry, chemical in-dustry, machinery, materials industry, credit control, geology, and drilling, and requires close cooperation between enter-prises and research institutions. It also requires close collab-oration and joint efforts between relevant departments, tenement holders, research institutes, and equipment sup-pliers. More importantly, funds, talented personnel, time, experimental bases and protection of rights and interests are needed for the research and development, implementation, and achievement transformation of the project, while an or-dinary entity does not have such a systematic capacity, strength and perseverance. Field visits by the author also show that while a number of market players are following under-ground coal gasification, few of them are devoted to in-depth research.

7.3.2 Recommendations for development

7.3.2.1 Key areas for technology research and development

Underground coal gasification technology R&D should be focused on:

① the establishment of a comprehensive evalua-tion system for feasibility studies. Technical, economic, safety, and environmental evaluation should be conducted for such feasibility parameters as coal quality, coal seams, hydrogeol-ogy and geology through a system evaluation method to guide project selection, obtain scientific, comprehensive, practical, and fast underground gasification evaluation systems and optimal projects, and to reduce risks of project decision-making;

② the research and development of technology and equipment for the comprehensive utilization of a variety of product gases separated by a single unit. Research should be done in air separation technology and theories, product mar-kets, technical and economic programs and equipment for the comprehensive utilization of gases separated;

③ the research and development of integrated, efficient oven-making tech-nology and equipment. Efforts should be made in the research and development of high-precision geological guide instruments (g-ray preferred), high-precision, long-range, high-torque, tractable downhole reamers and BOP holes, multi-angle, safe, and fast-drilling oven-making equipment, high-melting-point, low-cost pipes, high-temperature-resistance monitoring equipment, fast oven-building technology and processes, and oven-plugging technology, so as to build large sealed underground gasifiers in a rapid, high-precision, and low-cost way;

④ the research and development of technology for the monitoring and control of high-temperature and rapid gasification within the gasifier. Efforts should be made in the research of high-temperature and rapid-gasification theories, the relationship among the gasification agents and coal quality, product structure, gasifier type, gasification system and safety and efficiency, safe and convenient ignition and extinction technology, comprehensive monitoring and control inside and outside the gasifier, technology for the integration of coal seam gasification and protective seam mining, the relationship among gasification speed, coal calorific value and stability, and closed gasifier technology, so as to master rapid rovid-cation theory series technology and achieve the goal of scale underground coal gasification;

⑤ the research and development of heat insulation, thermal insulation, sealing and pressurized coke-oven gas gathering and transportation equipment. To ultimately attain the goal of safe downhole gathering and transportation of coke-oven gas, high-temperature, high-pressure, corrosion-resistant, leak-proof pipes, fittings, pumps and other materials and equipment should be researched, gas monitoring and anti-leakage devices should be developed, and safe, emergency equipment should be designed;

⑥ achievement of solideliquid air circulation and comprehensive utilization in a safe, energy-saving and environment-friendly way. Efforts should be made to research heat exchange efficiency and equipment for high-temperature coke-oven gas, catalyst type, quantity, technology and the modes of occurrence and mechanism of reaction with sulfur, nitrogen and other ele-ments, groundwater and gas migration, heavy metals and organic pollution mechanism, thermal action mechanism of hot rocks and its relationship with surface subsidence and groundwater level, to establish the centralized control system and integrated data analysis and feedback system, and ulti-mately to achieve the goal of basic use of waste heat, controllable migration of solid sulfur, solid nitrogen, heavy metals and organic compounds, and basically no surface deformation and no affected groundwater level;

⑦ the delivery of high added value and market design of gasification products. The economic goal of a large scale, low costs, product stability, and high added value should be ultimately achieved by studying the relationship between different addi-tives and different coal quality parameters in product structure, technology and processes for efficient purification and sepa-ration of coke-oven gas, and market demand for coke-oven gas by different products and corresponding technology and processes; and

⑧ the establishment of relevant industrial standards. Through the above research and practice, a series of standards for underground coal gasification technology will be developed as soon as possible.

7.3.2.2 Market positioning and economics of product

UCG enterprises can serve as a primary feedstock gas sup-plier and a gas pipeline transportation provider. Through all types of furnaces and processes, front-end UCG technology delivers the same goal as IGCC: to achieve useful components like CO_2, H_2, CH_4, and coke-oven gas containing a small amount of tar, hydrocarbons and other substances. After the removal of CO_2, N_2, O_2, H_2S, water vapor, dust and other use-less and harmful substances through purification, it is delivered directly to users through coal gas pipelines, just like natural gas. Depending on market demand, technological level and scale of investment, downstream users can choose to produce fuel cells (AFC) by hydrogen extraction or synthesize CH_4, methanol, dimethyl ether, acetic acid, acetic anhydride, formaldehyde and other subsequent chemicals through C1 chemical engineering. UCG enterprises can consider clean gas power generation or carbon capture and storage (UCGeIGCCeCCS) to make use of the supply surplus.

In technical and economic terms, technical feasibility should be put before economic optimization with a focus on whole-process overall economic indicators. The advantages and dis-advantages should be weighed considering the comprehensive benefits of all products, including safety risks, environmental costs, transport efficiency, energy efficiency, and waste recycling. Currently, efforts should be focused on the optimization of technical solutions, the stability and controllability of technologies, and the industrialization of equipment, so as to deliver qualified products, and smooth project implementation on a scale and to significantly reduce costs through scale effects.

7.3.2.3 Operational and management modes

In terms of industry access, strict control should be exer-cised to achieve the industrial chain goal of being efficient, environmentally friendly, safe, harmonious, and simple and avoid the mistakes of ground coal gasification. As under-ground gasification has fundamentally subverted the original modes of coal mining, coal washing and material transport, innovation in industrial management should be striven for. Meanwhile, as various intermediate processes are removed from underground coal gasification, a number of processes and the game of various interests involved in traditional mining should be mitigated and even removed, which may cause new problems, like safety, quality and property rights.

To deliver the goal of underground coal gasification, it is suggested that an integrated agency for innovation in pro-duction, education and research at the national level be established to solve such problems with technological devel-opment and scale operational management. It is recommended that relevant departments carry out research and planning as soon as possible to establish a mode of equity operation in which the upstream industries (petrochemical and coal) and downstream industries (power generation, coal chemical in-dustry and other end users of fossil fuels) work together, coal gas gathering and power transmission and distribution enter-prises participate in the construction, and research institutes and equipment suppliers provide assistance.

7.4 Conclusions

China will suffer a severe shortage of clean fossil fuels in the medium and long term. The insufficient production ca-pacity in China and a number of uncertainties in the international supply system have posed a threat to national security in China. One of the ways to ease the contradiction between supply and demand is to make good use of coal in a secure, environmentally-friendly, efficient and economical way. Through years of research and practice, underground coal gasification technology has demonstrated advantages such as being secure, environmentally-friendly, energy-efficient, and having integrated use of superior resources. This technology can serve as the front-end support and guarantee for coal chemical industry and IGCC. It will have a good economy if developed on a scale. At present, further technical research should be strengthened to overcome such problems as the technical and product positioning, management and operation of the underground coal gasification industry, to achieve the goal of optimization and innovation in the supply of fossil fuels in China.

References

[1] BP. BP energy outlook 2035. London: BP; 2015.

[2] Department of Energy Statistics, National Bureau of Statistics. China's energy statistical yearbook 2014. Beijing: China Statistics Press; 2015.

[3] China Energy News. To explore an innovative LPG industry operating pattern in the natural gas era. (2015-12-10) [2016-01-04]. http://news. xinhuanet.com/energy/2015/12/10/ c_128517458.htm.

[4] Resources and Environment Research Institute, The State Council Development Research Center. China's energy development report 2015: natural gas as a clean energy resource. Beijing: Petroleum Industry Press; 2015.

[5] Burton E, Friedmann J, Upadhye R. Best practices in underground coal gasification. Livermore: Lawrence Livermore National Laboratory; 2006.

[6] Zamzow KL. Underground coal gasification: history, environmental is-sues, and the proposed project at Beluga, Alaska. Bozeman: Center for Science in Public Participation; 2010.

[7] Klimenko AY. Early ideas in underground coal gasification and their evolution. Energies 2009;2(2):456e76.

[8] Ergo Exergy Technologies Inc. UCG is the new source of energy. [2016-03-11]. http://www.ergoexergy.com/eucg.htm.

[9] Wikipedia. Underground coal gasification. (2015-12-02) [2016-01-04]. https://en.wikipedia.org/wiki/Underground_coal_gasification.

[10] Yu Li. Utilization of abandoned coal resources to promote the develop-ment of underground coal gasification technology in China. Coal Sci Technol 2013;41(5):1e3.

[11] Wang Zuotang, Wang Jianhua, Zhang Peng, Huang Wengang, Xin Lin, Duan Tianhong. Study on index comparison between underground coal gasification in Huating mine and fixed bed coal gasification. Coal Eng 2013;1:99e101.

[12] Liang Jie, Cui Yong, Wang Zhangqing, Xi Jianfen. Gasifier type and technique of underground coal gasification. Coal Sci Technol 2013;41(5):10e5.

[13] Yang Lanhe, Liu Shuqin, Liang Jie. Numerical analysis of dynamic temperature field and concentration field in the process of underground coal gasification. J China Univ Min Technol 2003;32(4):349e53.

[14] Liu Shuqin, Li Jinggang, Mei Mei, Dong Donglin. Groundwater pollu-tion from underground coal gasification. J China Univ Min Technol 2007;17(4):467e72.

[15] Chai Zhaoxi, Dong Shuanggan, Nie Shixuan, Yang Xiudong. Under-ground coal

gasification technology in China: experiments and research on its industrialization. China Coal 2002;28(12):11e3.

[16] Hu Yuhong, Sun Xin, Zhang Wenbo, Zhang Binchuan, Sun Qinggang.

Study of impact of coal industry on environment. Energy China 2004;26(1):32e5.

8. Test of Applying Deep-Hole Loosening Blasting Instead of Advance Borehole to Prevent Outburst during Roadway Development Process in Severe Gas Outburst Area

Mr. Nengjun Yu is the corporate supervisor of HOT Mining; Yu has more than 35 year's experiences in coal mining industry.

Abstract: Because of the high frequency and strength of the outburst in soft layer in severe outburst area of the first low coal seam working face of Datong coal mine, considering the different characteristics between soft layer and hard layer about outburst, deep-hole loosening blasting to prevent coal and gas outburst test was arranged in hard layer. And it initially has achieved a good result.

Key words: Severe outburst area Hard layer Deep-hole loosening blasting technology Coal and gas outburst Prevention

8.1 Introduction

The first low coal seam working face of Datong coal mine is N2702, which has a buried depth of about 500m. Actual gas pressure of this working face is 3.52Mpa and gas content is 34.0m3/t. The thickness of coal seam is less than 0.8 meters including soft layers with a thickness of 0 to 0.4 meters and an average thickness of 0.2 meters. The average $\overline{K_1}$ value of soft layers is 0.834 and average $\overline{S}$ value is 6.55kg/m. The f value is 0.1. The same data of hard layers separately are 0.324, 2.54kg/m and 0.45~0.55.

During the developing roadway of 790m level, there were nine times borehole outbursts through the advance boreholes in soft layer. The average outburst strength was 29t, and the largest outburst reached to 100t. The maximum gas emission was 14910 m³. Every outburst occurred in soft layer. There are no borehole outbursts in the hard layers below and above soft layer. Neither gas ejecting nor pipe sticking happened during drilling process in hard layers.

Since March 1998, advance drainage boreholes have been arranged in hard layers. And extra drilling boreholes were arranged as inspection boreholes. If potential outbursts detected, then drainage boreholes would be added in soft layer. Practice shows that this method can prevent borehole outbursts, However, the effect of methane drainage is poor and ineffective. Therefore, the deep-hole loosening blasting experiment was carried out to instead of advance drilling to prevent outbursts.

8.2 Deep-hole loosening blasting test

Location: East cutting roadway of N2702, which its length is 133m. In the east part and west part of roadway, 17 drainage boreholes have been arranged in advance on each side. The diameter of boreholes is 65mm. The distance between boreholes range from 0.5m to 1m. The depth of boreholes range from 35m to 37m. The middle of the roadway (61m) is still in original condition. The thickness of coal seam ranges from 0.5m to 1m. The thickness of soft layer ranges from 0.1m to 0.4m. The average thickness is 0.19m. There is a 0.7 m drop of normal fault obliquely through the middle. The roadway was developed from east to west. And the I-beam support was applied.

Method:Arrange depth-hole loosening blasting holes in hard layer away from soft layer 0.1m to 0.2m. The diameter of the hole is 42mm. The depth of the holes are 8m to 8.8m. Through experiments we know that the effective radius of loose blasting is 0.8 meters. And control range of edge is 2.5m. Number of holes is 6. To prevent the outbursts causing by air pressure, worker should push coal powder to bottom of hole with wooden tamper before loading explosives. Then load 0.2m stemming and emulsion explosive in sequence. The length of emulsion explosive should be remaining hole depth minus 5.5~6.0 m. At last, fill length of more than

2 meters of stemming to seal the borehole. The explosive is assembled with 5~7 explosives as a group, each assembled add a millisecond detonator, which foot line is lengthened by $0.5mm^2$ copper core wire and connected by series connection. All the holes in the soft layer are filled with yellow mud, not filled with explosive.

Two hours after the explosion, five φ42mm inspection holes should be drilled in the soft layer.If the measure is not effective, φ65mm drainage hole s shall be drilled in the soft layer until the test is valid.

During the development, no less than 5m advance distance should be reserved.

8.3 Effect inspection and analysis

8.3.1 Index change before and after loosening blasting

In 11 times of loosening blasting test, 3 times test was directly successful. The rest of tests were drilled φ65mm drainage holes. Index value changes before and after the loosening blasting test is shown in Table 1.

	$\overline{K}$	$\overline{S}$ (kg/m)	K_{max}	S_{max} (kg/m)
Before test	0.834	6.55	1.16	2.1
After test	0.414	4.06	1.60	8.6

Table 1 Index value changes before and after the loosening blasting test

$\overline{K}$ Value of after test decline by 50.36%, and $\overline{S}$ value of after test decline by 38.02%. The strength of outburst is also greatly reduced, which indicate the loosening blasting effective.

8.3.2 Gas emission changes before and after the loosening blasting and development blasting

Using gas monitoring system to measure the gas concentration in return air after loosening blasting and development blasting. Figure 1 shows the trend of gas concentration in return air after two hour of blasting. Table 2 shows the changes of gas emission content after loosening blasting and development blasting.

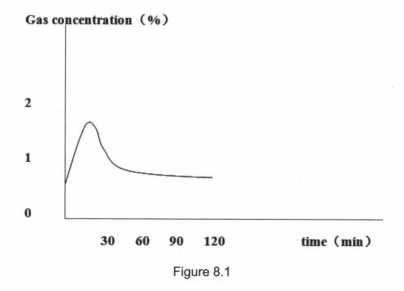

Figure 8.1

No.	Loosening blast			Inspection hole		Increment gas emission	
	Loading explosive (kg)	Detonator (quantity)	Gas emission** (m³)	Total (quantity)	Over standard hole (quantity)	The first cycle (m³)	The second cycle (m³)
1	8.8	10	14.4	4	1	4.8	8.4
2	11.6	10	18.4	4	2	6.3	8.6
3	12	10	42	4	2	4.2	23.1
4	14.8	12	70	4	0	14.1	10.4
5	14.4	12	50.6	4	0	10.8	19
6	12	10	34.5	4	0	17.2	19.6
7*	15	12	29.3	4	2	3.1	13.1
8*	15	12	15.8	5	1	3.6	10.1
9	12.2	10	52.6	5	3	4.1	9.6
10	15	12	46.4	5	2	14.7	11
11	10.8	9	42.2	5	3	5.3	10.3
Total	141.6	119	416.2	48	16	88.2	143.1

* Fault

** Increment gas emission after two hours of loosening blasting

Table 8.2 Changes of gas emission content after loosening blasting and development blasting and test results

After loosening blasting, gas emission amount increase with loading explosive amount and detonator amount. The effect of loosening blasting became poor in the fault zone. And coal slide happened along the fault plane after blasting. The number of boreholes with outburst risk decreased by two-thirds. The increase of gas emission within 2 hours after loosening blasting accounted for 64.26% of that of loose blasting and development blasting. In development process, the increment gas emission in second cycle is 1.62 times of emission in first cycle. This is due to the fact that the coal wall of the first cycle face is exposed for a longer period of time than the second cycle, and the coal body has naturally discharged more gas.

8.3.3 Study on Effective Radius of Loosening Blasting

According to the upper level survey data, the effective radius of 7# layer loosening blasting is 1m. In the first 3 tests of the area, the drill hole is arranged according to the effective radius 1m, the charge (length) is the effective hole depth minus 6m, but the outburst risk is not eliminated after the blasting. From the fourth test, the drill hole is arranged according to the effective radius 0.8m, and the charge quantity is 5.5m minus the hole depth. As the result, the 4th to 6th test of loosening blasting were successfully completed (eliminating the risk of outburst). The 7th to 9th test had poor effect of loosening blasting because of faults. For the 11th and 12th, outburst was not completely eliminated. This is because the huge ground pressure leads to the hole deformation, resulting in improper charge.

8.3.4 Benefit comparison

If using φ 86mm advanced drilling technology to prevent and control outburst, roadway excavation can reach to average of 1.03 meters a day. If using deep-hole loosening blasting technology to prevent and control outburst, roadway excavation can reach to average of 2.10 meters a day, which increased by 107%. Compared with φ 86mm advanced drilling technology, deep-hole loosening blasting technology can reduce cost form 140 yuan/m to 58 yuan/m.

8.4 Conclusion

8.4.1 The K1, S values of soft layers in the test area are about 2.5 times of the hard layer, the f value of hard layer is about 5 times the soft layer. During drilling process in hard layer, there are no hole eruption, hole collapse and pipe sticking. Therefore, according to the different characteristics of soft layer and hard layer, avoiding construction prevention outburst hole in soft layer in high outburst area can protect personal safety, reduce construction workload and improve work efficiency. And deep-hole loosening blasting technology is an optional measure.

8.4.2 The value of $\overline{K}$ after loosening blasting decline by 50.36%, and value of $\overline{S}$ after loosening blasting decline by 38.02%. The increase of gas emission within 2 hours after loosening blasting accounted for 64.26% of that of loose blasting and development blasting, which can significantly reduce the gas outburst risk in coal mines.

8.4.3 Appropriate loosening blasting effective radius is 0.8 m. The length of emulsion explosive should equal to the hole depth minus 5.5m.

8.4.4 In the tests, due to the influence of the faults and the rock pressure, the blast hole cannot reach the predetermined position or the loading is not appropriate, resulting in such phenomena as the flaking along the fault plane and the breaking working face. Therefore, deep-hole loosening blasting technology only can apply in normal seam condition with stable hard layers. It should not be applied in the tectonic zone.

8.4.5 Compared with φ 86mm advanced drilling technology, deep-hole loosening blasting technology can increase excavation efficiency by 107% and reduce cost by 82 yuan.

9. Studies on Failure Characteristics and Normal Height in Steeply Inclined Coal Mining Activities

Abstract: In order to research the failure characteristics of steeply inclined coal mining activities, this article takes steeply inclined coal seam of Datai Coal Mine as example; the two similar material models were employed to research the caving zone failure characteristics and the normal height of deep mining and shallow to deep mining. The failure pattern and normal height of caving zone due to steeply inclined coal mining of Datai Coal Mine were measured by the high resolution geophysical rovideson. The results showed that the caving zone forms Trapezoidal arch structure due to the deep mining and the normal height was about 2.5 times of the mining thickness. The caving zone form zonal distribution due to the shallow to deep mining and the normal height was about 5.0~6.0 times of the mining thickness. The geophysical exploration results showed that the caving zone form zonal distribution and the normal height were about 5.6 times of the mining thickness. The results of geophysical exploration and similar material model were identical.

Key words: steeply inclined coal seam; Caving zone; Failure characteristics; Normal height; Geophysical exploration

There has large stratigraphic dip of heavy pitch coal seam, it reflects the formation process and after formation process of coal seam, suffer from the violent geological con formation movement. Get phase ratio with the gently inclined coal seam, the mining of heavy pitch coal seam has complicated mining subsidence disciplinarian and failure mechanism of terrane. At present, some scholars at domestic and international have carried out some relevant research work from the aspects of theoretical analysis and in-situ measurement of rock formation. Alvarcz Fcmandcz proposed the N-K influence function and studied the table movement calculation of steep coal seam mining. Based on the actual observation data, Tianquan Liu summarized the law and characteristics of overlying strata movement in steeply inclined coal seam mining. The document [5-6] using testing data, the similar model test on heavy pitch coal seam to mining variation law of the surrounding rock is studied. The document [7-9] is numerical simulation method is used to study the movement rule and control method of surrounding rock in the mining of steep coal seam. The document [10-11] is numerical simulation method is used to study the movement rule and control method of surrounding rock in the mining of steep coal seam. The document [12-14] is numerical simulation method is used to study the movement rule and control method of surrounding rock in the mining of steep coal seam. The document [15-17] is destruction of overburden rock and the stability of waterproof coal pillar in steep seam are studied. From document [18-20] is using color drilling television,

194

transient electromagnetic and microseismic techniques, the height of overburden destruction in mined-out area was monitored and analyzed. It follows that, the research on the failure characteristics and normal height of the caving zone in steeply-inclined coal seam is not yet sufficient. Based on this, the author takes the steep seam in Datai Coal Mine as the research object, it similar material model test was used to simulate the rock failure of steeply-inclined coal seam mining, and the geophysical prospecting technique was used to study the damage characteristics and normal height of the caving zone in No.3 coal seam.

9.1 The establishment of similar material model 1

The model 1 based on the section 2 of Datai Coal Mine, a two-dimensional similar material model was established. The vertical boundary of the model and the boundary of the floor are fixed bi-directional, and the ground is free, self-weight loading is carried out to simulate mining the deep-300m level coal seam in No. 3 coal seam. The vertical height is 100m, the average thickness is 2.3m, and the average dip angle of the coal seam is 73 degrees. The depth of physical simulation is 600m, among them, and-210mi level above the coal seam is reversed, and the average dip angle of the coal seam is 80 degrees. The model 1 scale is 1:500, the bulk density ratio is 0.6, the strength ratio is 0.001, and the time ratio is 0.0447. According to the similarity constants, the relevant parameters of the model are calculated. Quartz sand is used as aggregate, gypsum and lime mixture as cementing material, and the model is made. The parameters of each rock stratum are shown in Table 1. After laying out the observation points after laying the model, 1 and 5 observation lines were laid on the surface and rock section respectively. In order to analyze the roof movement status after coal mining, 3 observation lines were laid along the coal seam, and 215 observation points were set up, including 4 control points. Among them, 14 observation points were laid on the surface observation line. 35 observation points were arranged for each observation line on the rock section. The horizontal distance between each measuring point was about 50mm. The vertical distance between the inclined observation lines was about 120mm, and the distance between the measuring points was about 100mm.

Table 9.1 Ratio parameters of each rock stratum of model I

	Mixture ratio	Total weight/kg	Material weight/kg			
			Quartz sand	Lime	Gypsum	Water
Basalt	8:7:3	65.11	57.87	5.07	2.17	6.51
Metamorphic rocks	9:8:2	12.79	11.52	1.02	0.25	1.27
No.3 coal seam	10:1:0	9.98	9.08	0.90	0	1.00
Packsand	9:7:3	126.50	113.84	8.86	3.80	12.64
Medium-sandstone	10:8:2	101.82	92.56	7.40	1.86	10.18

Lithology	Mixture ratio	Total weight/kg	Material weight/kg			
			Quartz sand	Lime	Gypsum	Water
Siltstone	12:8:2	217.67	200.94	13.39	3.34	21.76
Longmen conglomerate	10:1:0	28.12	25.56	2.56	0.00	2.81
Basalt	8:7:3	65.11	57.87	5.07	2.17	6.51
Metamorphic rocks	9:8:2	12.79	11.52	1.02	0.25	1.27
No.3 coal seam	10:1:0	9.98	9.08	0.90	0	1.00
Packsand	9:7:3	126.50	113.84	8.86	3.80	12.64
Medium-sandstone	10:8:2	101.82	92.56	7.40	1.86	10.18
Siltstone	12:8:2	217.67	200.94	13.39	3.34	21.76
Longmen conglomerate	10:1:0	28.12	25.56	2.56	0.00	2.81

The total station is used for observation, and the displacement accuracy is less than ±0.2mm. For the first time, the model was observed after the model was dried for 3-5 days. According to the actual mining situation, the roof is managed with all the collapse points, and the observation is again after the ground movement is stable. The layout of the model 1 station and the formation of rock strata are shown in Figure 1.

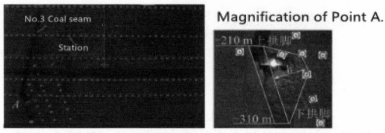

Fig1. Layout of the model 1 station and the formation of rock strata

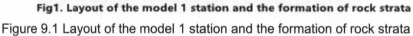

Figure 9.1 Layout of the model 1 station and the formation of rock strata

9.1.1 The establishment of model 2 of a similar material

Model 2 is mainly based on the 12 profile of Datai coal mine. The experiment simulate to exploit the-310m horizontal coal seam of No. 3 coal seam, the mining area is from shallow to deep. The vertical height is 650m, the average mining thickness is 3.0m, and the average dip angle of coal seam is 65 degrees. The scale of model 2 is 1:600, the volume-weight ratio is 0.6, the ratio of strength is 0.001, and the time ratio is 0.0408. The matching parameters of each rock stratum are the same as that of the model 1.

According to the actual mining conditions, the mining elevation of No. 3 coal seam is +350-310m. We laid along the surface 1 observation lines, there are 12 observation points at each rock observation line, vertical spacing between each observation line is 100mm, measuring point average distance is 50mm, a total of 340 observation points (including 4 control points), the observation method and precision is the same as the model 1, model 2 measuring points layout and strata collapse drop shape as shown in figure 2.

9.2 Analysis of failure characteristics of caving zone and determination of normal height

9.2.1 Model 1 deep partial mining

(1) The deep partial mining of No. 3 coal seam, a stable non isosceles trapezoid arch structure formed by the overlying strata collapse zone in the goaf. In the early stage of mining No. 3 coal seam, the coal seam above the goaf first collapsed at the roof rock layer, with the increase of the goaf area, the roof bend upward to mountain along the direction of the rock normal line, and the asymmetric arch structure appears. The upper and lower arch feet are located in the upper and lower coal seams of the goaf, respectively. With the continuous expansion of the mining area, the damage range of the caving zone is continuously enlarged, the normal height of the caving zone increases gradually, and the lower arch foot decreases with the increase of the mining depth. When the mining area reaches a certain size, the vertical component of the overburden load in the normal direction is greater than the maximum tensile stress of the pressure arch in this direction, the arch structure is unstable and fractured, the rock layer is collapsed, and the goaf is filled.

Due to the dilatation effect of the caving blocks, the continued collapse of the rock on the side of the lower arch foot is prevented, and the upper arch foot side transfers upward along the collapse of the rock stratum, forming a new arch structure.

Fig2. Layout of the model 1 station and the formation of rock strata

• The failure of the floor rock is not obvious, the damage degree of the upper boundary of the caving area is great, and the damage degree of the lower boundary is significantly reduced. The damage degree of the rock layer is closely related to the internal stress balance arch of overlying strata above Goaf. The greater the mining degree, the greater the height of the development of the stress arch.

(2) The normal height of the roof caving zone in the deep part of the coal seam No. 3 is 5~6 m, which is about 2.5 times the thickness of the coal seam.

9.2.2 Model 2 shallow-deep complete mining

(1) No.3 coal seam shallow-deep complete mining. The trapezoid arch structure formed by the caving zone in model 1 disappears, and the movement of the shallow and deep parts of the caving zone formed by the

impact of the roof and floor is close to that of the bottom. The collapse area is generally banded and parallel to the coal seam, and the failure range on one side of the roof is far larger than the bottom side.

(2) The mining of No.3 coal seam is shallow, and the surface outcrop is seriously damaged and the collapse pit is formed.

(3) Compared with all mining in the shallow and deep part of the model 1,3 coal seam, the height of the caving zone is increased and tends to be stable, which is 15~18m, which is 5.0~6.0 times of the thickness of the coal seam.

9.3 Analysis of geophysical exploration

9.3.1 Survey line layout and data acquisition

The downhole survey was carried out in the seam roof of No.3 coal seam at the level of-210 m in the West Sixth Mining Area. One trend profile and one strike profile were measured, all of which were located in the goaf section. The mining conditions were similar to the model 2. Because the pro-profile test is carried out from top to bottom along the south side of the roadway, a fan-shaped detection area is formed in front of the exploration area, and the spatial relationship between the exploration area and No. 3 coal seam is shown in FIG. 3.Mine geophysical prospecting usingmmS – 1 three-component seismic instruments for data collection, comprehensive plane method is adopted to form multiple coverage of observation system, the measuring line layout shot point and geophone array, each trigger, the shot point and the whole arrangement is moving forward at the same time a certain distance, until the whole section.

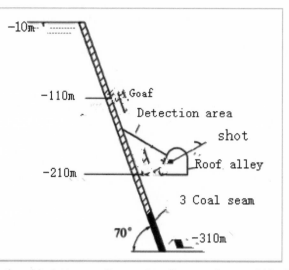

Fig.3 Spatial relationship between the exploration section and No.3 coal seam

9.3.2 Caving zone to determine the normal height

(1) Pro-profile. According to the results of the superimposed spectrum of the post-dip profile, we can see that there is a certain angle between the rock strata and the survey line ahead of the dip profile, indicating that there is a mining failure zone of the No. 3 coal seam in front of the rock strata. The average time width of the damage zone is about 12ms.Based on the physical property conditions of the working area and the rock failure mode after mining, the wave velocity of the rock is 4.5m / ms in the intact rock formation, 4.0m / ms in the fault zone and 3.0m / ms in the damage zone,The time is 10ms, calculated that the normal height of the caving zone of No.3 coal seam is about 17.3m.

(2) To the profile. The length of the exploration strike is about 40 m. The results of the superimposed color spectrum show that there is a

mining failure zone of No.3 coal seam in front of the strike profile, and the average duration of damage zone is about 11.2 ms. According to the workspace of rock physical conditions and mining failure pattern of rock, rock wave velocity and inclined section, the same to the profile from the mining damage with the top interface average time width of about 11.5 ms, may go to no. 3 coal seam caving zone method to the height of about 16.8 m.

9.3.3 Analysis of geophysical results

(1) The test results clearly show the destruction status of roof and floor rock strata and the distribution of caving zone in steep seam mining. The caving area on one side of the roof is approximately parallel to the coal seam with a zonal distribution.

(2) The normal height of roof caving zone in No.3 coal seam mining is 16.8~17.3m, which is 5.6 times of the coal seam thickness.

The above analysis shows that the geophysical prospecting and similar materials model test collapse zone collapse characteristics and the normal height of the basic agreement.

10. Analysis and Prospect of Coal Preparation Development in China

Author: JunDi Zheng, Master of China Coal Preparation Engineering Design

In this paper, the construction scale and technical development level of coal preparation in China are introduced in detail. In particular, the characteristics of coal preparation equipment in China are summarized. With technology development, this paper introduces two typical coal preparation plant in China, one is the Anhui province Huaibei area Guobei coal preparation plant, the other one is Shanxi Province East open-pit Pingshuo Mine Coal Preparation plant

China's coal production and consumption ranks first in the world. In order to reduce the emissions of coal dust and SO2 and NOX during the coal use, the Chinese government has formulated a series of policies and regulations to enforce the clean and efficient utilization of coal. Coal preparation, as the source technology of clean and efficient utilization of coal, must be vigorously developed. The *"Action plan for the prevention and control of air pollution"* issued by the State Council of China clearly stipulates that: We should further speed up the adjustment of the energy structure, increase the supply of clean energy, control the total amount of coal consumption and promote clean utilization of coal. Also, increasing the proportion of raw coal washing is much important, and the new coal mine should synchronize the construction of coal cleaning facilities, and the existing coal mines should speed up the construction of a matching coal preparation plant.

Since twenty-first Century, China's coal preparation industry has achieved the world's advanced level through the Sino-foreign cooperation, technology import, technology innovation and management improvement. The successful application of some new technologies, new processes, new equipment and new materials in the design and production of coal preparation plants has achieved good corporate, social and environmental benefits. Part of the coal preparation methods and equipment have filled the blank of the world coal preparation industry.

10.1 Analysis on the situation of coal preparation processing in China

10.1.1 A large increase of coal preparation amount and rate

In 2010, China's coal production was 3 billion 240 million tons, the amount of raw coal preparation is 1 billion 650 million tons and the raw coal preparation rate is 50.9%. In 2015, the amount of raw coal preparation is 2 billion 470million tons, the raw coal preparation rate reached 65.9%. As of 2016, there are 2000 coal preparation plants that have been recorded, with a total coal preparation scale of 26 million tons and 23.45 million tons of coal preparation amount. Among them: The amount of coking coal washing is 985 million tons, and the amount of steam coal preparation is 1 billion 360 million tons. The total coal production is 3 billion 450 million tons whose sieving amount is 100%. The total preparation amount is 68.9%, the coal preparation ability and total preparation amount ranked first in the world.

10.1.2 The number of coal preparation plants in the scale of 12 million tons or more ranks first in the world

Before 2000, there are only several coal preparation plant that annual capacity is more than 10 million, such as Antaibao coal preparation plant, Pingshuo; Heidaigou coal preparation plant, Zhungeer; Daliuta coal preparation plant of Shenhua company. After 2000, steam coal preparation plant that annual capacity is more than 10 million, like Pingshuo east open-pit coal preparation plant put into production. And, coking coal preparation plant that annual capacity is more than 10 million, like Linhuan coal preparation plant put into production. There was upsurge of construction of large and super large coal preparation plants. Since 2000, a large number of large and super large coal preparation plants with advanced world level coal preparation technology and equipment have been built. By the end of 2016, a total of 75 coal preparation plants with annual capacity of 10 million tons of raw coal have been put into production, among them: there are 11 coking coal preparation plant, the total annual capacity is 1450 million tons. And there are 64 steam coal preparation plant, whose annual capacity is 9550 million tons. At present, the annual capacity of the largest coking coal preparation plant is 16 million tons, and the capacity of largest steam coal preparation plant is 3500mt/year. The amount of coal preparation plant with ten millions of annual capacity ranks first in the world.

10.1.3 Rapid development of dense medium coal preparation technology

Heavy medium coal preparation technology is of the highest precision coal preparation technology in industrial separation at present. In recent years, dense medium coal preparation technology has reached the world advanced level of simplification of process system, large-scale washing equipment, automatic production process and efficient separation index. Large dense medium shallow-slot separator, large diameter dense medium cyclone, and pressure free three product dense medium cyclone with China's independent intellectual property rights and other dense medium separation equipment have been developed and put into use, which makes dense medium coal preparation entry into the track of rapid development. The washing capacity of single system in dense medium coal preparation plant can reach 5.00Mt/a. It plays an important role in reducing the investment and production cost of basic construction, improving the proportion of dense medium coal preparation and improving economic, social and environmental benefits in China.

10.1.4 Coal jigging process tends to be improved

Coal preparation jigging technology has the characteristics of simple technology, electricity saving and low operation cost. It is one of the main coal preparation technologies in China, and has obvious advantages in easy-processed coal preparation. The dynamic sieve jigging process is widely used in the 300~40mm raw coal processing, which is characterized by its characteristics: Large amount of waste, small amount of water, simple system. Two types of domestic movable sieve jigger: hydraulic transmission type and mechanical transmission type. The hydraulic transmission type has a good effect, but the failure rate is high and the hydraulic system needs to be imported. The mechanical transmission type has simple and reliable mechanism, which is more suitable for the operation level and management level of our country at present. The domestic moving sieve jig has a great advantage in price compared with imported equipment. With the further increase of the handling capacity of single machine, the application of waste predischarging process in coal preparation plant will further expand.

10.1.5 Rapid development of dry coal preparation

China's coal reserves have more than 2/3 distribution in the west, when using jigging, heavy medium and flotation, the water consumption is large and the cost of investment and production is high. Dry coal preparation has no water use, less investment, quick construction and many other features, which providing useful technical method for the coal preparation of easily muddy coal and water shortage area. The series of composite dry coal preparation equipment produced in China has been applied to many enterprises in China.

10.1.6 Remarkable development of coal preparation equipment technology

In recent years, through cooperation with foreign coal preparation companies, we have introduced large scale dense medium shallow-slot separator, large diameter dense medium cyclone, banana screen, tension screen, centrifuge, TBS and other advanced equipment.

(1) Dense medium shallow-slot separator

There are 6 series of dense medium shallow-slot separator, the slot width is 3.6~7.9m. The dense medium shallow slot separator of 7.9m wide slot, processing capacity is up to 800t/hour, a single system can be equipped with large coal preparation plant of 5~ 6mt/a.

(2) Dense-medium cyclone

The Dense-medium cyclone has many advantages, including low wet cleaning limit, large processing power, the high accurate readings and adaptable for coal washability, this machine has been used in coking coal preparation plant and steam coal preparation plant. The diameter of dense-medium cyclone production of MIC for mixed coal from 710mm~1500mm, formed more than ten series of products, including most be used diameter of main equipment are 1.2m, 1.3m, 1.45m, 1.5m main equipment. The feeding in pressure dense-medium cyclone has 750~800t/h throughput, single system can forming a complete set 5~6 million t/a large coal preparation plant.

The free-flow three-product dense-medium cyclone has intellectual property of China. After the processing of machine there are three products can be produce, the cleaned coal, middling coal and reject, it has obvious advantages of simplification for process system and high separation precision. No-voltage feeding coal no pressure feed coal is compared with pressurized feed materials, materials don't need to mixed with dense-medium into the cyclone by high-pressure pump, low coal degradation rate, low slime production, and low processing cost, it has been used in thousands of coal preparation plant in China.

In order to reduce the processing cost, increase the amount of flotation slime, the dense medium cyclone is Chinese independent research and development product, the main separation of slime from 0.5~0.2mm, processing cost is 60% lower than flotation.

(3) Jig

In 90s, Chinese has developed 35m^2 sifting air plenum, adjustable coupling 1.5 million t/a coal preparation plant for mixture washing, in recent year Tangshan coal academy made some improvement of SKT series jigs from air valve, wind chamber and reject discharge mode, aim at power coal to develop wide slot single block jig, it can raise ceiling at 200mm for wash, in order to make up the shortcoming for washing limit of jig, which is lower than dense-medium shallow slot before. Yao Kunliang develop minus sieve flexible air plenum (equivalent to setup air spring at minus sieve, which can let gas pass), it's beneficial to motion balance along the with direction of jigger-bed, it provided space for jig with wider cell body, this technology has been used for the 35m^2 jig in the Shaanxi Huangling coal preparation plant and Jiaozuo Zhaogu II mine coal preparation plant. Chang Jianyong develop YTZ type jig, it assimilate advantages of jig, which was manufactured by German KHD company, adopt new type of air supply mode, and the specification of this jig is 4.6×6m. It is used to washing anthracite of Jingcheng mining area, the processing power is 600t/h, the ash content of reject discharging is above 80%, obtain better separation effect, received favorable reception from washery owner.

(4) Coarse slime cleaning equipment

At present, homemade spiral, teetered bed separator(TBS), Dense-medium slime separator and triple water-medium separator, all machines are used to separation of 1~0.2mm coarse slime.

(5) Flotation equipment

There are three kinds of slime flotation equipment in China: agitation forth machine, ejector flotation machine and flotation column. The volume of single slot coal slurry in agitation forth machine is from $4m^3$~$90m^3$, the ejector flotation machine is from $4m^3$~$40m^3$, and the diameter of flotation column is 3~5m.Some domestic coal preparation plants also imported the flotation equipment from Germany, the US and Poland, but it is proved from the effect of separation and difficulty of operation, the Chinese flotation machine has some advantages, including large processing power, low reagents cost and high cost performance, it has strong market competitiveness.

In order to get flotation effect, equipment for flotation equipment including pulp preprocessor, slime surface property modifier and other equipment. The flotation reagents are fully exposed to the slime to improve the separation effect. The flotation reagents developed in China are non-toxic, innocuous and good in use.

The main features of the technology are as follows:

① Washing coal without water. For dry and water shortage areas and in winter cold areas, the compound dry method has special significance.

② Low cost of production and less investment in construction. The process of coal preparation is simple. Labor productivity is high, and the need of staff is less.

③ Low water content of commodity coal after washing. It is suitable for all kinds of gangue discharge, and does not increase the moisture of the product. It has a certain dehydration effect on the surface moisture of coal, which can reduce the effect of water on the heat. The technology of compound dry coal preparation has been popularized in 26 provinces, cities and autonomous regions in China and exported to the United States, Russia, Ukraine, South Africa, Turkey, Brazil, Indonesia, Philippines, DPRK, Mongolia, Vietnam and more than ten countries. Shaanxi Chenghe mining bureau has been successfully used to improve the market competitiveness of commercial coal.

The development and application of infrared intelligent waste selection technology

The raw coal slips through the chute to form a thin layer waterfall and passes through the×ray analyzer, and the particles are sequentially scanned by the×ray.×rays pass through the raw material layer based on the atomic number of the components of each particle, then×ray will form different image of coal and gangue. According to the analysis of imaging grayscale completes particle composition, the horizontal air jet array will spray the compressed air flow according to the predetermined program and separate the gangue particles into the gangue flow.The coal particles will be remitted to the clean coal stream according to the normal trajectory. The principle is shown below.

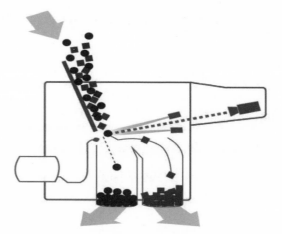

10.1.7 The automation level of coal preparation plant has been improved obviously

With the rapid development of electrical and electronic technology, in coal preparation plant the integrated automatic control, automatic adjustment of the proportion of sorting, automatic adding medium, liquid level automatic monitoring and adjustment, automatic temperature measurement of large motor bearings, automatic filling, automatic detection and control of coal slurry concentration, automatic detection and alarm equipment fault, coal quality on-line detection and remote management, automatic blending and automatic washing have been developed rapidly. Coal preparation plant can fully realize high yield and high efficiency operation. The total efficiency of some large coal preparation plants has reached over 300t/person. The medium consumption, power consumption, water consumption and fuel consumption index of most coal preparation plants have reached the international level.

10.1.8 The results of intensive management are remarkable

Due to many mining areas actively develop coal washing technology, in Shendong company, Huainan, Ningxia coal, Pingshuo as the representatives of the large state-owned coal enterprises, the establishment of coal or coal washing plant center to achieve the unified management and contracting operation of production technology, procurement, maintenance, human and property. Intensive management makes the management level of coal preparation plant further improved, and good enterprise benefit has been achieved.

10.2 Typical case of coal preparation plant

10.2.1 Huaibei Coal Mine,

XuanBei Coal Preparation Plant is a coal-based circular economy Guoyang project covers an area of 520 acres and a total investment of 1.6 billion yuan, the design year selected 12 million tons of coal, the largest amount of 15 million tons into the wash, the main selected Guoyang Mining Area Of raw coal, the product is coking coal, fat coal and other rare coal, has broad market prospects. After the project is completed and put into operation, it will become the largest centralized coking coal preparation plant in Asia. The main product coke and fat coal produced by the project are sold to large-scale chemical enterprises and steel enterprises in the country. Based on the coal preparation plant project, the project extends the 4×300,000 KW coal gangue power plant, produces 10,000 tons of polycrystalline silicon, as well as new-type building materials and pulverized coal and ceramsite to form "coal-electricity-chemical-building material" Industrial chain, promote the transformation of value-added resources, improve the level of comprehensive utilization of coal.

1) Coal Preparation Method:

50-0mm raw coal is adopted pressureless three-product HM cyclone separation, coarse slime separation by slime separation, slime removal by fine slime, flotation clean coal by pressure Filter dehydration, coal tailings pressure filtration recovery, to achieve closed loop washing water.

• The main product is clean coal:

Coking coal (or fat coal) coals: cleans ash Ad≤11.00%, Mt≤10.00%;

Lean coal coals: cleans ash Ad≤10.50%, Mt≤10.00%;

1/3 coking coal coals: cleans ash Ad≤9.50%, Mt≤10.00%.

2) By-product:

Middlings, coal slurry, gangue and other by-products produced at the coal preparation plant are sold, backfilled or dumped into low-calorific value fuels for power plants in the industrial zone.

3) equipment selection

• Raw coal grading screen

Raw coal grading screen using 4 sets of 3.6×7.5m high efficiency combination unit screen. This machine has larger amplitude, stronger vibration intensity and higher screening efficiency than banana screen. It has strong adaptability to raw coal with high moisture content and large viscosity and large processing capacity, which can simplify the system and reduce the number of equipment.

• coal crusher

Selection of the introduction of four double-rollermmD500×2000mm-type crusher, the handling capacity of the device, reliable operation, suitable for crushing coal containing hard ore, crushing rate is low, you can ensure the requirements of coal particle size.

• Heavy medium cyclone

Design recommended pressureless three product heavy medium cyclones use φ1300 / 920 type

• Medium draining screen

Clean coal, gangue products, the introduction of screening with the introduction of 3.6x7.3m linear vibrating screen, the removal of coal products used in the screening of imported 3.6x6.1m linear vibrating screen. The material on the linear vibrating screen has a longer residence time than the thick sieve, and is suitable for the de-introduction of fine-grained materials with higher mud content, which is more suitable for the process and coal quality of the factory. The device has high vibration intensity, large capacity and low noise.

(5) Centrifugal dehydrator

Clean coal, middlings coal centrifugal centrifuges selected in the import of Φ1400mm horizontal centrifugal centrifuge, powder clean coal, powder dehydration in the selection of domestic Φ1200mm vertical slime centrifuge. The equipment capacity, product moisture is low, a small amount of maintenance.

(6) Slime heavy medium cyclone

The design uses domestic heavy medium cyclone Φ350mm type, the device has been widely used, reliable performance, small footprint, large capacity, high sorting accuracy, the production cost is relatively low.

(7) Magnetic separator

Magnetic separator used 40 pairs of countercurrent Φ1200×3000mm double drum separator, multi-pole, large magnetic field gradient, large capacity, magnetic separation efficiency of up to 99.8%, low price, suitable for large viscosity slime.

(8) Flotation machine

Flotation machine selection 12 20m3 mechanical agitation flotation machine, the flotation machine has the advantages of large capacity, small footprint, high flotation efficiency, and mature technology.

(9) Pressurized filter

Domestic pressure filter has been widely used, with high cost, large capacity, low moisture, high degree of automation. Design selection of 10 120m^2 pressure filter.

(10) Pressure fan

Compressor is the workshop with high load of high-voltage motor in coal preparation plant. The equipment selection has a great influence on the power consumption, investment and maintenance cost of coal preparation plant.

Pressurized fan selection 200m^3/ min centrifugal fan, the main plant pressure filter for the wind.

Also taking into account the fast-opening diaphragm presses and wind clearance, barrel mixing, pneumatic gates, pirated version of the wind, because these winds are intermittent with the wind, centrifugal fan does not apply, so choose another three 60m3 / min screw Pressure fan.

(11) Thickener

Native slime thickener using 4 sets of Φ30m thickener.

Tail coal thickener 4 sets ofΦ50m thickener, and the other hand need to build an accident sedimentation tank.

Native slime thickener and tail coal thickener are center-driven, with imported torque detection and protection devices, with automatic rake device.

• Filter press

Selection of 32 domestic 650m^2 quick-opening diaphragm filter press, the device handling capacity, high degree of automation, strong adaptability to the characteristics of slime, reliable system, low moisture products.

4) Process layout

• The total layout of the ground craft

Located at the east side of the existing coal preparation workshop (outside the east wall) of the existing coal seam of North Xuanbei Mine, the coal preparation plant of Xuanbei is adjacent to the existing Xuanbei Mine, with the Guoyang-Yongcheng Highway on the east side and the planned integration on the east side of the highway Utilize the power plant, north of the North volcanic mine railway station yard, south of North volcanic coal mine approach road. The entire plant was elongated east-west topography, flat. The total layout of the ground craft layout based on the following principles and requirements:

Can meet the two coal washing at the same time, two coal

unloading, storage, loading, transport system independent;

Foreign coal by rail transport, the use of K-hopper transport;

By coal pit double share the entire column head traction unloading car, the length to meet the 17 wagon at the same time unloading car;

Considering the need of multi-coal storage and washing, the original coal bunker is designed according to 10,000t / block and one of the silos reserves the interface to the power plant.

Set product storage, clean coal place into the product storage;

The fine coal is considered to be equipped with a fast loading station and transported by railway.

Coals can be stored in medium-coal storage, railway loading and transportation, and can be sold to the power plant. Coal slime to dry field storage, drying, land sales, and save coal mud to power plant interface.

The facilities of the factory are all arranged in the south side of the railway and divided into three zones according to their functions: the northern region is the railway station, which is responsible for the unloading of the raw coal and the loading and unloading of the products. Central area for production facilities, decorate a screening crushing plant, raw coal, the main factory building, enrichment workshop, filter workshop, pin positions, etc in fine coal, gangue, coal flow is smooth, layout reasonable, beautiful and coordination; The southern region is for production control and living areas. The whole partition uses the road interval, rational layout green belt, the beautification production, the office environment is also guaranteed.

• Railway station

On the premise of meet the coal loading and unloading facilities layout, make full use of existing facilities, fields is to minimize both building demolition to move, to meet the design of the loading and unloading line length, and create conditions for yard design cohesion and extended on both ends. The original station bearing the same YuanZhuangChe line 6, 7) position unchanged, instead of coal gangue loading the line, 8.5 m up north plant rapid loading line, (5), south   IV departure line (9), (3), (2), (1) way for coal unloading line, the original (2), IV road north, respectively, to 0.7 m, 0.5 m.

The station is changed from end to through. Extends to the west, to avoid building xue village, 220° turn north station, radius of about 800 m 44 '41 "curve, while still pressure – northwest corner of the village, but extends to the departure of two, the bearing is appropriate, loading and unloading of north bend the local and the brick wall Angle, end up to 750 m radius of the curve, and recover the slope Angle of shoulder retaining wall, do not take a brick factory land as far as possible.

• Electric Automation

In the southeast corner of the coal preparation plant located 110 / 10kV substation, two substations 110kV power supply from Jiao Lou 220 / 110kV substation 110kV different bus section overhead lines 15km.In addition to the coal preparation plant, the 110 / 10kV substation is also responsible for supplying power to other facilities in the entire industrial park. Based on the data provided by Party A, other loads are to be considered at 12000kVA after compensation. The 110 / 10kV substation uses two indoor units of 50,000kVA change. Under normal circumstances, two 110kV lines and main transformer are supplied with power at the same time and run in different stages. When there is a fault or overhaul in one time, the other one can meet 100% load of the whole plant.

The production control system consists of four parts: control system, dispatching monitoring system, management monitoring system and industrial television monitoring system

According to the principle of economy, practicality and efficiency, and combining with the development of technology, site maintenance and usage, the 110/10kv substation has the load regulating transformer, and the main transformer model is sfz10-50000/110/10kv. The control system host selects the 1756 series PLC of AB company.

• Environmental protection, safety health and fire protection

The environmental protection, safety and health and fire protection engineering and the main project are simultaneously designed, constructed and put into production at the same time, and the environmental protection, safety and sanitation and fire control measures meet the requirements.

The designed coal consumption per ton of coal is 9.11kw · h / t. In 2014, the actual coal consumption is 8.60kw · h / t; the designed coal consumption is 1.5kg / t; the actual coal consumption per ton in 2014 is ≤1.22kg / t. Tons of coal consumption, consumption and indicators are in the world's leading level. Magnetic recovery ≥ 98%, circulating water concentration reached 2.8g / L, reaching the world's leading level.

In 2013, the yield of refined coal was 46.03%, the ash content was 10.78%, the moisture content was 10.64%.In 2014, the yield of refined coal was 47.62%, the ash content was 10.76% and the moisture content was 10.96%. The product ash content, moisture content and processing capacity all meet the design requirements. In 2013 alone, 2.787 million tons of refined coal was produced and the sales revenue was 2.55788616 million yuan, creating significant economic benefits for Huaibei Mining Group Company.

10.2.2 Shanxi Pingshuo Mining East open-pit preparation plant

Dongan coal preparation plant is located in pinglu district, shuozhou city, Shanxi Province, and designed the processing power of raw coal: 25m t/a. Total investment in the project was RMB 258, 72.37 million.

1) Washed coal: No. 4 coal seam is a long flame coal with high ash content, high volatility, low sulfur, medium calorific value and high ash melting point, and a small amount of gas coal. Coal seam No. 9 is a high-ash, high-volatile, high-sulfur, medium-high calorific value, high ash melting point of gas coal and long flame coal. Coal seam No. 11 is a high-ash, high-volatile, high-sulfur, medium-high calorific value, high-ash gas coal and long flame coal.

2) Coal Preparation Methods: Coal Preparation Plant washing system is divided into two parts of the selection system and gangue system.

The selection system of the process using 150~13mm heavy medium shallow tank primary re-washing sorting, 13~1.5mm heavy medium cyclone main wash sorting, 1.5~0.15mm spiral sorter sorting,- 0.15mm slime Not sorting process.

The process of the gangue system adopts 150~13mm heavy medium shallow tank sorting, 13~1.5mm heavy medium cyclone sorting, 1.5~0.15mm spiral sorting machine sorting,-0.15mm slime sorting process.

• product structure

There are three main types of coal at the coal preparation plant, determined by calorific value: high-quality thermal coal with Qnet and ar> 6,000 (5,600) kcal / kg; thermal coal with Qnet and ar ranging from 5,000 to 5,600 kcal / kg; Heat Qnet, ar ≥ 4,000kcal / kg of washed mixed coal.

(1) high-quality steam coal:

a. High quality steam coal Ⅰ : Particle size 50~0mm, Ad% <14.00%, St, d≤1.00%, Qnet, ar> 6,000kcal / kg;

b. High quality steam coal Ⅱ : Particle size 50~0mm, Ad% <14.00%, St, d≤1.30%, Qnet, ar> 6,000kcal / kg;

c. High-quality steam coal Ⅲ : particle size 50-0mm, Ad% <20.00%, St, d≤1.00%, Qnet, ar> 5,600 kcal / kg;

d. High quality steam coal Ⅳ : Particle size 50~0mm, Ad% <20.00%, St, d≤1.30%, Qnet, ar> 5,600kcal / kg

(2) General thermal coal:

Grain Size 50~0mm,Ad%=18.00~25.00%,Qnet,ar=5000~5600kcal/ kg

• The mixed coal:

Grain Size 50~0mm, Ad% is about 32%, Qnet, ar is above 4000kcal/ kg

• Bypass coal:

Grain Size 50~0mm, Ad% around 28%, Qnet, ar is around 4600kcal/kg

• Equipment selection

A total of 5 coal preparation systems were selected in the coal preparation plant, in which the main washing system of block coal was about 7.9 meters in width, with a total of five units, and the rewashing system of the lump coal rewashing system was made up of 4.9-meter width and 4.9-meter width. The main washing system of the coal heavy mesocyclone has a total of 5 sets in diameter, and 1.15m diameters of the coal rewashing and rewasher are 4 sets.

• Plant layout (according to a set of coal washing system)

Belt conveyor head through water chute into the two double banana screen (upper seam sieve 13mm, the lower sieve seam 1.5mm) for wet grading mud, the upper sieve sieve material into one shallow slot for sorting. The overflow of the shallow tank enters the two single-layer 3.6×6.1 line sieves (the discharge terminal length L=1200mm, which is 50mm grading segment) to remove, dehydrate and grade. Oversize + 50mm piece of plant, after breaking into the high quality steam coal product belt conveyor, undersize material (50-1.5mm) (decorate on centrifuge dehydration may be reserved) into high quality steam coal product belt conveyor. The heavy product of shallow groove is lifted back into the chute by scraping plate, and then it is divided into a shallow slot after fixed sieve. Piece of plant medium screen and select shallow slot heavy product qualified medium under fixed screen return lump coal main wash barrels, qualified medium and then by the pump up to the main wash shallow trough separator recycled, dilute medium under medium screen gravity to double drum magnetic separator, dielectric recovery, coal ore concentrate of magnetic separation machine from qualified medium into the coal main washing barrels, tailings of magnetic separation machine into magnetic separation tailings barrels, the pump was adopted as flush of desliming screen. Then choose shallow trough the overflow into one single linear sieve to medium, dehydration, sieve content after crushing into mixed coal belt conveyor, then choose shallow trough heavy product into a piece of waste rock medium to medium screen. After the removal of as the final product into the gangue product belt conveyor. Piece of coal and waste rock medium screen qualified medium return lump coal washing qualified medium bucket again, and then by the pump lift to wash shallow trough separator recycled, dilute medium under medium screen gravity to choose loose medium bucket again, shifted from pump into the double drum magnetic separator, recycling for medium, magnetic separator for re-election lump coal concentrate from flowing into coal wash qualified medium bucket again, tailings of magnetic separation machine into magnetic separation tailings barrels, the pump was adopted as the lump coal desliming screen flush.

10.3 Outlook

The 13th Five-Year Plan for the Development of the Coal Industry (2017-2020) promulgated by the China's National Development and Reform Commission and pointed out: "By 2020, coal production and development will be further concentrated in large-scale coal bases with a total output of 4.74 billion tons , Accounting for 95% of the national coal production ".By 2020, the rate of primary coal will be reach 75%. Combined with the national coal construction "compression in eastern, central and northeastern limit, optimization of the west" strategy pattern, the future development of shaanxi, Inner Mongolia, xinjiang power and chemical industry with coal, development of large coal preparation plant will become the main development direction of coal industry in the future.

China's coal preparation technology and equipment manufacturing have reached the international advanced level, and the coal preparation plant design, research, construction, management personnel close to 40,000 people. Some of the world's coal preparation methods, China has, other countries do not have the method of coal preparation, China has all too. To further improve the management level, China is building a coal preparation plant in accordance with the model of intelligent factory. At that time, China will comprehensively lead the development of coal mining technology in the world.

Author: Zheng Dundi (1955-), male, Xianyang Shaanxi Province, graduated from China University of Mining and Technology in February 1982 with a major in coal preparation, a professor-level senior engineer, national design master in the coal industry, and a senior consultant in China Coal Xi'an Design Engineering Co., Ltd.

Assistant Email: *kira.zhang@hot-mining.com*

11. How Could Coal Washing Plant Be Better?

A flexible flow sheet would bring better operation performance, it doesn't matter that R.O.M coal is good or not, because the process has high adaptability. Basis on similar experiences in China, the coking CHPP with flexible flow sheet can win more about 22 million RMB per annum than those without suitable flow sheet (Capacity: 3.5 million tons per annum).

If the process is not suitable enough, the net benefits would loss. Additionally, due to the weak adaptability, CHPP would meet with unnecessary shutdown. The worst possibility, CHPP would have another upgrade project without planning.

Case Study

Wangzhuang Coal Mine Coking CHPP located in Changzhi, Shanxi Province, it belongs to Lu'an Group which is listed in the TOP 10 coal mining companies in China. Wangzhuang CHPP. Before its upgrade, the capacity is about 0.6MTPA, the major process technology is Jig + Small Cyclone + Flotation + Spiral + Thickener. After upgrade, the capacity designed to be 6.0 MTPA, actually, it could process about 8.0 MT ROM coal per annum. The new process technology is Heavy Medium Vessel (Bath) + First Cyclone + Secondary Cyclone + TBS + Spiral + Flotation + Filter Press + Thickener. Now the operation performance is much better than before.

For better comparison, we convert the capacity into 3.5 MTPA. (Old CHPP & Upgraded CHPP)

Figure 10.1 3D engineering designs of coal preparation plant

Picture, courtesy by HOT Mining

Technical & Benefits after upgrade

So, it's better to visit some similar CHPP projects and discuss more details with professional engineering or technical consulting companies before inviting for tender. It could help to minimize potential risks and save cost. If coal mining companies wants to import equipment from China, it's better to visit those equipment' performance in real CHPP (coal washery, coal washing plant, coal handling preparation plant).

Below translation, by Ms. Serena Fu

[Engineering Design, thecrucial factor of Coal Washing Plant Delivery]

During 2002-2012, the coal washing technologies have been improved rapidly. These changes has promoted the design document's quality and technology standard of many Chinese engineering company and some state-owned state institute becoming better, also the documents' content has changed a lot, mainly as follows:

11.1 More Strict Requirements on Coal Quality Analysis

11.1.1 The Expansion and Extension of Coal Usage

Recently, coal is not only the raw material of power fuel and coking, but also the valuable material of some high-added value industry which could replace the petrochemicals, such as modern coal chemical industry and coal-based compound fuel oil. Some industries such as clean coal technology, coal liquid, coal liquefaction and coal gasification has got good development chance, for example: supercritical, super-supercritical pulverized coal fired boiler, large circulation fluidized bed boiler, coal based syngas to methanol, methanol chemical products(rovides l ether, acetic acid and the following down-stream product), methyl alcohol made alcohol ether fuel, methyl alcohol made olefin, poly-generation, direct liquefaction, indirect liquefaction, smouldering and Lignite drying quality.

The usage of coal has been greatly expanded and extended. Different coal usage method has different requirement about coal property, which pushes coal preparation engineers to expand the knowledge width.

11.1.2 More Strict Requirements Towards Coal Property Analysis

The coal property analysis and processing performance analysis play important roles, because it' one of the basic factors in determining the product orientation and structure after being washed.

11.1.3 The Content of Coal Property Analysis is More Comprehensive

Besides the regular industry analysis and elemental analysis, the coal processing performance index analysis, micro coal rock structural analysis, degree of coalification analysis and metamorphic grade analysis shall also be included. The design document shall reflect original data of geologic report. The coal property information listed in the design document sometimes is not complete, and pointless. Mainly reflected in the following questions:

• When used as thermal coal, usually lack of some index related to boiler corrosion, such as chlorinity and fluorine content, also some index related to slag removal, such as ash fusion point, clinkering property and dirt property.

• When used as raw material of coal chemical industry, usually lack of some important index related to moving (fixing) coal gasification and gasifier efficiency such as machinery anti-crushing intensity, thermostability, and convert ratio to CO and so on.

[Case Study] Meagre coal in Lu'an coal mine district has low intensity of machinery anti-crushing, and easily smashed during transportation. Some plant in Taiyuan is the lump coal user of this coal mine, which is used as gas generating. During the transportation, the lump coal is smashed, and caused contract disputes. It suggests that the meagre coal in this mine is not suitable for gas generating.

• When the coal is applied as liquidation, sometimes lack of vitrinite reflectance parameters related to coal's micro-coal rock composition, degree of coalification and metamorphic grade, and some indicator reflects the carbon hydrogen ratio, oxygen content, hydrogen content, grindability, coal ash fusibility, flowing temperature and etc.

• When coal is applied as the raw material producing the synthesis gas, and the coal gasification processing is the water coal slurry gas flow bed processing, sometimes lack of analysis about coal water slurry.

[Case study] The non-caking coal of some coal mine in Shanxi Yushen coal mine is the raw coal base of indirect liquidation project with 1mt per year capacity for one coal group in Shandong. This processing of this project adopts the Texaco coal-water slurry flow bed, which lack analysis of slurry character. The non-caking coal's slurry character is very bad, with only 59.5% of the coal-water fluid concentration in lab data, but the indirect liquidation project feasibility study designed coal-water concentration is about 65.0%. Which has many adverse impact on the gasification processing.(With the add of coal consumption and oxygen consumption, the investment has added hundreds of millions)

11.1. 4 The Requirement of Coal Quality Analysis is More Sophisticated and Accurate

Quality characteristics and presentation process performance index is not accurate enough, there is no strict accordance with the various division level coal quality indicators relevant national standards or industry standards to express. It should be noted that these standard dynamic management, with the passage of time and technological progress, all kinds of coal quality division level standards are constantly revise and improve. We must grasp the new "standard."

11.1.5 The Coal Type and Sulfur Content Two Important Factor When to Determine the Direction of Coal Products, Which Cannot be Ignored. It Is Necessary to Point Out It.

State applies the principles of classification of coal resources and the use of optimal allocation (Industrial Development and Reform Commission [2006] No. 1350 text). Coal type and sulfur content, involving questions of principle relating to national resources and reasonable utilization. According to the State Environmental Protection Administration, the State Economic and Trade Commission, Ministry of Science and January 30, 2002 jointly issued documents (UNCED [2002] 26) the provisions of Article 3.1 of "no new coal seam around stars more than 3% of the sulfur mine"; in "coal, peat geological exploration specification" (DZ / T0215-2002) Appendix E proposed to estimate the amount of coal resources index, the maximum sulfur content of 3%; the national development and reform Commission Notice No. 80 of 2007 "coal industry policy" tenth three also pointed out, "the State applies protective exploitation of special and scarce coals, limiting sulfur, high ash coal resource development." Thus the Ministry of Land and attaches great importance to the project approval countersign these two issues. For example: gas coal (1) Huainan Mining Guqiao and coking coal mines will not be a problem for power generation; (2) high-sulfur coal mine Songzao (St.d> 4.0%) resources, development and utilization of the question whether it is reasonable . National Development and Reform Commission approved the two projects were met Ministry of Land and countersigned in question. Another expert again demonstrated. So, when designing special and rare types of encounters other purposes or high-sulfur coal resources need to be developed, the need for development and utilization of rationality should be demonstrated. Often they lack the necessary design files such arguments, especially the development of Yunnan, Guizhou, and Sichuan area of high-sulfur coal mines.

[Case Study] Guizhou Zhijin coal mine fertilizing overall high sulfur coal seams is one of the main coal quality characteristics of Ida, where the 7th, 23rd floor average sulfur coal were up 4.22% and 4.10%, are sulfur coal.

However, the feasibility study of the occurrence of high-sulfur coal resources Ida mining, the use of reason, necessity lack the necessary proof and elaboration. Guizhou Province is rich in coal reserves, but high-sulfur coal more resources. For example, sulfur fertilizer Tianjing Tian> 3% and 3% of coal reserves almost half and half. So that high-sulfur coal resources are fully rational use is unavoidable reality.

Only from the following three aspects of the grounds of high-sulfur coal mining provide some ideas for the Feasibility Study prepared to consider:

• For mining, Sulfur within Ida> 3% sulfur coal and sulfur 3% of the coal resources are staggered symbiotic. For example, a group of three coal, coal seam No. 6-1 average sulfur content 3%, while the average sulfur content of coal seam No. 7> 3%. In the mining process, if not crossed the 7 layers of high sulfur coal mining, continuing the lower part of the coal seam mining, the coal seam No. 7 would have been caving destroyed. Even in average sulfur content 3% in the same coal seam, there is also sulfur> 3% block segment, for example, No. 6 coal seam average sulfur though 2.59%, but the fluctuation range of sulfur was 1.88%-3.21% of the between. In the mining process, it is impossible not crossed the segment of high sulfur coal mining blocks. In short, the underground mining process is difficult to achieve only low-sulfur coal mining, high-sulfur coal not mined. The reality is that low-sulfur coal mined in the same time, if not high-sulfur coal mining, the high-sulfur coal resources will be destroyed and cannot be preserved intact. This is a waste of precious fossil energy resources at once.

• For the coal property, in view of the high sulfur Ida sulfur iron ore mainly composed of inorganic sulfur (nearly 80 percent), low content of organic sulfur, which provide a very favorable conditions for washing desulfurization. PRECISE geological report data show that the theory of high-sulfur coal washing desulfurization rate of nearly 70%. 7 wherein sulfur coal can be reduced to 1.32% from 4.22%; 23 coal can be reduced to 1.44% from 4.10%. For this high-sulfur coal mines, the through washing and processing coal in most of the sulfur is removed. Using washing desulfurization power plant boiler flue exhaust desulfurization + combination treatment, fully able to effectively control SO_2 pollution of the environment, meet the national environmental requirements, high-sulfur coal mine based rational use of resources provide a viable condition.

• In addition to this high sulfur anthracite mine, the other quality characteristics: such as high – especially high calorific value, especially phosphorus, arsenic low, medium ash softening temperature, high thermal stability, high crush strength and other characteristics are in line with high-power electricity coal gasification and quality requirements. From the protection of national resources considerations, the high sulfur anthracite coal mine exploitation should be, and make full use by Comprehensive Utilization.

11.2 The Coal Product Direction And Structure Need to Be Market Oriented.

The direction of coal products, the product mix should be based on market demand. With the higher demands of the market adaptability, than the initial period of planned economy and a market economy has been a qualitative change. So when the feasibility study report review, the target market for coal products require more precise analysis, user requirements are more implemented, with the general requirements of the target user's coal supply agreement initialed as a support document.

Target market analysis, implementation is important because it is one of the bases of coal products to determine the direction and positioning of the product mix.

11.2.1 Determine the Base of Coal Product Direction and Structure.

Coal product direction and positioning of the product mix is mainly based on two: First, coal quality characteristics; second is the market demand. Target market is not implemented, given the direction of the product is not accurate, when completed will result in passive and losses.

[Case study] Jibei Mine coal preparation into the wash of the main mine production No. 3 coal seam. 3 inherent low ash coal seam and Yanzhou coal mining area within the gray similar. However, the yield of light density material level much lower than Yanzhou. Now a two coals Yanzhou Coal and 3 # 3 #coals in Jibei Mining contrast as follows:

	Yanzhou (3 #)	Jibei Tangkou (3 #)	Jibei Xuchang (3 #)
Accumulated float coal ash content %	8.54	8.52	8.57
Floating rate cumulative production of coal content%	87.32	70.43	71.88

Thus, the economic coal mine in the north under the production of low ash product, the yield is much lower than Yanzhou Coal Mining (lower by about 16 percentage points), its cost may be much better than Yanzhou good. Coupled with extremely rich East China gas coal reserves, and the local market for coking coal is used with gas coal and coking coal demand is very limited. Jibei mine production of low ash coking coal product cannot be with the neighboring gas coal Yanzhou quality competition, so after the election ash products should not be set too low. According to the economic analysis of a Coal Mine in the North # 3 coal drifting data obtained when producing high-quality thermal coal ash ≤12%, the biggest increase in its yield. Than the production of 9% ash coking coal product, increase the annual production of about 180,000 tons, an increase of about 20 million yuan profit. Therefore, it is recommended Jibei mining coal preparation product positioning, should be to produce a high-quality thermal coal ash ≤12% based.

[Case study] Weakly caking coal mine in Shaanxi Province Huangling a mine, although having low internal waters, low ash, low sulfur, high calorific coal quality characteristics, however, is not the ideal blast furnace injection of coal. Higher due to evaporation (Vdaf = 33.75% in the case of high volatile) points, points higher phosphorus (Pt.d = 0.067% in the case of phosphorus), low ash content can be used as injection coal particles under high temperature conditions skeleton Al2O3 content (only 21.67%), as a blast furnace injection of coal is not ideal.

Injecting Coal limited domestic market demand, the need for blast furnace injection of coal 20.00Mt / a or so. The coal mine and coal quality reasons regard as blast furnace injection of coal is not ideal, as compared with neighboring provinces such as mine in Jincheng, Yangquan mine anthracite, lean coal Lu'an Mining, the quality gap is large, as a blast furnace blowing coal market less competitive, market difficult to open. In addition, weakly caking coal coking coal market as little more amount. Therefore Huangling II coal mine blast furnace with coke and injection coal as the main product direction, substantially all coal washing, the principle of low-ash coal production and processing products, is endless reasonable.

It is understood that during the preparation plant test run, because blast furnace injection of coal and coking coal market push is not open, the end of the coal product sales are sluggish, resulting in the Coal Dense

Medium Separation System and interference slime bed sorting system long idle, resulting in waste.

This case fully proved coal quality conditions and market demand has a significant impact on determining the correct product orientation, to develop a reasonable product structure, with the typical sense.

11.3 The Common Questions in the Market Analysis of Feasibility Study

(1) Market analysis covers international and domestic, vague content, and research itself is not closely linked.

• The target user market analysis is not specific enough; the lack of end-user demand for coal intent agreement text.

Detailed analysis of the target market and user text coal supply agreements are one of the important projects of the National Development and Reform Commission, it is indispensable, should not air to air. (The most simple truth: If no users, there is no need mining, countries that do not promote the use of the newly opened mine to run existing product market, which is a waste of resources.)

11.4 Methods to Improve the Grade of Fine Coal by TBS

The conventional separation technology of coking coal is, 50.0-0.5mm heavy dense medium cyclone processing, 0.5-0mm fine particle flotation, the mature separation technology based on coarse coal heavy dense medium process and slurry flotation has been formed.

As the developing capacity of coal washing plant, the requirement for capacity of heavy dense medium cyclone is higher and higher, the development trend of heavy dense medium cyclone is large-scale. Due to the increase of effective separation lower limit of grand diameter cyclone and decrease of feeding particle size of microbubble flotation column, the coarse coal slime (1.0-0.3mm) has become the dead zone of coal washing technology. To adapt the change of coal property, coal washing technology has improved and developed in recent years. As the popularization and application of TBS coarse coal slime separator, the technology has been formed as the following picture:

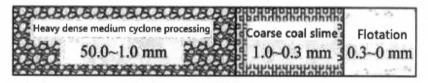

Heavy dense medium cyclone processing 50.0~1.0 mm	Coarse coal slime 1.0~0.3 mm	Flotation 0.3~0 mm

Figure 11.1 TBS coarse coal slime separator

The flotation technology of coarse coal slime heavy dense medium is mature, while coarse slime separation technology is relatively weak. So, coarse slime separation work is the crucial point of increasing fine coal productivity and improving coal company economic benefit.

11.5 Analysis about TBS Cleaned Coal Ash Higher

TBS coarse slime sorting machine is the most common machine in Chinese coal preparation industry including Zhuang shuanglou coal preparation plant, Ji Er coal preparation plant, Pan Nan corporation and Liang Bai coal preparation plant, and sorting result is satisfactory.

Taking example by the experience of above-mentioned company,

Centre coal preparation plant used two Φ3000mm TBS coarse slime sorting machines in first-stage project. But they didn't get a desired result, concentrate ash content is higher. Because TBS sorting machine is based on interfering terminal velocity for delamination. Within a certain particle size, it is easy to sort low density of fine particle and high density coarse particle. And it is hard to sort high density of fine particle and low density of coarse particle. The following form is the result of Concentrate small screening test

粒级/mm	质量/g	产率/%	灰分/%
+0. 500	54	10. 80	3. 03
0. 500 ~0. 250	213	42. 60	4. 05
0. 250 ~0. 125	155	31. 00	7. 44
0. 125 ~0. 075	33	6. 60	20. 61
0. 075 ~0. 045	29	5. 80	46. 37
-0. 045	16	3. 20	50. 31
总计	500	100. 00	10. 02

Table 11.1 Analysis about TBS Cleaned Coal Ash Higher

By above knowable, TBS Concentrate ash degree is 10.02%. +0.075mm material accumulated ash degree is just 6.28%,but-0.075mm material accumulated ash degree is 47.77%. This part of the fine particle materials account for 9% of the concentrate. Most direct and effective way to improve the concentrate grade is to reduce the concentration of-0.075mm high content of gray matter.

11.5.1 Measures to Improve the Grade of TBS Concentrate

There is some adjustment to coarse slime separation system in order to improve the grade of concentrate and realize blending of TBS concentrate to clean coal.

11.5.2 Reducing Pipe Diameter of Recoil Water

In order to meet the required conditions of coarse slime separation, make the materials to maintain the necessary continuous turbulence state in the tank, reducing pipe diameter of recoil water to improve pressure of recoil water. The water supply pressure is maintained at 70kPa and keep it stable. At this pressure it can provide some ascending fluid velocity, it will make high density material settled in the ascending fluid while low density material floated to realize the separation by density and particle size. It will lower the frequency of Ad≥11% of special coal sample by adjustment.

The change of pipe diameter is shown as follows:

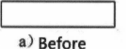   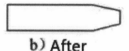

a) Before   b) After

Figrue 11.2 The change of pipe diameter

11.6 Grading Cyclone Bottom Drain Port Adjustment

Adjust Φ500mm Grading cyclone bottom drain port from 100mm to 90mm in diameter. After adjustment, TBS coarse coal slime separator into the material grade 0.125mm granular material mass fraction was reduced by 3%-4%, Then reduced the TBS concentrate high ash content of fine clay materials, reduced the ash content of TBS concentrate.

11.7 Centrifugal Liquid Process Piping Transformation

As a result of the centrifuge (mesh 0.4mm) centrifugal fluid contains a large number of fine grain material, ash content is higher, at 22%. There is a big gap with concentrate 8% ash content requirements. It has a serious pollution of production quality. Transfer the original barrel to concentrate centrifugal liquid discharged to the TBS tailings slime centrifuge. Blend it into the coal products after dehydration treatment. Fundamentally solved the centrifugal liquid high ash of fine clay material in concentrate system build-up of pollution problems, improved the TBS concentrate grade.

The following form is TBS concentrate screening test results after change.

粒级/mm	质量/g	产率/%	灰分/%
1.000 ~ 0.500	84	21.00	2.95
0.500 ~ 0.250	174	43.50	4.69
0.250 ~ 0.125	103	25.75	8.02
0.125 ~ 0.075	23	5.75	18.37
0.075 ~ 0.045	2	0.50	42.06
−0.045	14	3.50	54.86
总计	400	100.00	7.91

Table 11.2 TBS concentrate screening test results after change

Through the data contrast can be seen that the changed to 0.075mm material decreased by 55.56%, and the concentrate ash content reached 7.91%, reduced by 21.06% compared with the previous.

11.8 Selection of Slurry Centrifuge Basket Sieve Pore

The content of high ash of fine slime in slurry is high when the the content of coal gangue is up to 40%. Because the-0.045mm fine particles cannot be separated by classifying hydrocyclone, and TBS is also not good for fine particle coal slurry separation, so the high ash of fine slime will float to clean coal with TBS over flow. This will make the ash content of product different. Coal washing plant will solve this problem by the following desliming measures: In general the slurry centrifuge basket pore is 0.4mm, when processing the 1/3 coking coal which with high gangue content, the bask pore should be 0.6mm. In this way, it can increase the rate of fine slime through screen. Finally this part of fine slime will be separated by centrifuge force and the ash content in product is reduced.

Here is the screening test results of TBS throughing 0.4mm basket pore as below:

粒级/mm	质量/g	产率/%	灰分/%
+1.000	64.00	12.80	2.67
1.000~0.500	206.00	41.20	5.26
0.500~0.250	88.00	17.60	8.26
0.250~0.125	51.00	10.20	11.82
0.125~0.075	48.00	9.60	36.87
0.075~0.045	28.00	5.60	64.46
-0.045	15.00	3.00	65.32
总计	500.00	100.00	14.28

Table 11.3 screening test results of TBS throughing 0.4mm basket pore

The screening test results of TBS throughing 0.6mm basket pore as below:

粒级/mm	质量/g	产率/%	灰分/%
+1.000	0.50	0.13	4.16
1.000~0.500	163.00	40.80	3.50
0.500~0.250	118.00	29.54	5.38
0.250~0.125	63.00	15.77	8.34
0.125~0.075	37.00	9.26	33.72
0.075~0.045	17.00	4.26	67.88
-0.045	1.00	0.25	63.90
总计	399.50	100.00	10.51

Table 11.4 TBS throughing 0.6mm basket pore

Through the comparison of the data found that the replacement of 0.6mm sieve, concentrate the yield of-0.075mm decreased from 8.60% to 4.51%, reduced by 47.56%, ash from 14.28% to 10.51%, reduced by 26.40%.

11.9 Application Effect

After through reform of the above the process of coarse coal slime separation system and equipment found concentrate product average ash decreased from 10.02% to 7.91%, TBS concentrate from the part o f the mix, implements all blended to clean coal, The clean coal yield increased from 47.62% to 49.53%, clean coal yield increased by 4.01%, Every day producing more clean coal 286.5t, according to current gas-fat coal coal market value, every day can increase the income of 180,500, a nnually for the enterprise to increase economic benefit 64.98 million Yuan.

11.10 Conclusion

Currently, large diameter cyclone with independent intellectual property rights (maximum diameter: 1.5M) and flotation column with a higher selectivity both are applied in coal preparation industry of China. With the gradual upgrading of coal preparation equipment,the technology of large particle materials gravity separation,fine coal slime flotation and coarse coal slime separation have been scaled greatly.So do a good job in the coarse coal slime separation are effective ways to improve economic benefit of coal preparation enterprises.The aboves are a exploration and transformation for coarse slime system and a good effect of ash reduction for TBS concentrate product.Although the TBS separator is applied in coarse slime separation,but the sorting accuracy is low,probably will lead to a large deviation.So studying on a new type of Coarse Slime Separator is the bounden duty of coal preparation workers.

Comment from Swadhin Saurabh (India):

I think that the four (4) most important factors that can improve the TBS performance are:

1. The top to bottom size fraction of the feed solid should be around 4:1. This ratio should not be more than 8:1. To ensure that the top and the bottom sizes of particles are precisely controlled, we should focus on classification of fine coal in classifying cyclones on the basis on D90 or D95 and NOT D50.

2. The maximum and minimum size of the particles that can be effectively separated in such gravity separation equipment is defined. One should not feed these equipment with size fractions beyond the limit s defined by the manufacturers.

3. It is continuous flow equipment. So the volumetric flow rate to the TBS should be controlled precisely to obtain the optimum result.

4. TBS also has limitations (both max and min) on the feed % solids (w/w). So, the feed % solids should also be controlled precisely.

If we follow these four (4) things while running TBS or even Reflux Classifiers, we should be able to get optimum performance out of these machines.

12. How Dense Medium Vessel Yield More Margin at Shanxi Coking Group

In May 2013, Malan Coal Washing Plant, Xishan Coal Electricity Group of Shanxi Coking Coal Group Co., Ltd conducted the process technical transformation about dense medium vessel bath. After one year operation, the coal in the gangue has reduced from 8% to 1%, the recovered raw coal is 60,000 ton in 2014, and added 30 million benefit.

Figure12.1 Dense medium shallow slot separation machine
Picture, Courtesy by HOT Mining

Due to the unadvanced coal washing process, the coal in the gangue takes large amount, which restricts the development of coal washing industry. In order to solve this problem, at the end of 2009, on the basis of investigation and survey, Shanxi Coking Coal Group Co., Ltd brought in the dense medium vessel bath technology, and tested in Xiegou Coal Washing Plant, Malan Coal Washing Plant, Xiqu Coal Washing Plant of Xishan Coal Electricity Group, Shanxi Coking Coal Group Co., Ltd and Lvneng Coal Washing Plant of Huozhou Coal Electricity Group of Shanxi Coking Coal Group Co., Ltd. "With dense medium vessel bath technology, the production efficiency has improved, the whole system operates well, reduced the coal waste, improved the process efficiency and accuracy"-Quoted by Mr. Jia Baolong, the Deputy Director of Malan Coal Washing Plant, Xishan Coal Electricity Group of Shanxi Coking Coal Group Co., Ltd.

As the professor of Coal Washing Major, the Deputy Chief Engineer of Coal Resource Comprehensive Utilization Department, Mr. Peng said, this technology has huge economic benefit and environment benefit, which could obviously improve the product quality and output.

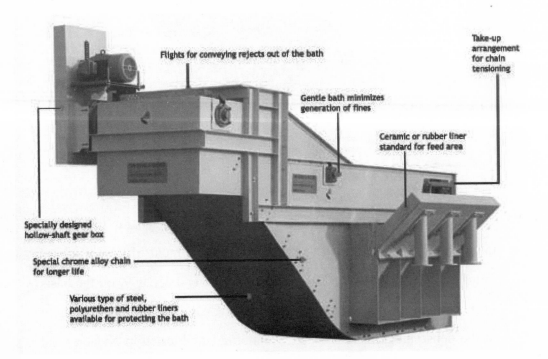

Figure12.2 Dense medium shallow slot separation machine

Picture, Courtesy by HOT Mining

Significant economic benefits. After the implementation of the heavy medium shallow slot separation in Ma Lan coal preparation plant, it has improved a lot compared to the past. The plant chief engineer Pang Liang said: "the original use of movable sievegangue coal and coal gangue with up to 8%-9%, sometimes can reach more than 10% coal gangue. Gangue with coal on the economic efficiency of enterprises is a huge loss. After adopting the shallow slot separation technology, less loss of 60 thousand tons of raw coal per year. "Shanxi Lv Lin of Huozhou coal coking coal preparation plant Zhang Chunhui calculations: Shanxi coking coal Huozhou coal preparation plant of Lu Lin to a year into the washing capacity of 10 million tons, of which more than 50mm accounted for 2 million 500 thousand tons of coal, this part of the coal adopts shallow slot separation technology, the amount of gangue is about 600 thousand tons, according to the traditional process, gangue contains 5% with the amount of coal reached 30 thousand tons, per ton of coal is calculated according to the market price of 400 yuan, a year can save 12 million yuan. The use of heavy medium shallow groove separation technology, greatly improves the discharging efficiency, not only meets the needs of production, but also solve the problem of mine and coal preparation plant resources selection. Since the system has been running, Shanxi coking coal Xishan Coal and electricity Xi Qu coal preparation plant coal gangue with coal amount from the original 8.20% down to the present 0.93%. Shanxi coking coal Xishan Coal and electricity Malan coal preparation plant form 8% down to 1%. Shanxi coking coal Xishan Coal and electricity Dianxiegou coal preparation and Shanxi coking coal

Huo Zhou Coal and electricity Lv Lin coal preparation plant coal gangue with coal loss close to 0.

Separation precision is improved. Liang Pang said: " Especially for 02# coal and 2# coal, the quantity efficiency is very low when we used vibrating screen before. The quantity efficiency of 02# coal is around 63% while 2# coal is around 77%. After we adopted Heavy-Medium Vessel Bath Refuse Discharge Technology, the quantity efficiency is more than 95%." After the operation statistics, 02#, 2# and 8# coal's quantity efficiency of Malan coal preparation plant are greatly improved, respectively increased from 63.19%, 77.61%, 95.26% to 90.72%, 99.25% and 99.25%; the quantity efficiency of Xiqu coal preparation plant increased from 80% to 99.6%.

Good for the following production. Chunhui Zhang said: "In the past, coal washing plants worked without waste discharge system. The effect of separation was not good and the wear of equipments was very large. Dense medium vessel bath waste discharge system sets up a good foundation for cyclone and decreases the wear of equipments. " The capability of main washing process can be fully developed with shallow slot separation technology. Less gangue will come into raw coal after separation. It will reduce the cost of main washing process when there is less gangue. The percent of gangue discharged by dense medium vessel bath is up to 30.31% in Shanxi coking coal Xishan Coal and electricity West Song coal preparation plant. It is increased by 11.63%. And it can reduce at least 100000 ton gangue coming into main washing process.

Labor intensity is reduced. " In the past, the vibrating screen and chute are always blocked, this increased our labor intensity. And the noise was too big. So we can not hand over to the next shift on time. But after using this system, our labor intensity, the dust and noise are redused greatly. The blocking and leaking situations are never appeared. So that we can hand over the next shift on time." Said Mr Ji Mi who is the captain with 23 coal washing experience of prepare workshop production two team in Malan coal washing plant. With high degree of automation and processing capability, dense medium vessel bath can ruduce runtime effectively.

Environmental indicators compliance. Shanxi coking coal in Xishan Coal and Electricity Malan mine gangue hill is buried by loess gangue, at the foot of the gangue hill never appeared "gangue traffickers". Jia Baolong introduced: "In the past, a lot of trafficker on the gangue hill, often some people pick up gangue. Now, no one wants to come here, because there are no sources. " With the decrease of the amount of coal not only reduces the pressure on the management of gangue hill, but also to avoid the phenomenon of spontaneous combustion of coal gangue.

13. Application of Solidworks in Pipeline System 3D Design of Coal Washing Plant

Abstract: The pipeline system of coal washing plant accounts for about one third of the total construction modulus. Although the parts are simple in shape, the total amount is large, which means that it will greatly affect the overall performance of the model if the file structure is unreasonable. In the preliminary design and detailed design stages, we can respectively use Solidwokrs' cross-section scanning and routing pipe plug-ins to improve efficiency.

Introduction

The pipeline system of coal washing plant is relatively simple compared with that of the oil industry, but it needs flexible designed vertical workflow and non-standard connections between devices. In addition, the coal washing design institute piping system design only needs to reach the general drawing level, which is used to guide the installation, not for production and processing. Therefore, solidworks, as a manufacturing-oriented and three-dimensional software, could sufficiently meet the requirements and balance each professional need in the whole design process.

13.1 Pipeline System Classification

The pipeline system of the coal washing plant is mainly for the process pipeline (medium pipe and slurry pipe), electric bridge (or called the trough), and heating pipeline layout. The coal washing plant pipeline system was shown in figure 1.

Figure 14.1 Pipeline System of Coal washing Plant

Picture, Courtesy by HOT Mining

The medium tube of process pipeline contains wear-resistant layer, it cannot be processed on-site. So it's necessary to count the quantity of elbows, tee and other prefabricated parts in the design and modeling process. In contrast, the production method of non-standard multi-tube is decided by the construction party according to their own technology. Processing details are not taken into account in the design.

The slurry pipe is the welded steel pipe without wear-resistant layer, it can be processed on-site. It doesn't need to count and draw tee, cross and other components in the design and modeling process. The rest requirements are the same as the media tube.

For electrical bridge, we only consider the location, direction and specifications, do not have to count other contents.

For heating pipeline, we only consider the number of heating groups, pipeline position, direction and the number of valves.

Only for the process pipeline, the hanger statistics and expression need to be considered.

13.2 Implementation Ways in Different Stages

The main purposes in the preliminary design is to quickly determine the direction of the pipeline, improve the visual effect of the model and provide professional CBWD for the construction units after winning the bid. After Pipeline Lofting, use the function of the welding parts to scan the pipe section, which can quickly generate the required pipeline information.

And the detailed stage will need a complete final drawings that can be used to guide the installation. Add a variety of information that can be used for statistics on the pipeline.

The two-stage model meets the different needs and can be interrelated.

13.2.1 Preliminary Stage

Use solidworks 3D sketch to draw the trend of centerline. See Figure 2. Use the weldment function to select the appropriate pipe size.

See Figure 3. Generate preliminary design scheme of Pipeline in the form of parts. See Figure 4. This stage doesn't generate the construction drawing.

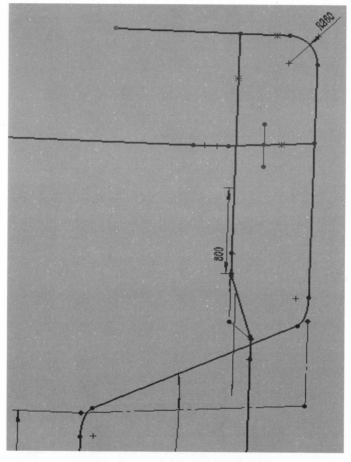

Figure 13.2 Pipeline Lofting Sketch

Picture, Courtesy by HOT Mining

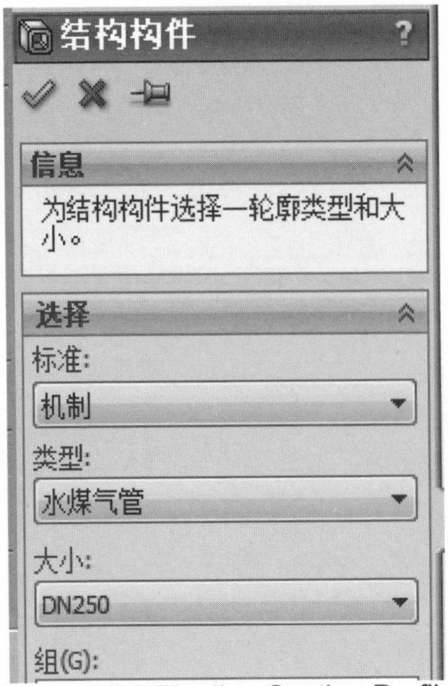

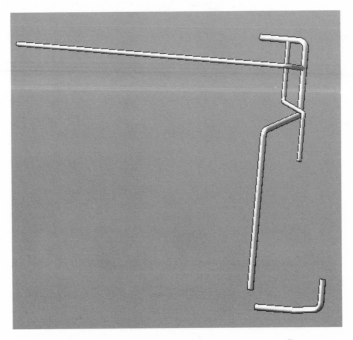

Figure 13.3 Pipeline Section Profile

Figure 13.4 Pipelines Lofting at Preliminary Stage

Picture, Courtesy by HOT Mining

13.2.2 Detailed Stage

Use the Routing function only in the detailed design of process pipeline. Because the needed statistical information is very limited, all needed valves could be added to Electric bridge and heating pipeline on the basis of welding parts.

13.2.3 Process Pipe Line

For partially reusable pipeline components which can be stored as stock in a common location and ready to be invoked. See Figure 5.

Figure 5 pipeline component library file

Picture, Courtesy by HOT Mining

The remaining pipes are drawn into the first fittings or valves in the sub-assemblies containing the weld out parts to activate the Routing pipeline function. This feature automatically enters the 3D sketch environment, without having to reposition the sketch position at this time, which directly coincide with the inflection points of the lofting parts sketch. As shown in figure 6., after applying this method, only the lofting parts need to be modified when the pipeline alignment needs to be changed.

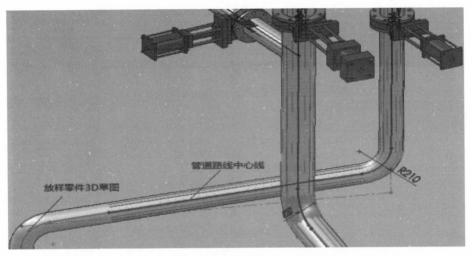

Figure 13.6 Linkage between initial setting and detailed data setting

Picture, Courtesy by HOT Mining

After drawing the 3D sketch, add the required valve / fittings to the line where necessary, and locate the direction and location (which can be modified in the assembly environment).Exiting the sketch, the system generates the elbow pipe automatically. See figure 7.

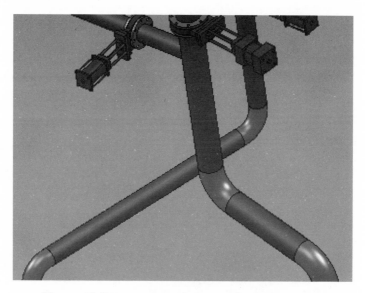

Figure 13.7 the system generates the elbow pipe

Picture, Courtesy by HOT Mining

13.2.4 Electric Bridge and Heating Pipe

The electric bridge generally does not draw the connecting piece etc. Information, only need the pipeline route, so generally no longer continue to deepen. See figure 8.

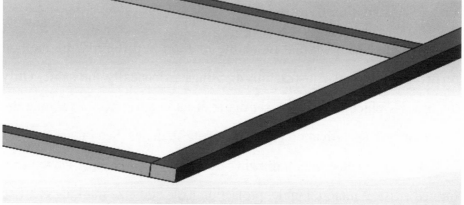

Figure 13.8 Electric Bridge

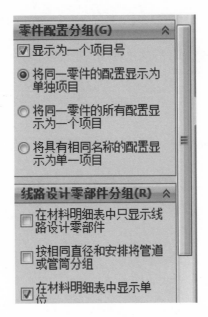

Figure 13.9 Material table attributes

The heating pipe method generates the subassembly at the place of the lofting part, and then inserts the required valve.

13.2.5 Construction Drawings

Although the detailed modeling method is different, the method of two-dimensional construction drawings is basically the same. Only the process pipeline needs to set material table attributes, determine the length of each specification pipe or separate statistics. See Figure 9.

The same construction drawing flow is projection three view plane, formed a list of material table, projection axis, add size marking etc. See Figure 10

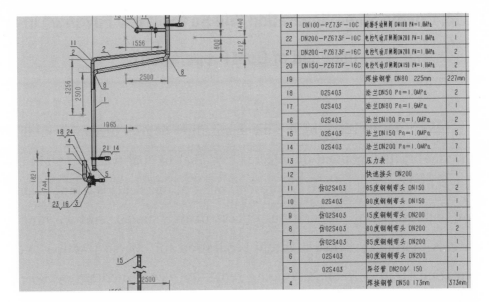

23	DN100-PZ73F-10C	附带手动闸阀 DN100 PN=1.0MPa	1
22	DN200-PZ673F-10C	电控气动刀闸阀DN200 PN=1.0MPa	1
21	DN200-PZ673F-16C	电控气动刀闸阀DN200 PN=1.0MPa	2
20	DN150-PZ673F-16C	电控气动刀闸阀DN150 PN=1.0MPa	2
19		焊接钢管 DN80 225mm	227mm
18	02S403	法兰DN50 Pn=1.0MPa	2
17	02S403	法兰DN80 Pn=1.6MPa	1
16	02S403	法兰DN100 Pn=1.0MPa	2
15	02S403	法兰DN150 Pn=1.0MPa	5
14	02S403	法兰DN200 Pn=1.0MPa	7
13		压力表	1
12		快速接头 DN200	1
11	仿02S403	85度钢制弯头 DN150	2
10	02S403	90度钢制弯头 DN150	1
9	仿02S403	15度钢制弯头 DN200	1
8	仿02S403	80度钢制弯头 DN200	2
7	仿02S403	85度钢制弯头 DN200	1
6	02S403	90度钢制弯头 DN200	1
5	02S403	异径管 DN200/150	1
4		焊接钢管 DN50 173mm	373mm

Figure 13.10 pipe two-dimensional drawings

13.3 Conclusion

Through the above operations, not only can meet the requirements of modeling details in each design phase, but also can reduce the consumption of hardware resources to the maximum extent. And each stage of the design results can be used at the next stage, reducing duplication of effort.

14. Course Slime Separation Will Be the "New Favorite" in the Field of Coal Preparation?

With the increase of the mechanization degree of coal mining, the fine fraction content of selected raw coal in coal washing plant is getting higher and higher. At present, most of our coals washing plant are using the coal preparation process of two stages joint washing, that is jigging or dense medium separation for coarse fraction and flotation for fine fraction. Jigging separator, dense medium cyclone, mechanical agitated flotation cell are the core equipment of jig, heavy medium and flotation process. The lower limit of effective separation of jigging separator is 1~2mm; the effective separation size of the heavy medium cyclone is between 0.25 and 2mm, and increases with the increase of the diameter of the equipment. The upper limit of the practical high-efficiency separation of the mechanical agitated flotation cell is 0.25mm. For the current coal preparation process and equipment development status, slime (<0.25mm) is for flotation. Slack coal(>2mm) rewashing technology has been quite mature, but the overall separation efficiency of coarse slime sized in 0.25~2mm is low. From the current production status and the potential growth of clean coal, the efficient separation of coarse slime has become the key to improve the yield recovery of clean coal in coal washing plant.

14.1 Source and Characteristics of Coarse Slime

14.1.1 Source of Coarse Slime

Coarse slime is a part of slime with particle size between the lower limit of the reselection effective separation and the upper limit of the flotation effective separation. According to the definition of the upper and lower limits of the coal preparation equipment, the slime in 0.25~2mm size fraction is coarse slime.

Coarse coal slime mainly comes from fine coal produced by coal mining and transportation. In China, the primary slime(excluding floating slime) accounts for about 20% of the amount of selected raw coal, and about 60% (The ash is below 10%), the recycling value is very large. In addition, the amount of floating coal in the primary slime is about 2% of the whole size fraction, which can be regarded as coarse slime. In the process of coal preparation, due to the secondary slime produced by collision between the coal briquettes and the collision between the device wall, and in order to achieve the full dissociation of refuse and meet the upper limit requirements of the separation equipment, there is some necessary crushing, which also produces the secondary slime. The sum of the two is about 8% of the amount of selected raw coal.

14.1.2 Characteristics of Coarse Slime

Coarse slime is a very important part of the selected raw coal, and its sieve and float-and-sink characteristics can be fully reflected in the comprehensive data of coal quality. However, compared with the selected coal, coarse slime has its own characteristics, mainly reflected in: Particle size is near the lower limit of separation of reselection equipment, the range of particle size is narrow; coal and refuse have been fully dissociated, the washability is good; the ash proportion of coarse slime is 2 to 4 percentage points higher than that of the reselection clean coal, the clean coal yield recovery is relatively high. For the coarse slime in the dense medium jig coal washing plant, the refuse has been excluded and the density is low; In the design of coal preparation process, the coarse slime is recovered separately, which provides favorable conditions for efficient separation.

14.2 Dense Medium Cyclone Separation Process of Slime

Figure 14.1 Dense Medium Cyclone Separation Process of Slime

14.2.1 Principle and Process

The coarse slime separation process based on slime dense medium cyclone is mainly applied to large-scale dense medium coal washing plant, which is an important supplementary process for the main process of lump coal, which can be used to make up the defect that the large diameter dense medium cyclone couldn't effectively separate the coarse slime. This process is divided into two types, they are pre-sliming and no pre-desliming, the principle of the two processes are shown below.

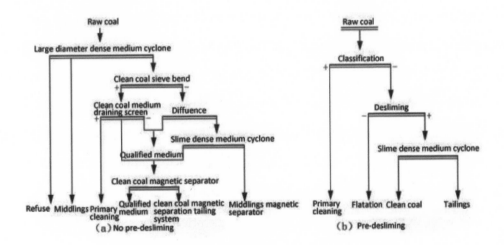

Figure 14.2 Principles and Process

14.2.2 Process Characteristics

(1)No pre-desliming

The cyclone feed in this process is the overflow of the large diameter cyclone under the clean coal sieve bend at the first stage, this part of slime is primarily separated by the large diameter cyclone, and will be further separated by the slime dense medium cyclone. Since the dense medium suspension has been classified and concentrated in the large diameter cyclone, the medium particle size of the slime dense medium cyclone is more suitable for the cleaning of slime, and the density of the suspension is close to the density of the slime, so that the qualified media preparation system of the slime dense medium separation system can be omitted. The overflow of the slime dense medium cyclone enters into the clean coal magnetic separator, and the clean coal separated by it will be dewatered and recycled through the clean coal magnetic separation tailing system; The underflow enters into the middlings magnetic separator, and will be recycled through the middlings magnetic separation tailing system, so there is no need to increase the specific product dewatering and recovery link, which simplifies the entire process.

The advantages of this separation process are the high precision of separation, the wide range of classification density, and the adaptability to the selected raw coal quality. However, the operation status of the large diameter cyclone directly affects the separation precision of the slime dense medium cyclone, the adjustment is difficult, the density fluctuates greatly and the separation effect is poor; The medium particle size of the slime dense medium cyclone is limited by the large diameter cyclone, and its lower limit of separation cannot reach 0, so it cannot completely replace the flotation.

• Pre-sliming

The cyclone feed in this process is the screen overflow of the raw coal desliming screen, this part of the coarse slime enters into the mixing tank and mixes with dense medium suspension, and finally it will be pumped into the slime dense medium cyclone and separated in a pressurized environment. The slime dense medium clean coal is separated by clean coal magnetic separator for medium draining, and will be the clean coal product after dewatering through its magnetic separation tailings recovery system. The tailings is separated by the middle refuse magnetic separator for medium draining and enters into magnetic separation tailings recovery system, finally it will be the middlings product after dewatering.

The advantages of the pre-deslimination of the dense media cyclone separation process are as follows: after the pre-deslimination of the raw coal, the load of the main system is reduced and the processing capacity is improved. The medium system of the coarse slime separation system is equipped with more adjustable density of material pressure suspension, which is benefit to improve the separation accuracy. But the separation system added a set of slime medium system, the number of equipment increased, and the process system becomes complex, so it cannot completely replace the flotation either.

14.2.3 Typical Process and Its Separation Effect

The combined separation process of slime dense medium cyclone with large diameter dense medium cyclone has been widely used in China coal washing plant, and has achieved good separation effect. Huang Yuxiang's study shows that the average possible deviation of the slime dense medium cyclone is 0.10 and the quantitative efficiency is 90%. The study of Su Zhuangfei shows that under the optimum process parameters, the possible deviation of the cyclone can be as low as 0.07, and the number of efficiency can reach 95.53%. The typical slime dense medium cyclone separation process and separation results of some coal washing plant in China were shown in Table 14.1.

Table 14.1 results of some coal washing plant in China were shown

No	Name of coal washing plant	Whether it is deslimed	Feed ash	Overflow ash	Underflow ash	Quantitative efficiency	Possible deviation (g·cm⁻³)
1	Taiyuan CWP	Pre desliming	16.92	11.83	41.66	88.50	0.13
2	Xingtai CWP	Pre desliming	13.50	5.00	57.00	95.50	0.07
3	Shuangguang CWP	Pre desliming	15.28	7.51	29.53	94.30	0.07
4	Nantong CWP	No desliming	17.55	16.22	40.35	87.15	0.09
5	Ruzhou CWP	No desliming	28.19	18.16	40.19	82.35	0.11

14.3 Spiral Separation Process

Figure 14.3 Spiral Separation Process

Picture, Courtesy by HOT Mining

14.3.1 Principle and Process

The spiral has the advantages of simple structure, no running parts, small footprint and convenient operation and management. In China, the coarse slime separation process based on the spiral is mainly used in the thermal coal washing plant. The principle is shown below.

In a certain range of particle size, when separating with a higher density, the equipment has a high separation precision and lower limit of separation; it can produce clean coal, middlings and tailings, and can be adjusted flexibly. But it often cannot meet the separation requirements of difficult separation coal and clean coal with low ash content.

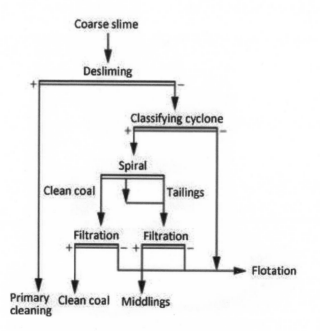

Figure 14.4 Principles and Process

14.3.2 Process Characteristics

After the desliming of selected raw coal by 2mm desliming screen, the slime under the screen enters enters into the concentrate cyclone group. After classification and concentration, 2~0.1mm slime enters into the spiral. The spiral clean coal enters into concentration and dewatering system for dewatering and finally become clean coal product. The spiral tailings turn into middlings after concentration and dewatering. The overflow of cyclone group and slime under the dewatering screen enter into flotation or concentration system, after further separation, they become a clean coal product, or directly as a tailings product.

The main advantages of this separation process are: the spiral itself has a low running cost and high effective separation density which is usually above $1.60g / cm^3$; it can be installed double or even three helix to improve the processing capacity of a single device. But the unit processing capacity is small; generally, there is a need for multiple joint use; When the raw coal quality changes, the equipment process parameters are not easy to adjust; When the separation density is low, the separation effect gets worse.

14.3.3 Typical Process and Separation Effect

Relying on the characteristics of the liquid flow, spiral is separation equipment which is used to separate different density under the influence of gravity and centrifugal force, and has been widely used in the domestic thermal coal washing plant in recent years. The factors that affect the separation effect of the spiral are mainly structural factors and process factors. The structural factors mainly include the outer diameter of the separation tank, the shape of the spiral groove, the diameter of the spiral, the number of spiral groove, etc., The process factors mainly include pulp throughput, ore concentration, feed size, baffle plate position,etc. The separation effect of the equipment is mainly evaluated by the efficiency and imperfection of the equipment. The typical separation process and separation effect of the spiral in some coal washing plants in China are shown in the following table.

Table 14.2 some coal washing plants separation effect

No	Name of coal washing plant	Feed ash	Clean coal ash	Tailings ash	Imperfection	Quantitative efficiency
1	Majiliang CWP	15.71	8.82	40.12	0.29	89.40
2	Xiyi CWP	28.32	16.49	68.79	0.26	96.13
3	Panyi CWP	37.98	7.51	68.20	0.32	85.30

14.4 TBS Teetered Bed Separator Separation Process

Figure 14.5 TBS

14.4.1 Principle and Process

TBS has a good separation effect for coarse slime in the coal washing plant, and this equipment is used for coarse slime separation in more and more coal washing plants for separation coarse slime and has achieved good economic benefits. Compared with other coarse slime separation equipment, TBS teetered bed separator has a wider scope of application, which can not only achieve the separation of fine coal and the cleaning of spiral clean coal under the desliming screen, but also recycle clean coal from the flotation tailings. The principle and process of coarse slime separation based on TBS teetered bed separator is shown in the following figure.

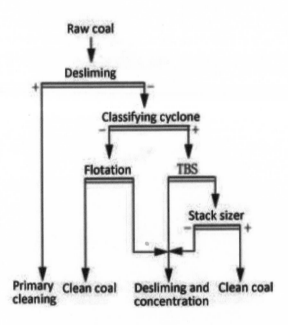

Figure 14.6 Principles and Process

14.4.2 Process Characteristics

After the dewatering, the slurry enters the thickening and classifying cyclone, and its overflow enters into the flotation system to be processed. The underflow is separated by TBS teetered bed separator, and TBS clean coal is dewatered by high frequency screen to be clean coal products, TBS tailings enters into the concentration system.

The main advantages of the TBS teetered bed separator process are: high separation precision and efficiency, low operation cost and simple process system.

The obvious shortcomings of the separation process in domestic applications are: through the real-time control of the underflow to achieve the stability of the separation process, the underflow is measured by the rising water flow rate that is automatically adjusted, but the current measurement and control means cannot achieve the synchronization and adjustment of rising water, which has a certain negative impact on the quality and quantity of the clean coal; the separation range of the equipment is narrower, which requires a higher classification of the material; The separation density can be controlled at 1.40~1.80g / cm^3, but this is achieved through the interference, which is difficult to precisely control.

14.4.3 Typical Process and Separation Effect

Key factors in the application of the separation process include particle characteristics, feed concentration, water flow rate, feed pressure, feed water pressure, etc. The size of the general separation material is between 0.15 and 3mm, and the separation effect is best when the particle size ratio of large particles and small particles is 4:1, the excess ratio is easily to cause mismatch problem and reduce the separation effect; if the feed pressure is too high, the bed will be not Stable, which results in the increase of ash. The separation effect of the separator is evaluated by the possible deviation, imperfection and quantity efficiency. The typical process and sub-effect of the TBS in some coal washing plants in China are shown in the following table.

Table 14.3 the typical process and sub-effect

No	Name of coal washing plant	Feed ash	Clean coal ash	Tailings ash	Possible deviation (g·cm⁻³)	Imperfection	Quantitative efficiency
1	Liangbei CWP	20.96	13.72	66.74	0.06	0.15	92.00
2	Zhaoguan CWP	27.25	10.87	54.52	0.098	0.19	91.00
3	Liyi CWP	41.18	9.44	78.60	0.12	0.20	91.50

14.5 Water Medium Cyclone Separation Process

Figure 14.7 Water Medium Cyclone Separation Process

14.5.1 Principle and Process

The water medium cyclone belongs to the autogenous medium type equipment, which uses the fine ore particles in the feed as the medium to realize the separation of the material under the centrifugal force. It is mainly used for the separation of coarse slime. At present, this equipment is mainly used for high sulfur coal and difficult flotation weathered oxidized slime processing. The principle and process of coarse slime separation based on water medium cyclone are shown in the following figure.

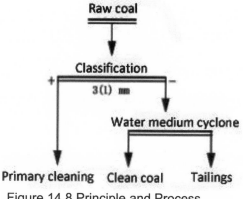

Figure 14.8 Principle and Process

14.5.2 Process Characteristics

The raw coal is graded by the classifying screen, and the screen underflow is fed into the mixing tank to stir, the feed pump is tangentially supplied to the cylindrical part of the cyclone, and then the spiral motion is formed. In the effect of centrifugal force, the high-density particles move down along the wall, and then discharged from the bottom of the mouth, after dehydration to become refuse products, low-density particles come to spiral upward movement, and finally discharged from the overflow, after dehydration to become clean coal products.

The advantages of the separation process are as follows: simple equipment structure, large unit capacity, low investment, short construction, flexible process, easy to maintain the system, no need of any medium, and greatly reducing the production cost. But Its disadvantages are also obvious, its separation precision is low, and the overflow is difficult to achieve the ash requirements of clean coal without dewatering.

14.5.3 Typical Process and Separation Effect

The main structural parameters which affect the Application Effect of water medium cyclone include the diameter of the cyclone, the diameter of inlet, underflow outlet and overflow hole, the taper angle, the insertion depth of overflow tube,etc., the process parameters include the feed pressure, feed concentration and so on. The selection of cyclone diameter is directly related to the upper feed size. Generally speaking, the cyclone diameter is 20 times bigger than the upper limit of the feed size; Larger feed pressure causes increased flow rate and a corresponding increase in the separation density; feed pressure is generally 0.098~0.147Mpa, feed concentration is generally 15% , higher feed concentration causes a corresponding increase in the separation density, decrease in separation precision and increase in clean coal pollution degree. The separation effect of water medium cyclone is usually evaluated by quantitative efficiency, possible deviation and imperfection. The typical water medium cyclone separation process and separation effect of some coal washing plants in our country are shown in the following table.

Table 14.4 Typical Process and Separation Effect

No	Name of coal washing plant	Feed ash	Clean coal ash	Tailings ash	Possible deviation (g·cm^{-3})	Imperfection	Quantitative efficiency
1	Lvjiatuo CWP	32.83	10.89	54.59	0.10	0.29	76.56
2	Xiqu CWP	14.75	10.15	38.74	0.15	0.27	90.84
3	Xingwu CWP	18.34	7.62	54.74	0.06	0.10	94.11

14.6 Conclusion

The conventional coal preparation process based on jigging, dense medium and flotation has been relatively mature and perfect, and can meet the requirements of conventional washing technology. The research direction of coal preparation technology has been shifted to coarse slime concentration, slurry processing and so on. By adding the coarse slime separation link and rationally disposing the mature coal preparation equipment, construction of three stages joint coal preparation process is the future development trend of the coal preparation industry. At present, all kinds of coarse slime separation process are still not perfect, each has its own advantages and disadvantages. In the process design, the coal quality must be analyzed and compared seriously, and the most suitable process is selected according to the characteristics of the separation equipment and process characteristics.

15. Some CHPP Was Re-designed on a Large Scale After Being Put Into Operation, Why?

Coal washing plant design and construction level in China has been greatly improved, but the design level and engineering quality vary greatly. Some coal preparation plant was put into running after completion, neither the yield nor the quality can meet the design expectation, so it had to be re-designed on a large scale, even be closed. There are not only design reasons, but also decision-making reasons. Combining with the working experience in design, this article has discussed the problems which often appear in the design and construction of coal washing plant.

15.1 Construction Scale of Coal Washing Plant

Generally speaking, the coal washing plant construction scale of the mine type should be in line with the capacity of the mine it serves, and that scale of the central type should be determined with comprehensively considering the coal mine and coal resources around. But in the design process, the situation of "approve small but construct big" or "approve big but construct small" often appears.

(1) A coal washing plant in Binchang mining area of Shaanxi province, the design scale of the mine is 5.00 Mt/a, and the maximum hoisting capacity is 1500 t/h. The feasibility approval is 5.00 Mt/a, but the actual processing capacity of equipment is designed according to the maximum hoisting capacity of 1500 t/h, which is equivalent to a 8.00 Mt/a coal washing plant.

(2) A central type coal preparation plant in Erdos, Inner Mongolia, the feasibility approval is 8.00 Mt/a, but the actual transport system is designed according to the scale of 8.00 Mt/a coal washing plant, the washing capacity is designed according to the scale of 5.00 Mt/a.

The construction of above coal preparation plants is not only wasting investment, but also leading to the high redundancy and high costs of production and operation after being put into running.

15.2 Engineering Design Order of Coal Washing Plant

Coal washing plant design generally contains four stages. They are scheme design, feasibility study, preliminary design and construction drawing design. Each stage has different focus.

Scheme design belongs to the earlier stage design of the whole project, It's a solution which is made after fully understanding the requirements of the owner, and It's usually repeated several times; Feasibility study is the fundamental file of the project application, it mainly includes the researches of project construction, technical feasibility, economic feasibility, risks and countermeasures; The main purpose of the preliminary design is to guide the construction drawing design, guide the construction of coal washing plant, ensure smooth implementation of the construction technical scheme and reasonably control the construction investment; Design construction drawing design is for the project construction, which detailedly guides the construction of project.

At present, the design process of coal washing plant is still not so normative, existing the situation of supplementing the feasibility study and preliminary design after coal washing plant completion. The delay of preliminary design will restrict its function of guiding construction drawing and controlling investment. Usually, in the preliminary design review, the experts have put forward some important problems, such as technological process, equipment selection, etc., but the scene equipment has been purchased and the construction has nearly completed, then, these important opinions are missed. The consequences not only affect investment in coal washing plant construction progress, but also even affect the usage of coal washing plant after completion.

15.3 Design Data Collection

Coal washing plant design needs data of coal quality, factory condition, economic condition, and the user's requirements. But some users don't pay enough attention on it, they wouldn't be able to provide these data in time, which often results in design reworking and affecting the time limit for the project and project quality.

15.3.1 Geological Exploration And Geological Exploration Data

Geological exploration is the fundamental basis of building design. After determining the layout, the design institute directly makes geological exploration requests (or transferred it to Party A) to geological exploration units. But in fact, because it takes much time to do geological exploration, so in most projects, doing geological exploration is usually combined with design optimization, which results that sometimes part of the buildings has no geological exploration and can only refer to the neighbouring buildings. What's worse, some enterprises don't do geological exploration or only do primary exploration not detailed exploration.

(1) When designing a coal washing plant in Erdos, Inner Mongolia, the designers only referred to the geological exploration of the neighbouring places. But in the construction, the road surface of a gas Station in the west collapsed, then the emergency investigation of surroundings of the main workshop was taken. Fortunately, the main building area is not in the gob area, but the delayed construction time is about half a month.

(2) The coal washing plant in Inner Erdos, Mongolia was originally designed for coal washing plant + loading station in one. After the approval of feasibility study, the design institute had repeatedly communicated with Party A for half a year. Firstly, the main plant area was located in Shenhua Shendong gob area; Later, this project was redesigned to avoid gob area, the main building was changed to be located in Shenhua Shendong coal field; Finally, it had to remove the coal washing function and only retain the loading function, which not only wasted time, but also changed the original design and plan.

(3) The design of a coal washing plant in Shaanxi is based on the first edition of initial exploration. Later, the construction drawing was changed a lot, the most typical place is the concentration basin. According to the geological exploration report, the field belongs to collapsible loess

in the design with lime-soil compaction pile, 10.7m pile length, and the number of 4854. When it came to pile, the field was found to be rubber soil. Because it had started piling, in order to ensure the construction period, the construction had to continue according to the design, which increases the investment of project.

15.3.2 Coal Quality Data

The test data are mainly from raw coal (natural grade) size and float-and-sink tests, large sized broken coal (broken grade) size and float-and-sink tests, coal fines size and float-and-sink tests, slime flotation test, coal and refuse degradation test, and slurry settlement test. The test data is not only the basis of preparation process design but also the main basis of product structure positioning. The representativeness of experimental data is directly related to the quality of design process. The quality data in design process should be same or similar to that in operation after coal washing plant completion, or may result that the coal washing plant processing capacity couldn't reach the standard, even couldn't be put into a normal production.

Because the majority of coal washing plant is the new-built coal washing plant, the mine didn't produce coal when designing. So the designers can refer to the production sample near the coal washing plant to design, and consider the lump coal and smalls ratio and the slime amount.

15.3.3 The Price of Raw Coal and Coal Products

Coal price is an important indicator of whether the coal washing plant has economic benefits, especially for the central type coal washing plant. Compared with the mine type coal preparation plant, the purchase price of raw coal and the sales price of coal products have a great impact on the economic benefits of coal washing plant.

A central type thermal coal preparation plant in Erdos of Inner Mongolia, the design scale is 5.00Mt/a, the main production is 150~80mm coal, 80~30mm lump coal, 30~0mm smalls. After the completion of coal washing plant, due to the Group's limited coal production , the raw coal is mainly purchased from foreign coal. Because the raw coal in good quality also has a high price, and the poor quality coal has low recovery of clean coal after preparation, during the trial run of the project , the plant washed the 150~0mm and 50~0mm coal, but there is nearly no economic benefits. At present, the main use of this plant is providing loading services for the surrounding coal mine through its peripheral system. The entire coal preparation system (about 100 million yuan investment) is in a state of shutting down. In conclusion, the main reason is that the market research of the raw coal market and the washing coal products is not enough, and the product positioning is not accurate.

15.4 Product Structure Positioning

Product positioning is a process of target market positioning which is based on coal grades, physical and chemical properties, coal and rock characteristics, process performance indicators to determine the use of the product, and combines with the local market demand. After the accurate positioning, based on the local market prices, the products shall be further optimized according to the principle of maximum economic benefits.

The coal quality characteristics, process performance and application of a coal mine in Binchang Mine of Shaanxi province are summarized as follows: the coal seam in the area is in low water (Mad = 4.35%), low ash~medium ash (Ad = 15.21%), low sulfur (St, d=0.98%), low phosphorus (Pt, d=0.021%), rich in oil, high volatile (Vdaf= 32.25%), medium softening temperature (ST=1273 ℃), high calorific value (Qgr, d=27.49MJ/kg), non-caking coal No. 31 (BN31), and the coal with low grindability (HGI=59). The product structure is positioned as the lump coal for gasification coal and the smalls for spay-blow coal.

In fact, after the completion of the coal washing plant, due to the difficulty to open the spay-blow coal market, and the smalls sales is poor, which resulting in its smalls dense medium separation system and slime separation system in idle, the cost of idle equipment is more than 1800 million yuan.

15.5 Process Design

15.5.1 Does Raw Coal Need to Be Washed Thoroughly?

When designing a coal washing plant, it shouldn't blindly pursue the thermal coal all into the wash. To decide whether the power plant smalls need all into wash, we should carefully analyze the smalls quality and the requirements of power plant for smalls, and reasonably determine the lower limit of separation. In many domestic thermal coal washing plant design, the lump coal and smalls are respectively in the wash, and the smalls system is nearly closed after being put into operation, which results in equipment in idle and investment waste. Smalls are all into the wash, on the one hand, more slime and refuse are separated, the quality of clean coal is increased, but the yield recovery is reduced, which decreases the overall efficiency of the coal washing plant; On the other hand, in some coal-rich areas, like Shaanxi, Inner Mongolia, etc., many coal washing plant discharges the refuse with the slime, it results in the waste of resources.

15.5.2 Process Selection

Domestic common thermal coal washing plant adopts the process of lump coal into the wash, smalls in bypass process. Lump coal separation is commonly using dense medium vessel and jigging process. Both of the two preparation methods have their own advantages, disadvantages and application scope. The design selection should be comprehensively considered according to the coal quality, separation density, product structure and other conditions.

The advantages of dense media vessel process are: high efficiency of separation, wide range of adjustable separation density, high control precision, wide range of sizing size and high adaptability to the raw coal quality. The shortcomings are: Increase the dense medium recovery process, and this process is relatively complex; The abrasion of equipment pipeline caused by medium is more serious; when the required medium density is more than 1.8kg / L, the high density suspension is difficult to configure.

The advantages of the jigging process are: the technology is mature, the process flow is relatively simple, the maintenance and management is convenient, the processing cost is low; it won's be restricted by the separation density. The shortcomings are: the separation efficiency of jigging process is obviously lower than that of dense medium preparation when separation is difficult and it's difficult to choose coal. When the separation density is less than 1.4kg / L, the jig is difficult to control, which means that the normal separation couldn't be guaranteed; high consumption of circulating water causes the high load of slurry system.

15.6 Construction Organization

A large coal preparation plant construction project is generally subcontracted to a number of construction units, such as civil construction unit, equipment installation unit, distribution and control unit, pipeline installation unit, etc., so there is inevitably cross between each construction unit. At this point we should pay attention to the following question.

Assort the construction units with installation units. Generally speaking, the construction unit has installation conditions, and installation units comes into the installation, but it also occurred that, in order to catch up the progress, the construction unit build the installation wall of the main plant prematurely, which caused that installation equipment could only be hung in through the top of the main plant, greatly Increase the difficulty of the equipment installation.

15.7 Conclusion

Combined with the design practice in recent years, the author believes that to do a good design of coal washing plant, we must attach importance to the accuracy of data. And in the design of construction drawing, we should pay more attention to important points and the details. Finally, in the construction, we should pay attention to the coordination between each construction unit.

16. The Design and Choice of Preparation Process in Coking Coal Washing Plant

Abstract: By analyzing the design process of a coking coal washing plant in Guizhou, this article points out that when there is a large quantity of fine fraction and heavy product in raw coal, and the refuse is easy to degradation in water, the traditional dense medium process and flotation process exists many shortages. Besides, based on above analysis, this article also puts forward a novel coal preparation process.

Key words: Coal preparation process; Design; Dense medium process; Flotation; Coarse slime separation

16.1 Overview

In the last decade, the dense medium cyclone separation technology and equipment has been rapidly developed. Dense medium cyclone separation technology, with its large capacity, high separation precision, strong adaptability to different raw coal, simple process and easy to realize automation, has been highly accepted by more and more coal design and production companies. In the domestic newly-built coking coal washing plant with dense medium process, the most commonly used methods are mainly the "three products dense medium cyclone + slime flotation " and the "two stages two products dense medium cyclone + slime flotation" (hereafter "traditional dense medium process and flotation process"). Because of the many advantages of dense

288

medium process, and some misunderstandings in preparation, a lot of design companies and owners directly choose the above process without seriously studying the coal quality. But, when there is a large quantity of fine fraction and heavy product in raw coal, and the refuse is easy to degradate in water, the traditional dense medium process and flotation process exists many shortages. And by analyze the design process of a coking coal washing plant in Guizhou, this article also puts forward a novel coal preparation process.

16.2 Coal Quality

The main characteristics of the raw coal in the coking coal washing plant of Guizhou are: the coal is coking coal with high sulfur content and large heavy product content. The refuse is easy to degradate in water, fine fraction coal quality is good, and it has good slime flotability. The particle sizes of raw coal are shown in table 1, the float-and-sink component is shown in table 16.2, and the sieve analysis component are shown in table 16.1.

Size Fraction/mm	Yield Recovery/%	Ash/%	Total Sulfur/%
50 ~25	14. 13	36. 37	2. 71
25 ~13	17. 57	34. 63	1. 37
13 ~6	13. 05	31. 33	1. 81
6 ~3	12. 84	29. 71	1. 64
3 ~0. 5	17. 41	26. 31	1. 33
0. 5 ~0	25. 00	18. 32	1. 05
	100. 00	28. 29	1. 57

Table 16.1 The Particle Size of Raw Coal

Density Fraction/ g·cm⁻³	Floats And Sinks			Cumulative Floats		Cumulative Sinks		δ±0.1 Content	
	Ratio of Whole	Ratio of Same Size	Ash	Ratio of Same Size	Ash	Ratio of Same Size	Ash	Density	Yield Recovery
<1.3	8.40	11.57	5.35	11.57	5.35	100.00	31.39	1.30	67.86
1.3~1.4	28.45	39.16	11.47	50.73	10.07	88.43	34.80	1.40	67.62
1.4~1.5	8.13	11.19	20.85	61.92	12.02	49.27	53.34	1.50	22.30
1.5~1.6	4.02	5.53	29.44	67.45	13.45	38.08	62.89	1.60	11.09
1.6~1.7	2.24	3.09	38.07	70.54	14.53	32.55	68.57	1.70	13.11
1.7~1.8	1.18	1.62	46.72	72.16	15.25	29.46	71.77	1.80	8.75
>1.8	20.22	27.84	73.23	100.00	31.39	27.84	73.23		
Total	72.64	100.00	31.39						
Slime	2.36	3.14	38.48						
Aggregate	75.00	100.00	31.61						

Table 16.2 Float-and-sink Component of 50~0.5mm Raw Coal(%)

The raw coal coal quality analysis is as follows:

• The 0.5~0mm raw coal content is 25%, and has large amount of primary slime; The 3 ~ 0mm raw coal content is 42.41%, which occupy a large portion of the total. So we should carefully study the processing technology of 3~0mm sized coal in the design of coal washing plant.

Size Fraction /mm	y Ration of Same Size%	y Ratio of Whole%	Size Fraction /%
>0.25	39.38	9.85	18.25
0.25~0.20	17.66	4.41	17.42
0.20~0.15	7.90	1.97	18.25
0.15~0.125	4.81	1.20	18.48
0.125~0.10	5.53	1.38	18.75
0.10~0.09	4.58	1.15	18.71
<0.09	20.13	5.03	20.21
	100.00	25.00	18.56

Table 16.3 0.5~0mm Raw Coal Sieve Analysis Component

(2) <1.4 g/cm3 density fraction content is small, and the yield recovery of low ash clean coal is not high;>1.4 g/cm3 density fraction

content is large, and has large amount of middlings and refuse; Ash content in float-and-sink slime is 38.48%, and the phenomenon of refuse degradation in water is serious.

(3) When under the requirements of ash content below 10%, and separation density<1.4 g/cm^3, the washability is extremely small.

(4) >0.25mm content is 39.38%, and the coarse slime content is large; <0.09mm content is 20.13%, and the slimes content is small.

16.3 Product Structure

According to the raw coal quality, and the future market forecast of coking coal, in the design of coal washing plant, the quality index of clean coal preparation is confirmed as the following: Ad≤10.00%, Mt≤12.00%, the quality index of mixed coal preparation is : Ad≤32%, Mt≤12.00%. But in practical production, these indexes can also be adjusted according to the market.

16.4 Processes Selection And Analysis

16.4.1 Shortages of Traditional Dense Medium Process And Flotation Process

According to the raw coal quality, the author thinks that the traditional dense medium and flotation process have a lot of disadvantages, mainly include:

(1) In the raw coal,>1.4 g/cm^3 density fraction content is about 50%, and heavy product content is too large. If we choose the three products

dense medium cyclone to separate, the quantity of material which comes into the second stage of cyclone is large. And due to the limit of the throughput capacity, the processing capacity of cyclone will be greatly decreased. Thus, in order to improve the processing capacity, we have to enlarge the specification of the cyclone.

(2) In the traditional "two stages two products heavy medium cyclone" process, the clean coal products are separated in the first stage, but the processing capacity of the cyclone will be restricted because of the large concentration of underflow.

(3) The clean coal is separated first both in the "three products dense medium cyclone" and "two stages two products dense medium cyclone" , but in this plant, the refuse degradation of water phenomenon in raw coal is more serious, it should firstly discharge the reject, so the traditional dense medium process could not adapt to.

(4) There is no individual gravity separation of coarse slime in the traditional dense medium process, so the slime is all in flotation.But this plant has a very large quantity of the coarse slime, if all slime comes into the flotation, the construction investment and operation cost will be high, and lose clean coal easily.

16.4.2 Introduction of Recommended Coal Preparation Process

Through detailed analysis of the raw coal quality and comparison of several preparation plans, the final recommended coal preparation process is: 50~3mm sized coal is roughly separated by high density dense medium cyclone, 3~0.3mm sized coal is roughly separated by spiral,

13~0.6mm sized coal is cleaned by low density dense medium cyclone, 0.6~0.3mm sized coal is cleaned by RC slime separator, 0.3~0mm sized coal is in slimes flotation.The principle of the coal preparation process is shown in figure 1.

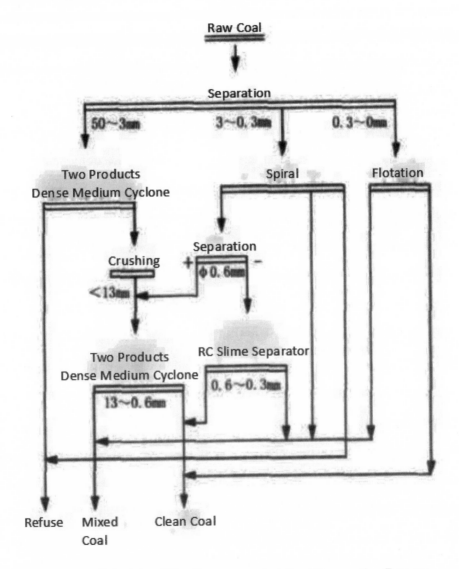

Figure 16.1 Principle of The Recommended Coal Preparation Process

16.4.3 Reasons For Selection of The Process

The recommended preparation process sticks to the coal quality. And there is a few application cases, which is worthy of study and discussion. The followings are introduction and analysis for several characteristic links.

16.4.3.1 Adopting stroke with aperture size in 3mm

The primary slime content in the raw coal <0.5mm is 25%. Adding the secondary and float-and-sink slime, the total slime content is about 35%. So the slime content is large, which means that it needs pre-election desliming process. One feature of the recommended process is to use stroke with aperture size in 3mm.

(1) 3~0mm content is 42.41%, which is large. With 3mm aperture size stroke, the 3~0mm sized coal and slime are removed from the raw coal, which can greatly reduce the throughput of the high density dense medium cyclone, and minimize the stroke and dense medium equipment specification, so as to reduce the construction investment and operation cost of the plant.

(2) According to the coal quality data, there is a large quantity of fine fraction raw coal. Dislodge the fine fraction raw coal in advance, and adopt the low-cost combined process of spiral and RC slime separator to separate effectively, which can effectively reduce the operation cost of the coal washing plant.

(3) The upper limit of separation of the spiral is 3mm, which can furthest take advantages of the low cost of spiral separation.

16.4.3.2 Adopting the two stages two products dense medium process, discharging reject at the first stage

(1) The heavy product content in the raw coal is about 50%, if using the traditional dense medium process, the clean coal products are separated in the first stage, but the processing capacity of the cyclone will be restricted because of the large concentration of underflow. And the specification of the cyclone in the first stage needs to be enlarged, which is not economic.

(2) Discharging reject by the dense medium cyclone in the first stage could reduce the refuse degradation in water, which will be beneficial for later separation and slurry system.

(3) After discharging reject in the first stage cyclone, its light product will be separated by the dense medium cyclone in the second stage, which helps improve the yield recovery of clean coal products.

16.4.3 30.3mm as the top size of flotation

(1) Flotation is a coal preparation method with high investment and high operation cost. So we should appropriately lower the top size of flotation to reduce the slime content in flotation.

(2) The most effective particle size of flotation is 0.3~0mm, coarse slime in 0.3mm or more is easily to be lost in tailings in the flotation process due to lack of bubble carrying capacity, which causes resources waste.

4.3.4 3~0.3mm coarse slime separation process

3~0.3mm coarse slime is roughly separated by spiral, its light products are cleaned by RC slime separator or dense medium cyclone according to the particle size.

(1) The effective separation density of the spiral is above 1.6kg/L, when separation density is lower than 1.6kg/L, the separation effect is poor. Spiral is an ideal equipment of roughing separation for coarse slime in 3~0.3mm with good desulfurization effect, low investment, simple operation and low processing cost. This design uses the spiral as roughing equipment of 3~0.3mm coarse slime and its light products will be cleaned in the next link.

(2) The separation mechanism of RC slime separator is similar to that of the teetered bed. Under the condition of higher ash content in the material, although we can wash out the qualified clean coal products through the separation of single equipment, the tailings cannot be disposed. Mixing with dense medium middlings, lead to mixed coal ash content exceeds bid; Mixing with refuse, cause waste of resources. Therefore, combining with the spiral is a better choice.

16.4.4 Main Characteristics of Recommended Coal Preparation Process

(1) According to the differences of particle size and washability, different size fraction of raw coal matches different separation process, which can give full play to the advantages of dense medium, spiral, slime separator and flotation process. It has a prominent effect to reduce processing costs and improve the overall yield recovery of clean coal.

(2) Use 3mm stroke for wet desliming, after selected products are separated by the 1.5mm dense medium, which can improve the dense medium separation effect, reduce duplication of separation process, and significantly improve the unit capacity and efficiency of the stroke and sculping screen. It also could reduce the fractional flow, the specifications of the dense medium module equipment, and the medium consumption and power consumption of the coal washing plant.

(3) Adopting two stages two products dense medium cyclone could precisely control the separation density in both two stages with high separation precision and less coal in refuse.

(4) Discharging reject by dense medium cyclone at the first stage could reduce the specification of the dense medium cyclone, reduce the refuse degradation in water, and improve the separation effect at the second stage.

16.4.5 Application of Recommend Coal Preparation Process

The combined coal preparation process has been successfully applied in Xiezhuang coal washing plant of Xinwen mining group. The design scale of Xiezhuang coal washing plant is 1.5 million t/a, the coal is gas coal and gas-fat coal. This plant get into operation from the end of 2006, and the main product is grade 11 clean coking coal. A year of operation practice shows that the technology is advanced and reasonable with high yield recovery of clean coal and low running cost. Finally, this process has created prominent economic benefits for Xinwen mining group.

16.5 Conclusion

In recent years, new technology and new equipment for coal preparation are developing fast, which provides a strong technical support for coal preparation process innovation. When choosing coal preparation process, we should base on the coal quality, market-oriented, advancing with The Times and innovation, and select the most pointed process on the technical and economic comparison, to ensure that obtain the biggest yield recovery of clean coal and minimize the capital investment and processing cost.

17. The Bright & Dark Side of China Coal Preparation Equipment Manufacturing

Note: The topic is a series, so we can call this paper as a preface. Follow-up is the related articles about coal preparation machinery will be ongoing and readers should continue to focus the updates.

As the user may encounter these situations (Coal Preparation Plant, Non coal mineral processing plant):

The Bright Side–Part of the product manufacturing level has been a world class:

Some imported cyclone underflow and other components are not as good as the domestic; it turned out that some big brands of wear-resistant parts are sourced from China...

A certain brand of dense medium vessel pure imported chain, tracing its source of origin, which originally is China sells to overseas, then overseas sell back...

Domestic filter plate has replaced some Austrian brand, Spanish brand. German brand is very well so that these foreign filter press manufacturing competitors all are purchasing the filter plate which made in China......

The China produced horizontal vibrating centrifuges are better than two major pure imported brands......

A domestic large vibrating screen and flip-flow screening machine which performance are better than all the foreign brands......

The Dark Side–In more representatively cases:

The rubber spring support of Firestone can be only used up to 3 months now; when the equipment just arrived, at least can be used for a year or two years...

A brand of new imported original parts of crusher even cannot be installed......

A brand of Centrifuge basket and scraper's service life are shorter......

A certain brand of imported centrifuge went wrong, the foreigner sent engineers to check it and found the corresponding serial number was not on, without this equipment......

A certain brand of imported large screen machine, shipped to the site, the buffer package actually has China mainland newspapers......

Large double roll crusher so far still cannot be copied successfully......

The large cyclone still has the wear-resistant lining whole molding technology......

The using effect of high-intensity magnetic separation is still far from the company of United States......

There is no denying that the coal machinery of China (including coal preparation equipment) is in the transition period of imitation – independent research and development ". Cheap, quality uneven, copycat, unfair competition...... This is the rising of "Made in China" that is being criticized on the coal market.

However, history is always surprisingly similar.

The national level, almost every technology leading countries has experienced this stage. Now known as the world industry benchmark "made in Germany", had met the same criticism with "made in China" .In 125 years ago, British people even labeled the German made products as "brazen". In 1871, after the reunification of Germany, numerous tasks remain to be undertaken; the economic booming was been needed. While it is not easy for Germany to enter the worldwide market, so those who pursuit their big dream are on the margins of other countries, finally they push themselves counterfeiting products from Britain and France, and relying on cheap price hit the worldwide market. On August 23, 1887, the British parliament passed the derogatory trademark law, and stimulated all products imported from Germany must be marked "Made in Germany". Therefore, "Made in Germany" become a legal term, which be used to distinguish "made in Britain", so as to differentiate shoddy goods in Germany and high quality products in British.

The enterprise level, now the several large brands companies which equipment is the copycat too at the beginning of making their fortune. After the company which be copied withdraw from the history, the copycat company will become the original. For example, a Finland company's large horizontal Vibrating screen technology, an Australian company's horizontal vibrating centrifuge technology, an USA company's Screen-bowl centrifuge technology...... Please note that I have not mentioned the China Company. Those are some of the world's top 500 have done already in the early stage.

History is a cycle.

I invite the reader to a prudent attitude towards the "cottage" the current situation of Chinese coal which is the stage of development decisions and manufacturers themselves need to upgrade as soon as possible to start a new independent research and development.

Chinese coal preparation machinery industry profiles

China's coal preparation machinery manufacturing enterprises widespread features as small-scale, scattered layout, low-end products and high-end market sales mix. And low-end products rely mainly on price competition while high-end products rely on equipment performance and services to expand the market space. This product structure unreasonable means superior enterprises have the comparative advantage of more outstanding in the integration of market future and formulate industry standards. These advantages make the enterprises easy to grow into equipment giant in the field of coal preparation technical services.

From the level of equipment, most of the domestic coal preparation equipment performance and reliability has reached to the international first-class level after nearly 10 years rapid development. Such as Dense medium vessel, Vibrating screen, centrifuge, Cyclone classification group, Express quantitative load-out system, filter press etc. However, part of the equipment performance and reliability still has a big gap with the international first-class level, such as Magnetic separator, Spiral chute separation, Double roll crusher.

Cost benefits provide China domestic coal machinery manufacturers a strong competitiveness in the market. In the case of the same type, the same model of coal preparation equipment, domestic equipment usually cheaper 25~50% than pure imported equipment, such as centrifuge, load-out station, automatic dosing device etc .Some domestic equipment even cheaper 50~80% than the pure imported equipment , such as double roll crusher, filter press etc. This is one of the main reasons for the domestic coal machinery manufacturers can get plenty of orders. Meanwhile, in the aspect of providing timely and comprehensive after-sales service, reasonable spare parts price, in-depth understanding of local customer's demand etc, compared with foreign suppliers. Also, when compared with foreign suppliers, the domestic high-end coal preparation machinery manufacturers have more advantages in providing timely and comprehensive after-sales service, reasonable spare parts price, and depth understanding of local customers demand.

Second, the classifications of the coal preparation machinery the features of coal preparation machinery are various and specialized, thus most products from the coal machine manufacturing enterprise are limited to a certain technology. In the range of worldwide, there are just several giant corporations with vast coal and mineral processing machinery product line, they are Finland's (Metso), Denmark's (Flsmith), Germany's (KHD), and the Netherlands's (TEMA), so it is not easy to see in manufacturing . In China, there are few enterprise has a broad product line , at present ,only Shandong Bo Run industrial technology co., LTD and TianDi science technology co., LTD have it. Metso is a strange brand in domestic coal. Except China, as a provider, Metso not only rovides the whole series of mineral products but also the excellence of coal preparation technology. Metso has business with China many years ago, the technology of metso's vibrating screen was used by An Tai Bao coal preparation plant in PingShuo, XiangShui coal preparation plant in Guizhou and so on, they are early modular in dense medium coal preparation plant project. As to the reason why metso lost such a big coal preparation technology services market in China, ahem...Metso didn't give me consulting fees so we skip it.

In accordance with the order of the dense medium coal preparation process and equipment's main functions, they are divided into XXXXXX (please consult Baidu, or read the book called *the mineral processing study*, published by China mining university). In order to save everyone's traffic, let's end it.

18. Coal Quality Analysis in the Designing Stage of Coal Washing Plant

Abstract: Through the example analysis, the paper puts forward the importance of the analysis about the float coal characteristics in the coal preparation plant design. The coal preparation plant which can manufacture coking coal and thermal coal should choose coal preparation methods flexibly. For fragile coal, when selecting coal, it is necessary to select the non-pressure feeding dense medium cyclone separator, and also consider the coarse slime reselection technique.

Keywords: *Design of coal preparation plant; Coal quality analysis; Coal preparation process; coal slime treatment.*

In the design process of a coal preparation plant, the correct analysis of coal is very important to help determine the reasonable preparation methods and processes. Besides, the analysis also provides a reliable basis to help investors further implement the target market and make the project decision. Through the investigation and the actual operation with some of the project, we found that the resources couldn't be rationally utilized, and even the finished project has to be rebuilt because of the improper coal quality analysis. Some views and experience with examples for the coal preparation plant designers are as follows.

18.1 Case Analysis

18.1.1 The internal ash analysis of coal is not enough.

There are 15 seams of coal in a mine in Yunnan province, from top to bottom: M4, M7, M8, M9, M12, M13, M16, M16, M16, M20, M21, M23, M23, M24 and M24. The main coal seams are M9 and M12. In the first 21a, they mainly exploited M4, M7 and M9 coal seam. The coal is a strongly viscous No.25 coking coal. The coal preparation methods which based on the metallurgical coking coal standard are: 50~0mm raw coal is preliminarily deslimed; 50~1mm raw coal is cleaned by the three-product non-pressure dense medium cyclone; 1~0.25mm coarse slime is cleaned by the teetered bed;-0.25mm slime adopts the combination method of flotation separation. When calculating, collect adjacent M9, M16 coal seams' production details, and synthesize them in proportion, then determine the theoretical separation density is 1.4g/cm3, the clean coal ash content is 10.72%, and the productivity of the clean coal is 50.12%. According to this calculation, the coal preparation plant's economic benefit is very good. But after detailed analysis, the following problems are found:

Float coal ash content. According to the coalfield geological exploration report which provides the coal quality and characteristics, the float coal ash content of those three seams which were exploited in term Pre 21a (-1.4g/cm3 density level) are shown in table 1, the Preliminary Coal Seam Mining Ratio and Float Coal Ash analysis are shown in table 2.

Coal Seam	M4	M7	M9
Ash Content(A_d/%)	18.91	16.17	10.92

Note: the float coal ash content of M12 coal seam in the later period is

13.99%.

Table 18.1 Float coal Ash Content Statistics of Preliminary Mining Coal Seam

Term		Pre 5a	6-11a	12-15a	16-19a	20-21a
Coal Seam Minging Ratio(%)	M4	100,00	75.78	52.98	37.38	24.62
	M7		24.24			75.38
	M9			47.02	62.62	
Average Ash in Float Coal(%)		18.91	18.38	15.15	13.90	17.28

Table 18.2 Preliminary Coal Seam Mining Ratio and Float Coal Ash analysis

From table 1 and 2, it can be seen that, when the theoretical separation density is 1.4 g/cm^3 and the production ash is 10.72%, the productivity cannot reach 50.12% .

• Miscalculated. The main reason for the miscalculation is the screening samples we adopted. The cumulative ash of the-1.4g/cm3 float coal is 10.10%, so the calculation results must be larger if the correction isn't made to table 2. Therefore, insufficient analysis of the internal ash content of coal will lead to the wrong conclusion.

18.1.2 Coal quality treatment scheme.

(1) Product positioning. In view of the characteristics of high ash content, strong bond and low sulfur content of coal, the product positioning of this coal preparation plant should be based on the production of other coking coal.

(2) The treatment of coal data. With referring to the simple samples which the coalfield geological exploration report provided, we should amend the ash content of the data which adopted by the density level, and calculate product solutions, make it more close to the actual production.

18.1.3 The coal preparation method has no specific characteristics of coal.

Jilin province is a large province in northeast China, but it's terribly short of coal resources. In recent years, it has developed a large mine of 1.8 Mt/a near Changchun city. The coal of the mine is ultra-low~low sulfur coal, and the clean coal's volatilization is 42%. The bond index is 12~93, and the average is 57.6. According to the national standard "China coal classification table", this kind of coal is the No.44 gas coal, and it is good coking coal. The joint process which the coal preparation plant adopted is: 200~13mm raw coal discharges rejects by dense medium shallow slot; 13~2mm raw coal discharges rejects by two-product dense medium cyclone; 2~0.15mm raw coal discharges rejects by spiral, slime is recycled directly. After the selection, the product is large sized coal, mixed medium sized coal and slack coal, the ash is about 20%, and the main usages are civilian use and power generation. The main problem of this coal preparation process is that it is not suitable for the preparation of coking coal, which causes sufficient use of resources.

The coking coal resources in northeast China are nearly exhausted, so it is very important to protectively develop and utilize coking coal resources in this area. The following factors should be taken into consideration in determining the washing process of a coal preparation plant by combining the characteristics of coal.

(1) In the field, coal caking index changes, and highest can reach to 93. Combining with drilling data, we should analyze the distribution mode of strongly caking coal, in the point form, or in the plane form. Then when formulating coal preparation method, we can attain "suit the remedy to the case", know fairly well.

(2) Further implement the users of coking coal and provide reliable basis for formulating coal preparation methods.

(3) The selection of coal preparation methods should be selected in the following two schemes, and the target market should be further optimized.

Plan one: 200~13 raw coal discharges rejects by dense medium shallow slot; 13~1mm raw coal is cleaned by three-product dense medium cyclone; 1~0.15mm raw coal is cleaned by spiral (or teetered bed). The characteristics of this system are to clean the high quality thermal coal, and the slack coal system has the flexibility of smelting blended coking coal.

Plan two: 80~1mm raw coal is cleaned by three-product dense

medium cyclone; 1~0.5mm raw coal is cleaned by spiral (or teetered bed). The characteristics of this system are mainly washing the blended coking coal, with the flexibility of making 80~50 (or 40)mm Lump clean coal.

• Whether the slime needs flotation should be further demonstrated bonding with the target market.

18.1.4 The particularity of coal is inadequate.

The low sulfur lean coal produced by Sanghuping coal mine of Hancheng,Shanxi mining bureau is a good blast furnace injection coal. In 2004, the mining bureau decided to build a coal preparation plant. The reject degradation in water of this coal wasn't too terrible, but the coal was so fragile, which includes about 25% of the primary slime. Adding the secondary and floating slime, the total content of slime can reach 30% to 35% in this-0.5mm raw coal. When choosing coal preparation method, combining with the aggregative indicator of this coal, the mining bureau finally decided to choose desliming pressure cyclone to clean the coal. And because of the large amount of coal slime, this process must add flotation technology. But after bringing into production, the real slime content was much higher than design value, which caused the processing capacity was less than 50% of the design value. Later, through investigation and research, the mining bureau decided to reinvest to add the slime cleaning system. After the completion of the renovation, the coal preparation plant finally entered the normal production process, but the whole delayed time reached 2a. This kind of situation also appeared in a coal preparation plant in Liangbei, Henan.

18.2 Experience

(1) With the strength of the coal exploitation in our country, some mine fields which has complex coal seam and special coal quality should construct a matched coal preparation plant. And when choosing coal preparation methods and technological process, we must give full consideration to the special factor of coal quality changing.

(2) If a new field does not have the condition to do a screening Float-and-sink data, we can use the nearby fields' data. But when designing, we should carefully analyze the Float-and-sink data of those simple samples in the geological exploration report, because the data directly represents the real characteristics of this coal seam.

(3) In areas where the coking coal is lack, if the preparation coal has a certain caking property, this kind of coal can be used as blended coal for coking. So to adapt to the market, and reasonably use the resources, the process and technology must be flexible.

(4) For the fragile coal in Weibei, Shanxi and zhengzhou, when choosing coal preparation methods, we should give preference to the non-pressure feeding way of washing, and try to reduce coal crushing. It shall also have a process of coarse slime separation at the same time.

19. How to Design a GOOD Coal Washing Plant?

During 2003-2013, China's basic construction management system and review procedure of engineering project design have changed fundamentally. These changes has promoted the design document's quality and technology standard of many Chinese engineering company and some state-owned state institute becoming better, also the documents' content has changed a lot, mainly as follows:

Figure 19.1GuoJiaHe CHPP, 15Mt/a,
Picture Courtesy by Techgart (Beijing) Engineering Ltd

Recently, coal is not only the raw material of power fuel and coking, but also the valuable material of some high-added value industry which could replace the petrochemicals, such as modern coal chemical industry and coal-based compound fuel oil. Some industries such as clean coal technology, coal liquid, coal liquefaction and coal gasification has got good development chance, for example: supercritical, super-supercritical pulverized coal fired boiler, large circulation fluidized bed boiler, coal based syngas to methanol, methanol chemical products (dimethyl ether, acetic acid and the following down-stream product), methyl alcohol made alcohol ether fuel, methyl alcohol made olefin, poly-generation, direct liquefaction, indirect liquefaction, smouldering and Lignite drying quality.

The usage of coal has been greatly expanded and extended. Different coal usage method has different requirement about coal property, which pushes coal preparation engineers to expand the knowledge width.

The coal property analysis and processing performance analysis plays important role, because it' one of the basic factors in determining the product orientation and structure after being washed.

Besides the regular industry analysis and elemental analysis, the coal processing performance index analysis, micro coal rock structural analysis, degree of coalification analysis and metamorphic grade analysis shall also be included. The design document shall reflect original data of geologic report. The coal property information listed in the design document sometimes is not complete, and pointless. Mainly reflected in the following questions:

(1) When used as thermal coal, usually lack of some index related to boiler corrosion, such as chlorinity and fluorine content, also some index related to slag removal, such as ash fusion point, clinkering property and dirt property.

(2) When used as raw material of coal chemical industry, usually

lack of some important index related to moving (fixing) coal gasification and gasifier efficiency such as machinery anti-crushing intensity, thermostability, and so on.

Meagre coal in Lu'an coal mine district has low intensity of machinery anti-crushing, and easily smashed during transportation. Some plant in Taiyuan is the lump coal user of this coal mine, which is used as gas generating. During the transportation, the lump coal is smashed, and caused contract disputes. It suggests that the meagre coal in this mine is not suitable for gas generating.

(3) When the coal is applied as liquidation, sometimes lack of vitrinite reflectance parameters related to coal's micro-coal rock composition, degree of coalification and metamorphic grade, and some indicator reflects the carbon hydrogen ratio, oxygen content, hydrogen content, grindability, coal ash fusibility, flowing temperature and etc.

(4) When coal is applied as the raw material producing the synthesis gas, and the coal gasification processing is the water coal slurry gas flow bed processing, sometimes lack of analysis about coal water slurry.

The non-caking coal of some coal mine in Shanxi Yushen coal mine is the raw coal base of indirect liquidation project with 1mt per year capacity for one coal group in Shandong. This processing of this project adopts the Texaco coal-water slurry flow bed, which lack analysis of slurry character. The non-caking coal's slurry character is very bad, with only 59.5% of the coal-water fluid concentration in lab data, but the indirect liquidation project feasibility study designed coal-water concentration is about 65.0%. Which has many adverse impact on the gasification processing. (With the add of coal consumption and oxygen consumption, the investment has added hundreds of millions)

Quality characteristics and presentation process performance index is not accurate enough, there is no strict accordance with the various division level coal quality indicators relevant national standards or industry standards to express. It should be noted that these standard dynamic management, with the passage of time and technological progress, all kinds of coal quality division level standards are constantly revise and improve. We must grasp the new "standard."

State applies the principles of classification of coal resources and the use of optimal allocation (Industrial Development and Reform Commission [2006] No. 1350 text). Coal type and sulfur content, involving questions of principle relating to national resources and reasonable utilization. According to the State Environmental Protection Administration, the State Economic and Trade Commission, Ministry of Science and January 30, 2002 jointly issued documents (UNCED [2002] 26) the provisions of Article 3.1 of "no new coal seam around stars more than 3% of the sulfur mine"; in "coal, peat geological exploration specification" (DZ / T0215-2002) Appendix E proposed to estimate the amount of coal resources index, the maximum sulfur content of 3%; the national development and reform Commission Notice No. 80 of 2007 "coal industry policy" tenth three also pointed out, "the State applies protective exploitation of special and scarce coals, limiting sulfur, high ash coal resource development." Thus the Ministry of Land and attaches great importance to the project approval countersign these two issues.

For example: gas coal (1) Huainan Mining Guqiao and coking coal mines will not be a problem for power generation; (2) high-sulfur coal mine Songzao (St.d> 4.0%) resources, development and utilization of the question whether it is reasonable . National Development and Reform Commission approved the two projects were met Ministry of Land and countersigned in question. Another expert, again demonstrated. So, when designing special and rare types of encounters other purposes or high-sulfur coal resources need to be developed, the need for development and utilization of rationality should be demonstrated. Often they lack the necessary design files such arguments, especially the development of Yunnan, Guizhou, Sichuan area of high-sulfur coal mines.

Guizhou Zhijin coal mine fertilizing overall high sulfur coal seams is one of the main coal quality characteristics of Ida, where the 7th, 23rd floor average sulfur coal were up 4.22% and 4.10%, are sulfur coal.

However, the feasibility study of the occurrence of high-sulfur coal resources Ida mining, the use of reason, necessity lack the necessary proof and elaboration. Guizhou Province is rich in coal reserves, but high-sulfur coal more resources. For example, sulfur fertilizer Tianjing Tian> 3% and 3% of coal reserves almost half and half. So that high-sulfur coal resources are fully rational use is unavoidable reality.

Only from the following three aspects of the grounds of high-sulfur coal mining provide some ideas for the Feasibility Study prepared to consider:

(1) For mining, Sulfur within Ida> 3% sulfur coal and sulfur 3% of the coal resources are staggered symbiotic. For example, a group

of three coal, coal seam No. 6-1 average sulfur content 3%, while the average sulfur content of coal seam No. 7> 3%. In the mining process, if not crossed the 7 layers of high sulfur coal mining, continuing the lower part of the coal seam mining, the coal seam No. 7 would have been caving destroyed. Even in average sulfur content 3% in the same coal seam, there is also sulfur> 3% block segment, for example, No. 6 coal seam average sulfur though 2.59%, but the fluctuation range of sulfur was 1.88%-3.21% of the between. In the mining process, it is impossible not crossed the segment of high sulfur coal mining blocks. In short, the underground mining process is difficult to achieve only low-sulfur coal mining, high-sulfur coal not mined. The reality is that low-sulfur coal mined in the same time, if not high-sulfur coal mining, the high-sulfur coal resources will be destroyed and cannot be preserved intact. This is a waste of precious fossil energy resources at once.

(2) For the coal property, in view of the high sulfur Ida sulfur iron ore mainly composed of inorganic sulfur (nearly 80 percent), low content of organic sulfur, which provide a very favorable conditions for washing desulfurization. PRECISE geological report data show that the theory of high-sulfur coal washing desulfurization rate of nearly 70%. 7 wherein sulfur coal can be reduced to 1.32% from 4.22%; 23 coal can be reduced to 1.44% from 4.10%. For this high-sulfur coal mines, the through washing and processing coal in most of the sulfur is removed. Using washing desulfurization power plant boiler flue exhaust desulfurization + combination treatment, fully able to effectively control SO2 pollution of the environment, meet the national environmental requirements,

high-sulfur coal mine based rational use of resources provide a viable condition.

(3) In addition to this high sulfur anthracite mine, the other quality characteristics: such as high – especially high calorific value, especially phosphorus, arsenic low, medium ash softening temperature, high thermal stability, high crush strength and other characteristics are in line with high-power electricity coal gasification and quality requirements. From the protection of national resources considerations, the high sulfur anthracite coal mine exploitation should be, and make full use by Comprehensive Utilization.

Figure 19.2 Simple 3D Design Diagram
Picture, Courtesy by Techgart (Beijing) Engineering Ltd

The direction of coal products, the product mix should be based on market demand. With the higher demands of the market adaptability, than the initial period of planned economy and a market economy has been a qualitative change. So when the feasibility study report review, the target market for coal products require more precise analysis, user requirements are more implemented, with the general requirements of the target user's coal supply agreement initialed as a support document.

Target market analysis, implementation is important because it is one of the bases of coal products to determine the direction and positioning of the product mix.

Coal product direction and positioning of the product mix is mainly based on two: First, coal quality characteristics; second is the market demand. Target market is not implemented, given the direction of the product is not accurate, when completed will result in passive and losses.

Jibei Mine coal preparation into the wash of the main mine production No. 3 coal seam. 3 inherent low ash coal seam and Yanzhou coal mining area within the gray similar. However, the yield of light density material level much lower than Yanzhou. Now a two coals Yanzhou Coal and 3 # 3 #coals in Jibei Mining contrast as follows:

Table 19.1 Two coal Yanzhou Coal and 3 # 3 # coal in Jibei Mining contrast

	Yanzhou（3 #）	Jibei Tangkou（3 #）	Jibei Xuchang（3 #）
Accumulated float coal ash content %	8.54	8.52	8.57
Floating rate cumulative production of coal content%	87.32	70.43	71.88

Thus, the economic coal mine in the north under the production of low ash product, the yield is much lower than Yanzhou Coal Mining (lower by about 16 percentage points), its cost may be much better than Yanzhou good. Coupled with extremely rich East China gas coal reserves, and the local market for coking coal is used with gas coal and coking coal demand is very limited. Jibei mine production of low ash coking coal product can not be with the neighboring gas coal Yanzhou quality competition, so after the election ash products should not be set too low. According to the economic analysis of a Coal Mine in the North # 3 coal drifting data obtained when producing high-quality thermal coal ash ≤12%, the biggest increase in its yield. Than the production of 9% ash coking coal product, increase the annual production of about 180,000 tons, an increase of about 20 million yuan profit. Therefore, it is recommended Jibei mining coal preparation product positioning, should be to produce a high-quality thermal coal ash ≤12% based.

Weakly caking coal mine in Shaanxi Province Huangling a mine, although having low internal waters, low ash, low sulfur, high calorific coal quality characteristics, however, is not the ideal blast furnace injection of coal. Higher due to evaporation (Vdaf = 33.75% in the case of high volatile) points, points higher phosphorus (Pt.d = 0.067% in the case of phosphorus), low ash content can be used as injection coal particles under high temperature conditions skeleton Al2O3 content (only 21.67%), as a blast furnace injection of coal is not ideal.

Injecting Coal limited domestic market demand, the need for blast furnace injection of coal 20.00Mt / a or so. The coal mine and coal quality reasons regard as blast furnace injection of coal is not ideal, as compared with neighboring provinces such as mine in Jincheng, Yangquan mine anthracite, lean coal Lu'an Mining, the quality gap is large, as a blast furnace blowing coal market less competitive, market difficult to open. In addition, weakly caking coal coking coal market as little more amounts. Therefore Huangling II coal mine blast furnace with coke and injection coal as the main product direction, substantially all coal washing, the principle of low-ash coal production and processing products, is endless reasonable.

It is understood that during the preparation plant test run, because blast furnace injection of coal and coking coal market push is not open, the end of the coal product sales are sluggish, resulting in the Coal Dense Medium Separation System and interference slime bed sorting system long idle, resulting in waste.

This case fully proved coal quality conditions and market demand has a significant impact on determining the correct product orientation, to develop a reasonable product structure, with the typical sense.

Figure 19.3 General Arrangement of CHPP site

Picture, Courtesy by Techgart (Beijing) Engineering Ltd

(1) Market analysis covers international and domestic, vague content, and research itself is not closely linked.

(2) The target user market analysis is not specific enough; the lack of end-user demand for coal intent agreement text.

Detailed analysis of the target market and user text coal supply agreements are one of the important projects of the National Development and Reform Commission, it is indispensable, should not air to air. (The most simple truth: If no users, there is no need mining, countries that do not promote the use of the newly opened mine to run existing product market, which is a waste of resources.)

20. Application of 3CDC 1500/1100 3-Product Central-feeding DMC in Changcun CHPP

Author: Gong Xuwen, Cui Xueqi, Jiang Runping, Ge Jiajun, Weihai Haiwang Cyclone Co., Ltd.

Abstract: Regarding the production capacity limitation of Lu'an Group Changcun Coal Preparation Plant, a new dense medium system is built with using one set of 3CDC1500/1100 3-product central-feeding dense medium cyclone researched and manufactured by Weihai Haiwang Cyclone Co., Ltd. The stand-alone testing result shows that for the new dense medium cyclone, Ecart probable (Ep) of the primary is 0.021 g/cm3 and that of the secondary is 0.028 g/cm^3. With separating organic efficiency of 98.4% and stable product quality, the equipment has a leading performance in worldwide.

Keywords: *dense medium system; 3-product central-feeding dense medium cyclone; stand-alone test; Ecart probable; organic efficiency*

20.1 Overview

Changcun CHPP is a large modern mine subordinating to Shanxi Lu'an Environmental Protection Energy Development Co., Ltd. The original design capacity of the mine is 4 million per year and currently it has been improved to 8 million per year. As a supporting construction project of the mine, original design capacity of the coal preparation plant is 4 million per year and washing capacity is 2.1 million per year, which cannot meet requirements of the mine. In 2013, modifications were made on the original jig system to improve the capacity, which was increased to 3 million per year; with considering the higher accuracy of dense medium separation, in order to adapt to the raw coal property and improve the whole separation accuracy of the coal plant, a new dense medium system with capacity of 3 million per year were built, by using 3CDC1500/1100 central-feeding dense medium cyclone researched and manufactured by Weihai Haiwang as the main separating cyclone, which is of the biggest diameter in Chinese coal preparation industry currently.

Main technical process of the dense medium system is: after de-sliming from de-sliming screen, the raw coal will enter into the central-feeding dense medium cyclone for separation. Overflow (clean coal) of the primary cyclone will pass sculping screen to remove medium and water; oversize clean coal will flow into centrifuge for further de-watering to generate the final products. Overflow (middling) of secondary cyclone will pass sculping screen to remove medium and water and oversize middling will flow into high-frequency screen for further de-watering to generate the middling products. Underflow (refuse) of the cyclone will be transported to refuse bin by belt after medium and water removal from sculping screen. Currently the raw coal washing capacity of all the systems in Changcun coal preparation plants are 6 million per year.

20.2 Principle and Features of 3-product Central-feeding Dense Medium Cyclone

20.2.1 Structural Features and Working Principle

Dense medium cyclone takes heavy suspension as separating medium to separate coal and refuse in centrifugal field according to Archimedes principle. Separation medium is introduced into the primary cyclone tangentially with certain pressure to form into inner spiral flow and outer spiral flow rapidly; materials will flow into the primary cyclone automatically from the top. With the function of centrifugal force and suspension resistance, particles will separate into layers rapidly in the cyclone from the center to the shell due to different density; light products that are lighter than suspension will gather around the center of cyclone and be discharged from the vortex finder along with the inner spiral flow; heavy products that are heavier than suspension will flow to the cyclone shell and be discharged from the apex (connection of primary and secondary) along with the outer spiral flow. Underflow of the primary cyclone is the feeding to secondary cyclone, which has the same separation principle with primary cyclone. Three products of clean coal, middling and refuse will be generated after the separation [1-4]. Structure of 3-product central feeding dense medium cyclone is as shown in figure 1 and the principle diagram is as shown in figure 2.

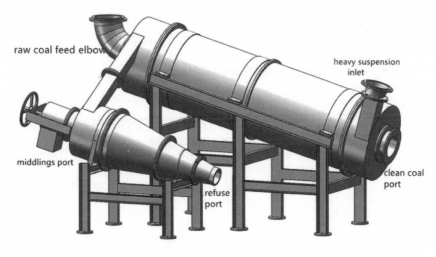

Figure 20.1 Structure of 3-product Central Feeding

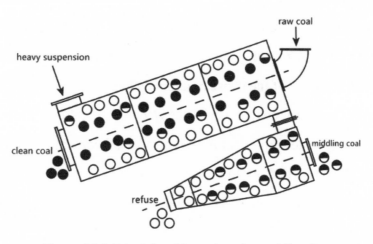

Figure 20.2 Principle of 3-product Central Feeding

20.2.2 Structural and Technical Features

The 3-product central feeding dense medium cyclone has below features:

The 3-product central feeding dense medium cyclone is mainly composed of raw coal feeding elbow, primary cylinder, clean coal discharging port, secondary cyclone, middling discharging port and refuse discharging port, etc. The designed reasonable specification, angle and dimension of these components have significant influence on the washing performance. With nearly 30 years' experience and data base accumulated on cyclone R & D and manufacturing, Weihai Haiwang can realize one-time precise design and model selection according to the raw coal features at site.

Low misplaced rate. The raw coal flow into primary cyclone along the axial direction by its own gravity; products of low density can enter into the inner spiral flow without getting through the liquid flow of high density, thus interaction between materials will be reduced, which means light products can get to its location easier to guarantee a higher separation accuracy of the dense medium cyclone [5].

Less secondary coal slime in the system. Compared with pressured feeding dense medium cyclone, raw coal of central feeding dense medium cyclone will flow into the equipment by its own gravity, which can diminish the smashing on coal from the pump and pipeline, impacting between coals, and reduce the secondary coal slime [6].

Adjustable secondary density online. Due to the special structure of 3-product central feeding dense medium cyclone, suspension fed to the secondary cyclone is concentrated by the primary cyclone with unknown actual density, so sometime separation density of the secondary cyclone appears to be higher or lower. This problem can be solved by adjusting the density of secondary cyclone online.

Customized ceramic technology with high –wearing feature. Liner of the cyclone is made of high wearing alumina ceramics, which has high alumina content. In addition, ceramic liners of Haiwang cyclone are all designed with customized structure and use thickening or integrate ceramic at special parts to improve the using lifespan of cyclone efficiently.

20.3 Analysis on Washability of Raw Coal and Evaluation on Cyclone Performance

Coal property of the raw coal (50-1mm) fed into the new dense medium system is as shown in attached table 1, and the corresponding washability curve is in below figure 3.

Table 20.1 Float-and-sink test result of raw coal (50-1mm) fed into the dense medium system

Density class/ ($g \cdot cm^{-3}$)	yield	ash	Cumulative floats		Cumulative sinks		Separation density ±0.1	
			yield	ash	yield	ash	Density class/ ($g \cdot cm^{-3}$)	yield
< 1.30	29.45	6.56	29.45	6.56	100.00	24.28	1.30	76.44
1.30 ~ 1.40	35.89	12.02	65.34	9.56	70.55	31.67	1.40	49.99
1.40 ~ 1.50	6.84	20.01	72.18	10.55	34.66	52.02	1.50	11.01
1.50 ~ 1.60	2.57	23.03	74.75	10.98	27.82	59.89	1.60	5.24
1.60 ~ 1.70	1.91	29.94	76.66	11.45	25.25	63.64	1.70	4.26
1.70 ~ 1.80	1.73	37.52	78.39	12.03	23.34	66.40	1.80	6.17
1.80 ~ 2.00	7.09	49.15	85.48	15.11	21.61	68.71	1.90	8.29
> 2.00	14.52	78.26	100.00	24.28	14.52	78.26		
Total	100.00	24.28						

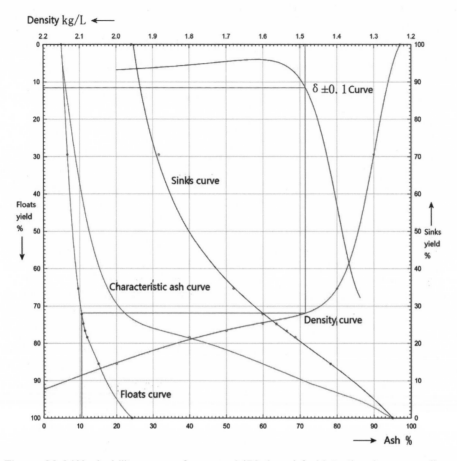

Figure 20.3 Washability curve of raw coal (50-1mm) fed into the dense medium

system

It can be seen from the table 1 and figure 3 that density of the washing raw coal has features that low yield for intermediate density class and high yield for the two ends of density class. The dominant density class is-1.30, and 1.30-1.40 g/cm^3.

Stand-alone test is carried out on the 3-product central feeding dense medium cyclone to check the performance and actual yield (see table 2) of each product is calculated based on the test result.

Table 20.2 Actual yield calculation of the 3-product dense medium cyclone

Density class/ ($\mathrm{g \cdot cm^{-3}}$)	Density distribution/%				$(c_i-t_i)^2$	$(c_i-t_i) \times (m_i-t_i)$	$(c_i-t_i) \times (f_i-t_i)$	$(m_i-t_i)^2$	$(m_i-t_i) \times (f_i-t_i)$
	Raw coal f_i	Clean coal c_i	Middling m_i	Gangue t_i					
< 1.3	29.45	41.85	0.00	0.00	1751.42	0.00	1232.48	0.00	0.00
$1.3 \sim 1.4$	35.89	49.73	2.02	0.00	2473.07	100.45	1784.81	4.08	72.50
$1.4 \sim 1.5$	6.84	7.54	5.88	0.00	56.85	44.34	51.57	34.57	40.22
$1.5 \sim 1.6$	2.57	0.75	33.35	0.11	0.41	21.27	1.57	1104.90	81.77
$1.6 \sim 1.7$	1.91	0.08	23.19	0.17	0.01	-2.07	-0.16	529.92	40.05
$1.7 \sim 1.8$	1.73	0.05	19.36	0.61	0.31	-10.50	-0.63	351.56	21.00
$1.8 \sim 2.0$	7.09	0.00	15.74	16.99	288.66	21.24	168.20	1.56	12.38
> 2.0	14.52	0.00	0.46	82.12	6743.69	6705.92	5551.31	6668.36	5520.22
Total	100.00	100.00	100.00	100.00	11314.43	6880.65	8789.17	8694.95	5788.13
					g_{01}	g_{11}	g_{02}	g_{12}	g_{22}

According to the calculation method provided in "GB/T 15715—2014 Assessment Method on Processing Property of Dense Medium Separation Equipment for Coal Products" [8] and combine the data in table 2, actual yield of cyclone each product is calculated as below:

$$\gamma\text{clean} = 100 \times (g_{01} \cdot g_{22} - g_{02} \cdot g_{12}) / (g_{11} \cdot g_{22} - g_{12} \cdot g_{12}) = 71.70\%$$

$$\gamma\text{middling} = 100 \times (g_{02} \cdot g_{11} - g_{01} \cdot g_{12}) / (g_{11} \cdot g_{22} - g_{12} \cdot g_{12}) = 9.83\%$$

$$\gamma\text{refuse} = 100 - \gamma_{精} - \gamma_{中} = 18.47\%$$

The actual ash content measured in the stand-alone test is 10.50%. It can be seen from the washability curve of the raw coal (50-1mm) fed into dense medium system that shown in figure 3, that when clean coal ash content is 10.50%, theoretical yield of clean coal is $\gamma t = 71.96\%$ and theoretical separation density is 1.485 $\mathrm{g/cm^3}$; content of $\delta \pm 0.1$ is 11.5%

after deducting the refuse (theoretical separation density is less than 1.7 g/cm3). According to GB/T 16417—2011 "Assessment Method on Coal Washability" [7], when clean coal ash content is 10.50%, washability of this kind of raw coal belongs to middle grade. At this point, the actual clean coal yield is $\gamma p = 71.70\%$, and clean coal organic efficiency of 3-product dense medium cyclone is $\eta e = 100 \times \gamma p / \gamma t = 99.60\%$, which is an ideal washing performance [9].

With yield of clean coal, middling and refuse, the yield of each product in total sample can be calculated and the corresponding distribution rate can be calculated consequently, which is as show in table 20.3.

Table 20.3 Products distribution rate calculation of 3-product dense medium cyclone

Density class/ (g·cm⁻³)	Density distribution/%						Distribution rate/%		mean square deviation
	Raw coal	Clean coal In total sample	Middling In total sample	Gangue In total sample	Calculated raw coal		Primary	Secondary	
					Primary	Secondary			
< 1.30	29.45	30.01	0.00	0.00	30.01	0.00	0.00	0.00	
1.30 ~ 1.40	35.89	35.66	0.20	0.00	35.86	0.20	0.55	0.00	
1.40 ~ 1.50	6.84	5.41	0.58	0.00	5.98	0.58	9.65	0.00	
1.50 ~ 1.60	2.57	0.54	3.28	0.02	3.83	3.30	85.98	0.62	
1.60 ~ 1.70	1.91	0.06	2.28	0.03	2.37	2.31	97.58	1.36	1.24
1.70 ~ 1.80	1.73	0.04	1.90	0.11	2.05	2.01	98.25	5.59	
1.80 ~ 2.00	7.09	0.00	1.55	3.14	4.68	4.68	100.00	66.99	
> 2.00	14.52	0.00	0.05	15.17	15.21	15.21	100.00	99.70	
Total	100.00	71.71	9.83	18.47	100.00	28.29			

According to regulations in "GB/T 15715—2014 Assessment Method on Processing Property of Dense Medium Separation Equipment for Coal Products" [8] and considering mean square deviation <1.4, the testing result is valid. The mean square deviation is 1.24 in this test, thus the calculation result is dependable. Distribution curve is drawn as below figure 4 according to the data in table 20.3.

Distribution curve can be got by fitting the data of 3-product dense medium cyclone distribution rate with antitangent mathematical model, and find out distribution rates that are corresponding with primary and secondary heavy products on the distribution curve are density of 75% and 25%. Potential deviation value that are corresponding to primary and secondary separation can be calculated with the formula E_p = （d75 – d25）/2 [10]. As a result, potential deviation value of primary and secondary cyclone is E_{p1}=0.021 g/cm^3 and E_{p2}=0.028 g/cm^3 respectively, which means the washing performance is ideal with rare material misplacement of primary and secondary cyclones.

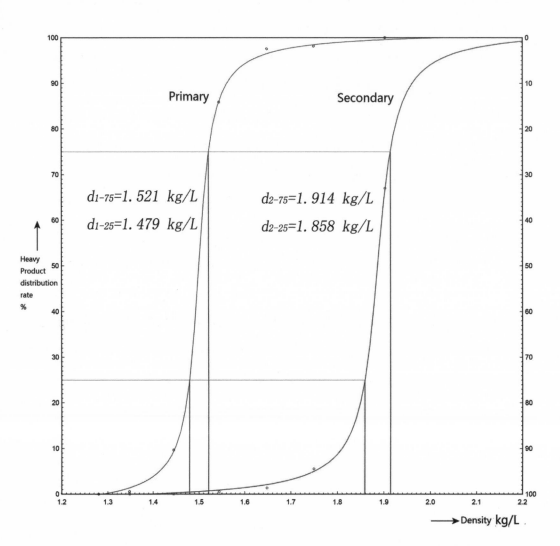

Figure 20.4 Distribution curves of dense medium cyclone primary and second-

ary heavy products

VI Conclusion

The stand-alone testing result of Haiwang 3CDC1500/1100

3-product central-feeding dense medium cyclone used in the new built dense medium system of Changcun coal preparation plant shows that ecart probable moyen of the primary is Ep1=0.021 g·cm^{-3} and that of the secondary is Ep2=0.028 g·cm^{-3}. With high separating efficiency, organic efficiency of η=99.6%, high washing efficiency, guaranteeing the stable performances and quality, the system creates significant benefits for Changcun coal preparation plant. In addition, Haiwang also attach importance on parameters like quality of medium powder, coal slime content in suspension and pressure in the actual production, which will have significant influence on the separating performance of dense medium cyclone and may cause changes on performance then affect the production if failing to control. So it is necessary for staff in the coal preparation plant to keep attention on these factors.

References

[1] Li Zhiyong, Ye He, Xu Sheng. New Technical Process on High Efficient Separation of Pre-desliming Dense Medium Cyclone with Non-pressured Feeding. [J]. Coal Processing and Comprehensive Utilization, 2008(5):1-3.

[2] Gong Xuwen, Cui Xueqi, Ge Jiajun, etc. Reasons and Countermeasures for Clean Coal in Middling of 3-product Dense Medium Cyclone. [C]//2013 National Coal Preparation Symposium Proceedings. Tangshan: Coal Preparation Technology-Editorial Dept. 2013:65-68.

[3] Deng Xiaoyang, Liu Peikun. Historical Leaps in Research of 3-product Dense Medium Cyclone [J]. Coal Processing and Comprehensive Utilization, 2007(1):1-4.

[4] An Hongmei, Gong Xuwen, Ge Jiajun, etc. Application of WTMC1200/850 Dense Medium Cyclone in the Modification of Datun Coal Preparation Plant, 2013(4)：17-19.

[5] Zhang Liqiang, Liu Shikuan. Development and Researching Status on Dense Medium Cyclone [J]. Coal Preparation Technology, 2007(4):137-140.

[6] Yin Dejiang, Luo Yuanfu, etc. Application ofφ1500/1100 3-product Dense Medium Cyclone with Non-pressure Feeding in Ertang Coal Preparation Plant [J]. Coal Preparation

Technology, 2016(2):43-47

[7] China National Standard Administrative Committee. GB/T 16417—2011 Assessment Method on Coal Washability [S]. Beijing: China Standards Press, 2011.

[8] China National Standard Administrative Committee. GB/T 15715—2014 Assessment Method on Processing Property of Dense Medium Separation Equipment for Coal Products [S]. Beijing: China Standards Press, 2014.

[9] Ou Zeshen, Zhang Wenjun. Dense Medium Coal Preparation Technology [M]. Xuzhou: China University of Mining and Technology Press, 2011:219-221.

[10] Xie Guangyuan, Zhang Mingxu, Bian Bingxni, etc. Mineral Processing [M]. Xuzhou: China University of Mining and Technology Press, 2005:304-309.

Email: gongxuwen@wh-hw.com Mr. Gong Xuwen

21. Capital Cost Estimating Methodology for Coal Handling and Preparation Plant

The Major Estimate Methods

Take off of quantities from progress plans, representative pricing by database, manuals, quotes, bid results, or experience adjusted for the conditions of the specific package. Crewed approach to labor and equipment, percent approach to general conditions, overhead and profit, contingency, and escalation. Some allowances carried for immeasurable items.

Brief:

Estimating methodologies are not static and must be flexible enough to adjust to the needs of the project's stage in the development process. The development process is described by the overall level of engineering design associated with the major development stages defined for the CHPP/Coal Washing Plant/Coal Washery/Coal Preparation Plant.

The capital cost estimating methodology used for the certain CHPP feasibility study provides capital costs within the battery limits of the facility. A summary of the approach to the capital cost development and resulting estimates is provided in FS stage.

The approach to capital cost development is a combination of factored equipment, project-specific vendor budgetary quotes, and scaled approaches using HOT Mining' in-house database, cost estimation software and cost model. The format includes separate evaluation of major systems and sub-systems for the entire plant.

The resulting capital cost is provided on an estimate form that recognizes each cost account for the plant. Each account in the estimate contains separate costs for equipment, materials, and installation labor, civil job, etc. These costs make up the total field cost, also referred to as the bare erected cost. The total capital cost estimate includes the cost of equipment, freight, and materials and labor for equipment installation and erection; materials and labor for construction of buildings, supporting structures, and site improvements; engineering, construction management, and start-up services (professional services); and project contingency.

HOT Mining has significant experience in the area of CHPP/Coal Washing Plant and recent cost estimates from vendors on other projects for major equipment in the on-site CHPP area.

21.1 Estimate Basis

21.1.1 Direct Cost

211.1.1 Scope documentation

To develop cost estimates to the level provided in this CHPP, the technology must be developed to provide the following source data:

General arrangement drawings;

Process flow diagrams;

Material balances;

Conceptual engineering drawings and sketches;

Project equipment lists;

Equipment data sheets;

Vendor budgetary quotes;

Equipment and pricing from historical data;

Construction labor and labor rate estimate based on study of area; andCivil job rates and materials, etc.

21.1.1.2 Estimate approach

The following approaches were used in developing the capital costs for the technologies described in the FS reports:

Factored equipment;

Vendor estimates;

Parametric modeling; and

Each of these approaches is described in more detail below.

Factored equipment

The majority of the estimate was developed utilizing the factored equipment method. Equipment pricing is developed using equipment parameters. Bulk materials costs and installation costs are developed by applying a factor to the established equipment cost to derive a total installed cost. Factors vary by type of equipment, metallurgy, and complexity, and conform to HOT Mining standards.

Vendor estimates

Vendor estimates vary from furnish-only to engineer-furnish-install.

In cases where vendors provided furnish-only pricing, the factored equipment approach was used to determine total installed costs.

Where vendors provided furnish-and-erect costs, a factor was applied to account for the foundation and bulks only.

In cases where vendors provided total installed costs, no additional factors were used.

Parametric modeling

In some cases, the HOT Mining estimating model was utilized to determine installation costs.

21.1.1.3 Plant equipment pricing

Budget pricing inquiries for major equipment/systems were issued based on specifications, data sheets, and/or bills of materials generated as a part of the engineering effort. Three categories of vendor pricing are considered in the methodology:

Vendor pricing – total installed cost

Pricing for equipment received from the vendors in the form of Total Installed Cost.

Vendor pricing– furnishes and erect cost

Pricing for the equipment received from the vendors in the form of a Furnish-and-Erect Cost.

Vendor pricing– furnish only cost

Pricing for the equipment received from the vendors in the form of a Furnish Only Cost.

21.1.1.4 Construction/installation

Construction is based on the owner retaining the services of an engineering/design/construction/EPCM firms and executing construction with multiple contracts. Construction/installation costs include the following:

Labor;

Construction management;

Contracting methodology; and

Contractor's indirect costs

Indirect costs include, but are not limited to, the following:

Mobilization and demobilization;

Warehousing and material handling;

Site supervision;

PPE tools (personnel safety);

Temporary facilities;

Conventional tools, such as tower crane, scaffolding;

Field office;

Small tools and expendables; and

Construction equipment, etc.

21.2 Contingency

Project contingency covers the "unknown unknowns" associated with a project. Contingency may cover things such as minor fluctuations in equipment or pipe sizing, unanticipated fluctuations in regional labor productivity, minor fluctuations in anticipated material escalation.

339

Normally, this level of contingency can be supported by historical data from past projects or from our local partners' experiences. In some cases, a specific or process contingency may also be included to cover things as mentioned above. There is always some level of change as a project progresses from concept to final design. As design concepts become solidified and project scope/definition improved, the level of contingency required will generally decline.

Contingency is not intended to cover significant scope changes, undocumented underground conditions, and removal/remediation of hazardous materials, discovery of archaeological artifacts, force majeure events, or escalation beyond that which could be reasonably predicted.

Contingency funds are different than the anticipated estimate accuracy. Contingency is viewed as a real cost which will be spent during the course of project implementation. The estimate accuracy range reflects the confidence level in the overall estimated project cost for the defined scope of work.

21.3 Inflation

Project costs were developed using constant fiscal year 2015/2017 cost estimates for the various project components. An inflation rate shall be applied to fiscal years F2015 to F2017 to develop an inflation adjusted cost estimate as at time of implementation. The rates are based on the official reports.

Interest during Construction (IDC)

The forecast capital costs include an amount for IDC, which is the cost of financing the project by the utility prior to the project being put into service. IDC is recovered in rates. Due to the nature of utility facilities, there are often long lead time equipment purchases and lengthy construction contracts that must to be financed by the utility. Adding IDC to an estimate ensures that the utility is not out of pocket for the costs of financing large utility projects that are for the benefit of rate payers that use the utility facilities. BC Hydro sets the IDC rate for transmission capital projects. An IDC rate which is provided by Australian banks shall be used for the project estimate.

21.4 Identification of Cost Reduction Opportunities

There are significant opportunities to reduce capital costs by source more equipment and steel structure work from emerging market. The most importantly, the sourcing capabilities and QA/QC experiences in emerging market is the key to success.

Furthermore, the integrated spare parts supply and back-up services on-site would also help CHPP to reduce operational cost.

You're concerning why HOT Know-How? (help to reduce capital cost in project execution stage)

22. Application of One Full Size (250x0.5mm raw coal) Dense Medium Separation

Author: ZHANG Yu-xiang, LIU Shan, TechGart (Beijing) Engineering Ltd

Abstract:

The innovated patent process technology of combined medium system for both heavy medium vessel and heavy medium cyclone is analyzed based on the application at China Songhe Coal Preparation Plant. The advantages of the easy plant operation, lower operation cost, and better plant production stability have been approved.

Keywords: *Coal preparation; heavy medium vessel; heavy medium cyclone; combined heavy medium system for both HMV and HMC*

Heavy medium separation method has been widely used in coal preparation plants due to its high efficiency comparing to water based separation. For coarse coal, heavy medium vessel (HMV) separation is efficient while heavy medium cyclone (HMC) is more efficient to process the fine coal. Two separated heavy medium systems for HMV and HMC have been applied worldwide.

In order to simplify heavy medium system, one innovated combined heavy medium system for both HMV and HMC has been studied and practiced by TechGart Beijing Engineering Ltd. (TBE) for more than a dozen coal preparation plants in China since 2004. Based on the successful applications, a patent of combined heavy medium system for both HMV and HMC has been awarded to TBE by China State Intellectual Property Office in 2013 with the patent number of ZL 2013-2-0102462.5.

22.1 Heavy medium vessel separation technology

22.1.1 Introduction of Heavy medium vessel

Heavy medium vessel (HMV) consists of the bath, the flight-type conveyor, the drive device and other components. Figure 1 shows the structure of the heavy medium vessel.

The raw coal is separated based on the float-sink principle. The clean coal is floated and discharged over a weir while the refuse sinks into the bottom and is transported by the conveyor and removed from the bath.

The feed box and the product overflow weir are located on the both sides of the bath. The feed box is provided with pipes for horizontal medium flow which pushes the clean coal toward to overflow weir. lThere are several hoppers at the bottom for the upward medium flow which keeps the constant single medium density through the heavy media vessel.

The medium is pumped to the vessel. The pinch valves are used on the feed pipe of HMV to regulate distribution of the medium throughout the bath. An adjustable dip plate at the feed box is used to ensure that all feed is pushed under the surface of the medium to endure raw coal is free to move and not get caught on the product rafts. The medium depth at overflow weir can be varied by adjusting the medium flow. The bigger the particle, the deeper the overflow weir will be required.

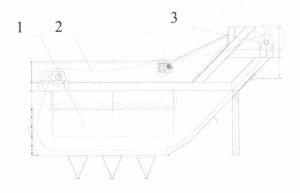

28-Bath 2-Conveyor 3-Drive device

Main-view

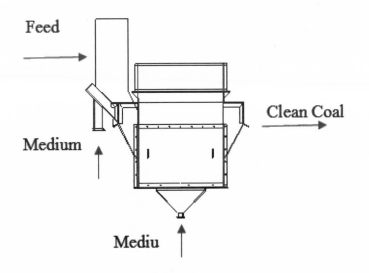

Side View

Figure 1. Structure of Heavy Medium Vessel

22.1.2 Characteristics of Heavy medium vessel

The characteristics of Heavy medium vessel are as follows:

1) Large feed top size: up to 250mm

2) High Efficiency, Ep = 0.02-0.05

3) High capacity of processing raw coal and discharging refuse

4) Less aggirillation of refuse since the separation in HMV is on gravity field not on centrifugal force field

5) Low moisture of product because of the uncrushed coarse product.

6) Low operating costs because of high capacity, gravity separation, low electric consumption, the low magnetite consumption.

22.2 Combined heavy medium system for both HMV and HMC

With above stated HMV advantages, HMV has been widely used to separate 250x13(6)mm raw coal while HMCs are used to separate 13(6)x0.5mm raw coal in coal preparation plants. Both HMV and HMC need each individual medium system to separate different size raw coal. The each medium system includes draining and rinsing screen for heavy medium recycle, magnetic separator for dilute medium recovery, the medium bleed/density gauge for gravity control and the magnetite adding system etc.

To simplify the operation of heavy medium systems, the combined one heavy medium system for full size raw coal (250x0.5mm) separation has been studied. The innovated patent process design for the combined

HMV and HMC medium system is illustrated in the Figure 2. Both HMV and HMC clean coal are combined into the same Drain and Rinse screen, so does the both refuse from HMV and HMC. The correct medium from the Drain section of screen flows to the HMV medium sump and the HMC medium wing tank. The bleed box, the density gauge and magnetite addition equipment are shared for HMV system and HMC system.

The dilute medium from the rinse section of screen is also combined to the dilute sump, so there is only one dilute pump and all separators are shared by HMV system and HMC system.

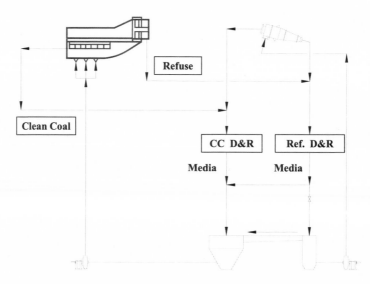

Figure 2. Combined HMV and HMC medium system

The one combined heavy medium system has the advantages as follows:

1) Improvement performance of Drain and Rinse screens and separators

Traditionally both HMV and HMC have its own Drain and Rinse

screens and separators. With the raw coal size distribution swing greatly, the screen and separator loads from one of the HMV or HMC circuit will be increased. The plant performance will be affected with the size distribution swing.

In combined medium system, the D&R screens and separators are shared. The loads of the screens and separators will be changed little with raw coal size distribution swing. The performance of screens and separators can be better guaranteed.

2) Easier to control the medium density

The medium density control is complicated and related with the sump level, the bleed box actuator position and the magnetite addition. Since there is only one medium system, the control of medium density in combined medium system is easier.

3) Reduction the product transfer units

The clean coal of HMC and the clean coal of HMV are processed at the same screens, so do the refuse. There is no transfer units for the clean coal or the refuse. The layout of the product transportation is simplified. The height of the main plant is lower and the power consumption is saved.

4) Saved capital and operation cost.

The volume of main plant is smaller and the length of pipe is shorter for combined medium system. The number of the dilute sump and pump, the density gauge, the transfer conveyor is reduced. As a result, the capital cost is lower.

The operation of plant becomes easy. The consumption of magnetite and power is decreased.

22.3 Applications of the proposed combined heavy medium system

Since 2004, the combined one heavy medium system technology has already been used in more than a dozen coal preparation plants which are EPC built in China by TBE. Songhe Coal Preparation plant is one of these plants.

Songhe Coal preparation Plant is located in southwest China. The plant capacity is 714t/h. The clean coal is primary coking coal with ash content of less than 10.5%.

22.3.1 Combined medium system in Songhe coal preparation plant

Figure 3 is the flow sheet of combined medium system in Songhe coal preparation plant.

• Raw coal screening, desliming

The 300x0 raw coal is wet screened at 8mm and desilmed and 0.75mm on double-duck screen to obtain three size fractions: 300x8mm, 8x0.75mm, and 0.75x0mm.

The screen underflow (0.75x0mm) is routed to the fine coal process circuits.

• HMV and HMC processing

The 300x8mm fraction is separated in HMV to produce coarse washed coal and coarse refuse, while the 8x0.75mm fraction is separated in HMC to produce fine washed coal and fine refuse.

The clean coal from both circuit are combined into clean coal

D&R screen with the single-deck 0.75mm opening on D&R section and 50mm on discharge section. Since 50mm is the top size limit of clean coal, 300x50mm washed coal is crushed down to 50mm and mixed with natural 50-0.75mm washed coal.

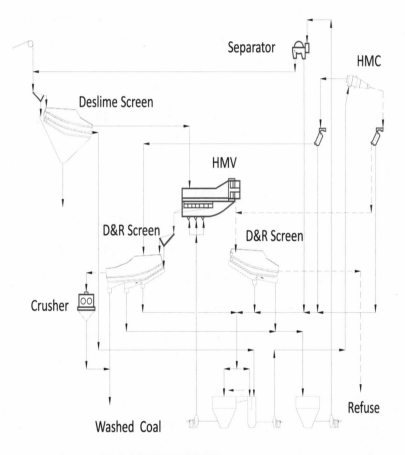

Figure 3 Flow sheet of combined medium system in Songhe plant

• Combined medium system

The correct medium from the drain section of D&R screen goes into ONE HMV sump and ONE HMC wing tank as recycle medium.

The dilute media from the rinse section of D&R screens goes into

ONE dilute media sump.

The bleed from the underflow of washed coal sieve bends will go into dilute medium sump.

Dilute medium is processed by the combined magnetic separators with highly concentrated magnetite piping back to correct medium sump and the tailings to the deslime screen.

22.3.2 Adjusting of medium densities of each HMV system and HMC system

As we all know that the maximum plant yield is based on the equal incremental ash from both HMV and HMC circuits, normally the separating density of HMV is always different from HMC. After we combine the both circuits as one medium, the challenge is how we can create two different medium densities between HMV and HMC.

The HMV is separating coarse raw coal at the gravity field. Its medium density from both clean coal and refuse are always same as the circuit recycle medium density, but the HMC process the raw coal at the centrifugal force field. The medium density of the cyclone underflow is 0.3-0.5 g / cm3 higher than feed medium density, while the medium density of the cyclone overflow of is 0.1-0.2 g / cm3 lower than the feed medium density. Therefore, we can easily adjust the medium density difference between HMC and HMV by controlling the amount of medium of cyclone underflow or overflow to the HMV sump and the HMC wing tank.

22.4 Conclusion

The patent process technology of combined medium system for both HMV and HMC has been approved with stable and efficient production at many coal preparation plants during last 10 years. This innovated technology can make one single heavy medium to process the full size (250x0.5mm raw coal) raw coal. The combined heavy medium system simplifies the process with compact layout, easy plant operation, lower operation cost, and better plant production stability.

Author Information

ZHANG Yu-xiang, Male, Executive Vice President & Chief Technical Officer, TechGart (Beijing) Engineering LTD.

He has more than 30 years of experience in coal preparation plant construction and operation and takes part in over 100 turn-key projects of coal preparation plants in China, United States, Russia, Australia, and Indonesia.

23. Separation process of easy-to-slime lignite with high ash content and water content

Author: (Steven) Heng Huang, Member of AusIMM (MAusIMM), Mining & Process Engineer

Translator: (Teresa) Xuezhi Zheng, Project Coordinator

It's estimated that China's proved lignite reserves account for 12.7% of China's total coal reserves, mainly in eastern Inner Mongolia, eastern Yunnan and Xinjiang. The lignite in China mostly belongs to aged lignite, and the volatilization is as high as 40%~50%. The ash content is generally 20%~40%; the total moisture content can reach 20%~50%, and the air dried basis moisture is 10%~30%; the net calorific power is generally 11.71~16.73MJ/kg.

Lignite has a low degree of metamorphism, which is easy to be weathered and easy to be muddied when encountering water. Therefore, the coal industry generally believes that lignite cannot be washed. This traditional understanding has been guiding and restricting the washing and processing of lignite. With the intensifying development of lignite resources in recent years, more and more attention has been paid to the problem of lignite upgrading. However, all the researches basically focus on the drying, dry selection and dry distillation, which cannot adapt to the situation of large-scale development of lignite coal resources due to its research results are not significant.

Coal No.4 in Xilinhot, Inner Mongolia, reflects the common nature of easy-to-slime lignite with high ash and water content in our country. This study uses this coal as an example to explore the feasibility of washing the easy-to-slime lignite with high ash and water content in China.

23.1 Conclusions of washability study

Coal is not fragile, and mainly enriches to the coarse-grain level;

gangue is fragile, and mainly enriches to the fine-grained level, especially to the level of less than 0.045mm and greater than 70% grained ash. It indicated that this level is basically gangue.

There is obvious difference between the gangue and coal of No. 4 coal in the degree of slime. The gangue is not only friable, but also easy to be slimed. After entering the water, it is easy to be enriched below 0.5mm, especially smaller than 0.045mm. Coal is not only non-friable, but also has a much lower slime degree than that of gangue. When the raw coal is turned over 30min in water, the grain size is still larger than 13mm, even if it is broken into fine particles, it is granular and will not become "sludge". When the gangue is turned over 30min in water, it is smaller than 0.5mm, and it is easy to be "slimed".

The basic characteristic of high ash lignite in China is the characteristics of slime. But the obvious difference between gangue and coal in the degree of slime has never been found and paid attention to. This difference indicates that the slimed process of high ash and water lignite in the water, in fact, is the process of lignite separation and ash reduction. Therefore, it fundamentally denies the traditional concept that the lignite is easy to be slimed and cannot be washed by water.

23.2 Conceptual design of process flow

23.2.1 Screen sizing

Because of the low ash content of lamp coal, it is recommended to screen with 100mm sieve hole. The material larger than 100mm granular is sold as merchantable coal; material less than 100mm granular is washed and processed. If the ash content cannot meet the requirements, it can also be crushed to less than 100mm particle size to washing.

23.2.2 Washing and processing

The lamp coal less than 100mm size should be washed completely. Heavy medium coal preparation cannot be used because of the difficulty of medium purification. It is suggested that the traditional jigging coal preparation method can be adopted, which is simple in the coal preparation process. It is better to design a jig for lignite sorting, because the lignite producing areas are generally relatively lack of water.

23.2.3 Product dehydration

It is recommended to use the centrifuge as final dewatering and the product surface moisture can be controlled below 12%.

23.2.4 Slime water treatment

Slime water treatment is the key to design a coal preparation plant. Because of the serious gangue slurry, the slime in coal slime water is basically gangue, so the slime is not necessary to recycle, but the washing water must be closed and recycled. Slime water treatment process should be simple and practical, but must have enough precipitation area, and adopt lime and other inorganic flocculants and polymer flocculants to help precipitate. The use of tailings dam or thickener and sedimentation tank process is suggested.

23.2.5 Drying

If the raw coal is dried directly, it is estimated that 10% moisture can be removed at most and the calorific value is less than 12.54MJ / kg. If the coal is washed and then dried, it is predicted that the calorific value will be over 16.72MJ /kg. Whether the product is dry or not can be determined according to the user's needs.

24. China Contemporary Technology & Preparation of Coking Coal Washing

Author: Yuxiang Zhang, Shan liu, Techgart (Beijing) engineering LTD

The distribution and production status of China coal resources and three stage of development of Chinese coking coal washing & preparation technology is discussed in this page; Taking Wangzhuang CHPP as an example, in order to introduce the six size ranges preparation technology of Chinese coking coal preparation plant, make whole plant to achieve maximum yield of coking coal, improve the economic efficiency of coal preparation plant; At the same time, this paper has made a brief introduction for flotation equipment and clean coal flotation dewatering equipment.

24.1 Coal resources and production in China

China is one of the countries with rich coal resources in the world. The explored coal reserves are 438 billion 100 million tons in 2011, there are 68.4% are suitable for underground mining, 31.6% is suitable for opencast working, and soft coal accounts for 53.1%, secondary soft coal accounts for 36.5%, recoverable reserves are 234 billion 600 million tons, there are 174 billion 400 million ton recoverable reserves in minefield where the mine has been produced. In 34 provinces of China, among them Shanxi, Shaanxi, Guizhou, Henan, inner Mongolia, Xingjiang, Ningxia, Gansu and Shandong have 84.18% coal proved reserves of China, they are leading coal producing province.

In 2011, Chinese coal gross productivity were 1.207 billion tons, the underground mine production capacity were 395 million tons, the production capacity of opencast working were 812 million tons. In 2011, there were about 1325 coal mines and 9.1 thousand and 6.11 hundred staffs in China, and coal production were 994 million tons, among them, the number of underground mining mine is around 9.5 thousand with 5.51 million staffs, the production capacity of underground mining is 315 million tons; the number of opencast working mine is 7 hundred and 88 with 3.7 thousand and 87 staffs, the production of opencast working mine is 679 million tons. The production of coal in 2011 and 2010 was basically flat.

24.2 Development of coking coal preparation technology and process in China in 20 century

The use of Dense-medium cyclone in coal preparation begins at 60s twentieth century. This equipment has high precision of flotation, small volume, large processing capacity of cubage and short assembly cycle. In 80s, The Chinese coking coal preparation adopt dense-medium cyclone for 0.5mm~0mm slime, use flotation process to selection flotation 0.5~0mm slime.

First smash raw coal to 50mm, desliming by 0.5mm screen, all oversize enter into two stages of two dense-medium cyclones, in order to separation the cleaned coal, middings and rejects. All undersize enter into the flotation system to separation cleaned coal and tailing. This separation process is simply, easy to operation and convenient in management, but in whole productive process, there are some shortcomings of 0.5mm as deslime grading granularity:

1. It's difficult to make classification for desliming; destructive sieve removal effect is poor, medium consumption, desilting grading equipment and more, high energy consumption.

2. The content of slime by dense-medium liquid is high, and density is instability. The dense-medium system has poor stability and precision is low.

3. Strict control open pore of desilting screen and medium draining screen, if 0.5mm is wear, so that will have more than 0.5mm coarse slime will enter into the flotation system, and make it get some low-grade coal, therefor if there get some wear, need to turnover immediately, the sieve

plate need turnover frequently.

4.Smaller than 0.5mm granular slime all static flotation system, resulting in large-scale slime water system, high operating costs.At the same time, 0.5mm as the upper limit of the flotation system brings the following problems need to be solved:

① 0.5~0mm flotation particle size is too wide, the separation result of it is not good. In order to ensure that all coarse grain level float, need to increase the dose, excess medicament will make the ash content of fine-grained product increase; So that reduce the ash content of the product, it is necessary to reduce the dosage of the medicament, which in turn causes the loss of coarse-grade coal to the tailings.

② Classification of de-sliming sieves by 0.5mm. With the wear of the sieve, about 15% of the floatation feed is coarse particle which is more than 0.5mm, and this part will almost be loss in the tailing.

Since 1990s, the coarse slime separation process has been widely used in the United States. The separation process of coking coal preparation plant change into three particle-grade separation system from two particle-grade separation system. The raw coal broken to below 50mm will be sent to wet classification with 1mm de-sliming sieves in the main building. The material of 1-50mm on the de-sliming sieve will be dealt with by two segment two product heavy medium cyclone to produce the clean coal, middling and gangue. The underflow of the de-sliming sieves will be classified by hydro-cyclone into coarse slime (0.15-1mm) and fine slime (0-0.15mm). Coarse slime will be separated from clean coal and gangue by coal slime separation equipment (such as spiral classifier and water medium cyclone).Fine slime will be separated from clean coal and tailing by flotation.

In this process, the size of the sieve holes for sculping sieves and de-sliming sieves is 1mm or 1.5mm, while that is 0.5mm in the previous process. The calculation of the opening rate in each size is as follows (It is assumed that the back width of the diagrid of the sieve surface is 1.6mm)

The opening rate (0.5mm) $=0.5 \div (1.6+0.5) =23.8\%$ (1)

The opening rate (1.0mm) $=1.0 \div (1.6+1.0) =38.5\%$ (2)

From the above two formulas, we can find that, when the size is 0.5mm, the opening rate is only 23.8%, and when the size is 1.0mm, the opening rate is 38.5%, it increases 61.8%. This can not only solve the blockage of sieve holes and the problem of small opening area, but also guarantee the water can flow down from the de-sliming sieves and the medium can flow down from the sculping sieves. As a result, the separation density is stable, the consumption of medium is reduced and the wear of sieve plate is reduced.

After improving the coking coal washing process, the lower limit of the heavy medium separation is 1mm, and its advantages are shown in the following aspects:

① Providing stable feeding conditions for the follow-up process, the effect of slime on the characteristics of suspension can be eliminated fundamentally. As the coal slime which is less than 1mm is discharged from the heavy medium system in advance, the change of the slime volume will not affects the separation density and the viscosity and stability of heavy medium suspension, thereby improving the output of clean coal.

② Improving lower feed limit of the cyclone and the separation effect is improved. The de-sliming process improves the lower feed limit of the heavy medium cyclone, and improves the separation effect of the cyclone, the output of the clean coal is improved as well.

③ Improving the sculping effect, reducing the flow rate of qualified medium, strict control of medium consumption, less water spray as well as lower production cost. Due to the small amount of slime on the sieve, the sculping effect is good, which further reduces the consumption of medium. Due to the reduction of slime in heavy medium system and the amount of sculping sieve will also be reduced. And then, the magnetic material amount entering the magnetic separator system will also be reduced, which effectively reduces the loss of magnetite in magnetic separation tailings.

④ Because the slime does not enter the heavy medium system, the slime can be avoided in the system for a long time and repeatedly soaking in the system, and the time of the surface oxidation reaction of slime and further argillaceous can be reduced, therefor the load of the slime water system can ease, and the water circuit can also be guaranteed.

⑤ The well stability of the medium system can make the density control be faster and more accurate, and it can also avoid the clean coal because of the circulating slime affects the actual separation density.

⑥ 1.0mm is the ideal upper limit of coarse slime separation in general. After this improvement, the upper limit of the floatation separation system is 0.15mm, this solves the problem that the clean coal has lots of coarse coal in the flotation system. And it can also avoid the loss caused by the raw coal bigger than 0.15mm flow into the floatation system when the raw coal is oxidized.

In summary, although a sorting system need to be added and investment will increase correspondingly, the output of cleaned coal can increase, the system will be more stable, the operation cost will be also reduced, and the return on investment can be higher.

Jim Walter coal preparation plant is located in Alabama, the original separating process is divided into two steps. First, 0.5-50mm raw coal is separated by two segment two product heavy medium cyclone and then, the 0-0.15mm raw coal is dealt with by floatation. The plant was reformed by Techgart (US) Company, The 0.15-1mm coarse slime separation system has been added, and the reformed processing capacity is increased from the original 1000t/h to 1400t/h.

Practice has shown that after increasing the coarse slime separation system, the separation effect of heavy medium system is improved, the water volume of coal slime is reduced effectively, and the production capacity and reliability of coal preparation plant are improved.

24.3 The development of technology and process of coal preparation for coking coal in China

In large-scale coking coal preparation plant design, in order to improve the yield of clean coal, the graded selected process is widely used. The raw coal preparation system only needs to break the raw coal to below 200mm, the raw coal of 13-200mm use shallow trough to separate, and the smaller coal will be separated by heavy medium cyclone. And the separation of coarse slime and fine slime is independent.

Wangzhuang coking coal washing plant is located in Changzhi, Shanxi province, China, the processing capacity is 2850t/h. The clean coal products are used as coking coal and middings is used as power coal. The plant selection classification, raw coal is divided into six different graded respectively, of which 200~50mm raw coal with medium shallow trough separator separation, 50~13mm raw coal with dense medium cyclone separation, 1-0.15 raw coal main separation and washing, using spiral classifiers 0.15~0.045mm raw coal with conventional flotation machine, is less than 0.045mm peat using air flotation column separation.

24.3.1 Multi-particle separation process

When the total fine coal ash content is constant, the individual grain size is sorted according to the equal elemental ash content and the total yield of clean coal is different .Table 1 coal washery coal shallow trough sorting system (hereinafter referred to as HMV) and coal at the end of the heavy medium cyclone separation system (HMC) under the condition of different separation density, when the total plant ash content was 9%, and the lump coal and slack coal separation plant output rate density under the condition of primitive ash content. As can be seen from the table, the total yield of refined coal is 30.29%, the sorting density in lump coal system is 1.483kg / L at this time, and the sorting density of the last coal system is 1.521kg / L, Coal in the respective sorting conditions, the elementary ash equal, are 21.60%. Lump coal and the end of the coal in the separation conditions under the condition of a large difference between the elemental ash, the total low-yield coal.

Figure 1. Relationship between total fine coal yield and gray-grade ash content of each grain grade

Dense shallow groove system		Dense medium cyclone system		Integrated coal	
Sorting density	Primitive ash	Sorting density	Primitive ash	Ash	Yield
kg·L⁻¹	/%	kg·L⁻¹	/%	%	%
1.350	9.33	1.562	24.77	9.00	28.80
1.375	11.12	1.560	24.61	9.00	29.48
1.400	12.51	1.554	24.13	9.00	29.80
1.425	15.8	1.547	23.60	9.00	30.10
1.450	18.27	1.537	22.85	9.00	30.22
1.475	20.65	1.526	21.94	9.00	30.28
1.483	21.60	1.521	21.60	9.00	30.29
1.500	23.19	1.513	20.93	9.00	30.28
1.525	25.29	1.498	19.80	9.00	30.19
1.550	27.85	1.481	18.50	9.00	30.03
1.575	29.34	1.464	16.92	9.00	29.78
1.600	31.93	1.446	15.11	9.00	29.42
1.625	33.87	1.425	13.55	9.00	28.86
1.650	35.07	1.406	12.62	9.00	28.16
1.675	38.13	1.384	11.46	9.00	27.22

Figrue 24.1 Relationship between total fine coal yield and gray-grade ash content of each grain grade

According to the data in table 1, the separation density of the block coal system and the ash fraction of block coal, the ash of the coal base and the curve relation of total fine coal yield. It can be seen from the figure that the total coal yield is the highest when the lump coal and the final coal ash are the same.

When the total refined coal production rate is highest, the sorting density of each particle sorting system is different; the selected ash is also different. Figure 2 shows the coal ash content of each particle size sorting system at the Wangzhuang coal preparation plant at the highest total coal yield.

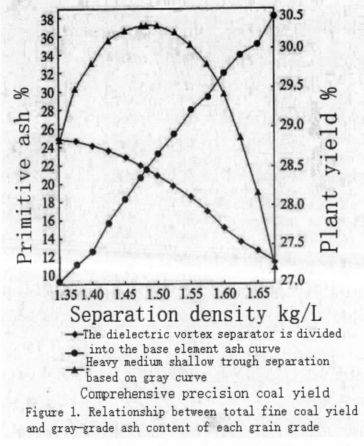

Figure 1. Relationship between total fine coal yield and gray-grade ash content of each grain grade

Figure 24.2 Relationship between total fine coal yield and gray-grade ash content of each grain grade

As is shown in the figure, when the elementary ash of each particle size is the same, the fine coal ash of the 200-50mm heavy medium shallow groove sorting system is 9.98%, and the 50-13mm particle size heavy medium cyclone sorting system The fine coal ash is divided into 9.37%, 13~1mm granular heavy medium hydrocyclone sorting system, fine coal ash is 8.69%, 1~0.15 grain class spiral separator system, fine coal ash is divided into 8.79%.

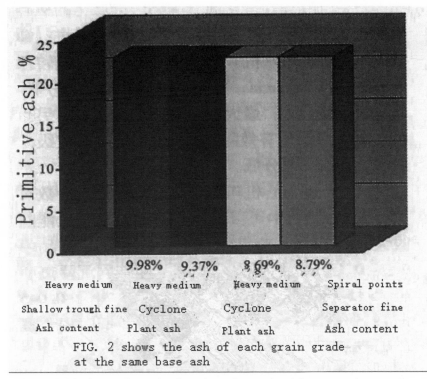

FIG. 2 shows the ash of each grain grade at the same base ash

Figure 24.3 shows the ash of each grain grade at the same base ash

The coal washing capacity of Wangzhuang coal washing plant was 17 million t / a. Using graduated candidates will increase the cost of washing and washing and increase about 0.5 yuan / t of raw coal, increasing the washing cost by 8.5 million yuan throughout the year. However, with the graded candidates, the yield of refined coal increased by 0.5%, the annual yield of refined coal increased by 85,000 tons, the price of refined coal at 1,000 yuan / ton, and the annual sales revenue increased by 85 million yuan. So, it can be seen that the net profit of Wangzhuang coal preparation plant increases by 76.5 million yuan through preparation of sized raw coal.

According to its raw coal character, Wangzhuang coal preparation plant adopting preparation of sized raw coal, following the principle of maximizing the yield of the clean coal, and choose 6 size ranges of separation process. And, different separation densities and equal elementary ash are adopted at separation of each size range, which maximum the yield of clean coal, bring great economic benefits to coal preparation plant and being recognized by international coal preparation industry. Meanwhile, this coal preparation plant was rated by the "Coal age" as the cover coal preparation plant in 1999.

24.3.2 Selection of flotation equipment

The coal slurry whose particle size is smaller than 0.13mm usually uses mechanical agitation separator and flotation column to do separation. By sieve analysis of slurry, the ash content of size range that smaller than 0.045mm is 8%-15% higher than it of size range 015mm-0.45mm. Therefore, coal slurry whose particle size is smaller than 0.045mm is hard to separation, and easy to pollute clean coal, causing high ash content of clean coal and cannot achieve largest yield. Because the quality of the two different sizes range of coal slurry, it is better to adopting stage flotation.

Compared with separator, the flotation column has the advantages of larger mineralized area, lower turbulence and more tiny bubbles; it is more suitable for the separation of micro particle size. Because the flotation column has the spray water for clean coal, it reduces the pollution of slurry of high ash and fine particle size in the clean coal. So, in large scale of coking coal preparation plant, common separator is used for the coal slurry of 0.045-0.15mm and coal slurry smaller than 0.045mm adopting aeration flotation column.

24.3.3 Dewatering process of clean coal flotation

Coking coal preparation plant usually use screen-bowl sedimentation centrifuge and filter press to recover the clean coal.

Screen-bowl sedimentation centrifuge realize solid-liquid separation of coal slurry water by centrifugal force produced by roller rotation, and unload the material through a spiral scraper. The rotating speed of screen-bowl sedimentation centrifuge is 900-1100 r/min, having the characteristics of large centrifugal strength and low water content of the product. The capacity of single machine is large, the maximum can reach 90t/h. It also another notable feature, that it can effectively recover coal slurry particles of larger than 0.045mm, and the product has low water content.

The work parameter comparison table between screen-bowl sedimentation centrifuge and slurry centrifuge is shown at table 2. It can be seen from the table, the slurry centrifuge can only recover coal slurry that particle is larger than 0.15mm, and the water content of product particle size 0.15-0.5mm is high. However, through the filtration of the material layer of screen-bowl sedimentation centrifuge, quite much coal slurry that particle size is 0.045mm can achieve efficient recovery. Also, because of the strong centrifugal strength, the water content of product is low.

Table 24.1 Work parameter comparison between screen-bowl sedimentation centrifuge and slurry centrifuge

Parameter		screen-bowl sedimentation centrifuge	slurry centrifuge
Type		Φ91.44×182.88cm	EBW36
Centrifugal strength/g		500	230
Solid recovery rate/%	+0.15mm	100.0	95.0
	0.15mm-0.075mm	95.0	5.0
	0.075mm-0.045mm	90.0	1.0
	-0.045mm	50.0	0.0
0.15mm-0.45mm product surface water content/%		9.0	13.0
Whether the wear of the sieve basket causes a decline in the yield of the product		No	Yes
Service life of sieve basket		10000	500

The dewatering process effect of flotation clean coal by screen-bowl sedimentation centrifuge and filter press is better than pressure filter, which has the advantages of low product water content, low solid content of filtrate, convenient operation, energy saving and so on. As shown in Table 3.

Table 24.2 Comparison of different dewatering method of flotation clean coal

Dewatering method	Pressure filter	Screen-bowl sedimentation centrifuge and plate-and-frame filter press
Recovering rate	< 100%, Filtrate cycle, Some of the clean coal is lost to the flotation tailings.	100%
Filtrate processing	Cycle, affecting flotation recovery, flotation reagent adding, and filter processing capacity	One time recovery, no cycle.
Product water content	High(Air pressure dewatering)	Low(Centrifugal strength dewatering)
Control system	Complicated	Easy
Control maintenance	Complicated	Easy

24.4 Conclusion

The separation process of coking coal should comprehensively analyze the relationship between system simplification and maximum recovery rate, according to raw coal quality and processing capacity of coal preparation plant. To prove it from several aspects: multi size range separation or single size range separation, desliming dense medium separation or non-desliming dense medium separation, desliming flotation or non-desliming flotation. So that separation process can achieve high yield of clean coal, stable, reliable,and efficient system and low operating cost.

Email: zhang@techgart.com

25. Coal Preparation Plant Process System Design Assessment Analysis

Author: Yanfeng Xu, TechGart (BeiJing) Engineering Ltd

Analysis all not a negligible issue of coal preparation plant process design, include castor stalk characteristics and transformation rules and eliminate uncertain elements, in order to avoid apply standard fossilized and consider the whole system; So that this article put forward average efficient productive time, manufacturing cost of average tons for coal, practical separation efficiency and the difficulty of a laparoscopic cholecystectomy for management, on this account to evaluate actual result of the coal preparation process system.

Coal preparation plant process even not have high-tech new challenges, but as for traditional application industry, with the development of the coal industry and the continuous development and application of new equipment, process design need to renewal too. Under the influence of many uncertain factors such as the change of the characteristics of the raw coal, and finish the reasonable application of process system design, it's difficult to evaluate the design effect objectively. Techgart has been in the domestic coal preparation plant design contract area for 10 years, and successfully designed and contracted to build 70 coal preparation plants. It has accumulated a large number of successful experiences. This paper intends to combine some of the coal preparation plant design and construction experience, in order to analysis of coal preparation plant design ideas and evaluation criteria. So that the decision makers and designers of the coal preparation plant process have a broader idea and understanding of the final process plan.

25.1 The Uniqueness of Process Design in Coal Preparation Plant

25.1.1Factors Influencing the Process Design of Coal Preparation Plant

Because there are too many uncertain factors in the process design of the coal preparation plant, therefore, in the process design should be adjusted to the maximum to adapt to and eliminate the influence of these uncertain factors. The main influencing factors are the following points.

(1)The characteristics of raw materials are different, such as coal seam condition, industrial analysis, process performance and industrial use.

(2)Raw coal processing performance differences, including particle size composition, optional, Gangue, top floor lithology and mud degree

(3)Different mining methods, raw coal gangue rate and grain size significantly different.

(4)Product market expectations and market positioning are different, resulting in different product structure.

25.1.2 Reasonable choice of process design in Coal Preparation Plant

The best process design that preserves all the advantages and circumvents all the shortcomings does not exist. For the design projects with the same quality requirements of coal and products, the design of coal preparation system can achieve normal operation even if different schemes are adopted. And to meet the final product quality requirements, the merits of it seems difficult to assess, more difficult to form a unified standard. Since there is no optimal design scheme, it is bound to need to choose a few schemes in multiple schemes to implement it. And what are the criteria for choosing more programs? And for the long-term experience of design practice, it is very important to reach a consensus before choosing a design scheme, and not limited to the following aspects.

The possible factors affecting the process are analyzed and the sequence is discharged in order to solve the main contradiction. First, the advantages and disadvantages of the main factors of process design are analyzed. Each scheme has advantages and disadvantages. It can't be generalized which is bad, but to analyze the actual situation of the project, as the advanced process can only be advanced in a particular case, and there may be a serious defect in an inappropriate occasion. For example, the pressure filter has a great advantage in reducing the moisture of the product and achieving the average performance of the product, but the dewatering effect of the slime is very bad for the serious slime.

Secondly, combining with the actual situation of the project, balancing and balancing the advantages and disadvantages of each scheme is the most important step in process design.Clearly what you want, what are the advantages Retention has the greatest probability of impact on project revenue, you must retain: What advantages, although obvious, but the probability of impact on the project a smaller probability, you can discard.Giving up unnecessary and eliminating serious shortcomings is equally important to the selection of process design. It is unrealistic to have a large area of argument or to try to find a solution without defect.For example, coal seams in a coal mine are very stable, and they can be mined for 15 to 20 years. However, the coal seam may change significantly after 20 years. If in order to adapt to all the coal mine, process design must be set aside more process to deal with, cause the process system in early is very complex, construction costs and processing costs will increase obviously, obviously this is not a wise choice.Similarly, a coal preparation plant with a clear user, a single product use, there is no potential for potential or potential use of smaller, blindly set aside or increase the product structure, set aside N multiple interfaces and the possibility of fear of the system Complexity and increased investment are also undesirable.

25.2 The issue of principle cannot be ignored in process design

Process design cannot be separated from the actual, must focus on the following issues, and the reasonable ways to solve these problems into specific design, this is a good process engineer must possess the potential.

25.2.1 Concerned about the characteristics of raw materials and changes in law

The variation of material properties plays a key role in the process design and the operation of the system in the future. The same process in the treatment of different coal, the operating effect of significant differences, the analysis of coal quality characteristics must be very cautious and comprehensive. In addition to the normal analysis of coalfield geological reports and the production of a large number of relevant information, but also pay attention to the following factors on the process design:

(1) Coal mining methods (external or mine supply)

(2)The conditions, thickness, number and lithology of the coal seam, geological structure and the variation trend of coal seam thickness.

(3) Mine mining plan and mining process, is integrated or put top coal mining and mining excavation approach.

(4) The influence of the characteristics of the link setting of the mine transport system on the change of coal quality, such as whether it has a bottom-hole coal bunker, and whether it has underground broken links, etc.

(5) investigation report on coal quality in similar mines and coal preparation plants. In the process design, these factors are often ignored, direct use of the production of large samples, so that the process design later risk greatly increases. The important information is to evaluate the representativeness of production, to revise the key points of the coal materials, and to eliminate the uncertain risk of the system.

25.2.2 Eliminating the potential uncertainties in the process.

According to the uncertainties that may appear in the change of coal quality and other factors that affect the process design, the main risk factors are listed according to the principle of weight loss and avoidance and the corresponding solutions are proposed.For example, in the process design of the Tagong coal preparation plant, the main problems that need to be solved are the large amount of gangue, serious muddy coal gangue and the selective fluctuation of coal slime on the overall system and fine coal ash content.To eliminate and control the risk, the company adopts full grain depth row of waste rock taggart, shallow groove and Shared medium cyclone separation system to walkthrough bottles of greater than 1mm material, effectively reduce the waste mud's influence on the subsequent process; The coarse coal sludge separation system adopts spiral separator and TSS, and the waste rock is expelled in advance, which greatly reduces the pollution of the waste rock to the coal ash. Before flotation, a small diameter cyclone was used to remove the sludge flotation, which ensured that the coal ash and yield of the flotation were reduced, and the drug consumption was reduced obviously.The practice proves that the process is successful and the whole system runs smoothly. The main reason is that the designer has fully implemented the idea of solving the risk of uncertain factors into the process design.

25.2.3 To avoid indiscriminately use specification

The particularity of process design in coal preparation plant does not mean that there is no chapter to follow, and the design code of coal preparation plant is actually the authoritative standard to guide the process design, but it is not advisable to apply the completely rigid use. Although the specifications listed by the process of the actual results of a large number of coal preparation plant by statistical analysis, however, the use of these standards still needs to be combined with the specific circumstances through the theoretical calculation of the verification, such as in the grading screen, the removal of mud screen, the sculping screen and other screen equipment, we must consider the size of the composition of the material characteristics, Average granularity and other indexes are calculated. The practical experience shows that there are obvious differences in the calculation results for different materials. Without the analysis, direct use indiscriminately to the specification, the future process system operation effect is obvious.

25.2.4 Mull the whole system selection process plan

Process design often has a focus on the local, ignoring the overall situation of the problem, often spent on a separate process advantages of a large number theoretical results for analysis and discussion, and draw the conclusion of the overall process plan, in fact, no matter how good the process is a prerequisite to achieve theoretical results, If you do not meet this condition or for meeting the conditions before and after the process,there will be adversely affected, eventually will make the overall process system effect, from the overall system point of view is not the most optimal solution. For example, the heavy medium shallow trough is the ideal equipment of the lump coal sorting, the theory effective sorting lower limit can reach 6mm, in order to play shallow trough this advantage, uses the 6mm powder process into the shallow trough sorting, the product which will be 6mm below the direct bypass is very good craft mentality. However, if the gangue is easy to muddy in the occasion, in order to reach the 6mm removal of powder there is a great technological risk, will make the heavy medium system encountered gangue mud and the final coal quantity of large problems, difficult to operate normally. Not only can not make shallow groove this advantage to play, but reduce the overall process reliability. Positive examples also have, for example, the existence of a separate set of coarse slime separation complex, the lack of separation accuracy is low, but from the perspective of the overall process system, it has its rationality, on the one hand, to eliminate the influence of slime on the heavy medium separation system, the precision of heavy medium separation is stable, while the coarse slime is effectively controlled in the flotation process. For conventional coarse slime separation process, it can be achieved by adopting the process system or controlling the feeding granularity range of the system, so as to achieve a stable ideal effect as far as possible.

25.3 Objective evaluation standard of process design effect

The coal quality, product requirement and other restriction conditions of each preparation plant are different, the method of process design will be changed accordingly. In addition, because different process design engineers have different analysis point of view,herefore even in the case of similar coal quality and other conditions, different process design ideas are adopted finally. In the practical application of these coal preparation plant can be normal operation, for this reason, the industry internal evaluation of which process better problem on a long-term debate, mainly reason is the choice of the scheme itself is a balance and trade-offs of the process. Because the position of thinking is different, the standard of project evaluation is different, the author sums up several main evaluation criteria, which are based on the same standard of the process system configuration, the system running normally, and can meet the design requirements of the process indicators and product number quality requirements.

25.3.1 System reliability – average effective production time

The reliability and complexity of the system are closely related to the adaptability of the system to the change of coal quality. During the running process of coal preparation plant, mechanical failures and failure in the process of adjusting parameters account for more than 80% of the total failures of the system. Therefore, the more the number of process links and the number of equipment in the whole system, the greater the probability of failure. In the process of adjusting parameters, the changes in coal properties, such as lump coal particle size, particle size composition and quantity of coal slurry, degree of gangue mud and gangue content all may cause failures, which cause system reduction or stop running. The probability of failure is directly related to the adaptability of the process system design and the complexity of the operation. Although the causes of these failures are numerous, and difficult to describe, but any failures will affect the efficient production time of the whole process system of the coal preparation plant. So, using average effective production time for multiple unit time periods to evaluate the reliability of different process systems is more objective and operable.

25.3.2 Ton coal processing cost –average ton coal processing cost

Every different process system will pay different price to get the same quantity and quality of qualified product, which is finally shown on the processing cost of ton coal. Obviously, the lower processing cost of the ton coal is, the better the process system is. To objectively evaluate the process system, author come with a new concept-average ton coal processing cost. To determine the direct processing cost of ton coal in several normal production shiftes, and to calculate the average value can objectively evaluate the running performance index of process system.

25.3.3 Actual separation efficiency-Ratio of actual yield of clean coal to theoretical yield

For a long time, evaluation method of calculation and prediction by single link combination theory is adopted in industry, because the theoretical prediction does not take into account the whole system, and the calculation of each link does not take into account the impact on the upper and lower processes, so even though the results are advanced, the efficiency is different from the actual operation. In a normal production shift, the actual clean coal yield of the system is obtained by the ratio of the total production of clean coal and the amount of separation raw coal. Then comparing it with the theoretical prediction yield, overall performance of the system can be obviously seen.

25.3.4 The difficulty of management-The number of operating posts and spot inspection posts

Assuming that there are skilled technicians in every operating post, and the management standards are the same. During production process, the more operating posts that need man-made operation in the system, the worse the stability of system is. Meanwhile, the more operating posts that need point inspection, the greater the workload of the system maintenance is, which cause a large failure rate and too much employ persons.

25.4 Conclusion

Combining years of experience in the design and construction of coal processing technology, Author has analyzed and discussed how to widen the idea of process design. Compared with specific technical details, although the details have been determined to be successful, the correct technological idea is the most important key to the success of the project.

26. How to Invest In International Mining Projects? China Has Paid Much Tuition!

Author: (Steven) Heng Huang, Director of HOT Mining, Member of AusIMM, Senior Engineer (Mining & Process)

Translator: (Luke) Ke Jiao, Mining Engineer, Chief Rep. Of HOT Mining Pakistani Joint Venture

For a long time, Chinese mining companies or investors are considered rich but fool. Until recently, we could still hear some jokes from mining brokers. "This mine has large reserves with high grade ore. It can be converted into gold XX tons..." Yes, until today, those completely unreliable guys are still active in the mining rights trading market.

Every time I heard this bullshit, I always want to ask: "Hi dude, could you please read more books before you intend to bamboozle others?"

This is just what happens in the China. How about international? In recent years, HOT has also done many international mining projects. Consequently, I've seen a lot of people with modified overseas resources projects to seek cooperation or financing. They are blind and impatient. They totally do not analyze clients' demand and intentions. They just want to sell the mining right as soon as possible, just like selling a house or a car. According to their way of work, you can image the quality of their projects.

One obvious fact is that the main target of these brokers is the investors from China. Probably, in the eyes of the mining rights traders all over the world, all Chinese mining investors are blockhead.

Deceptions are everywhere, no matter huge projects or small projects. It is not uncommon that data is modified to deceive investors or great plan is promised, which is actually cannot be achieved. There is no doubt that these projects are going to fail. But what if the projects are very good and they are all located in developed countries which have mature laws and regulations such as Australia and Canada, are these projects definitely going to be profitable?

Absolutely NO!

I have participated in a technical upgrade review work for a coal mine and coal preparation plant project in Australia. Strictly speaking, this project is a very good investment target. It is located in the mature mining area in Queensland. Its infrastructure is perfect and do not need to worry about water supply, electricity supply and transportation problems. It have great living conditions. It has very large reserves of coking coal. Its mining conditions are very good, and have been small-scale production for more than ten years. There is a coal preparation plant for this coal mine, and there is a special railway line that can transport products directly to the port. Because this project is already in operation, it is not difficult to update the environmental impact assessment and mining certificate renewal. Investors bought the vast tracts of land and pastures above the mineral rights in advance. Therefore the potential risks of conflict with local residents are solved.

From the perspective of Chinese investors, this project is "Extremely perfect". However, Investors are still suffering from serious losses.

What is the reason?

The reason is the location of this project. Yes, the reason is Australia, the place is considered that laws and regulations are perfect, and invest here is very safe.

The more perfect laws and regulations are, the more difficult it is for Chinese companies to work in the "Chinese way". To some extent, these various rules bring heavy burdens to the investment and development of Chinese companies.

First of all, Chinese companies are unable to send Chinese engineers and technical workers to Australia because of visa problem. Most Chinese employees can not apply for Australian working visa due to the strict Australian approval system. Therefore, hiring local engineers and miners is the only option. The problem is employment. It is a difficult to employ miners in Australia. For a underground mine, the situation is worse. During the several years from project preparation to project implementation, the overall experience of the chief engineer in charge is confined to the open pit mining. Even it's difficult to employ a chief engineer, and you can imagine what's going to happen for this project.

Besides, the engineer team also has problems. For example, due to the stubborn and arrogance of Australians, it is difficult for Chinese shareholders to get involved in decision making. For example, in Australia, miners can directly refuse to use if they feel the equipment has potential safety hazard, etc. Because of those, any partner and technical expert from China cannot really provide valuable and experienced advice.

They cannot work well with local employees. They are more like two separate operating systems.

Without considering the factors of the mine itself, the greatest risk of mining investment comes from the people involved in mine development and management. In this project, the management structure is unreasonable. In addition, the leading Australian chief engineer chose the long wall mining technology that was not suitable for this coal mine. Actually, the Chinese engineers have already pointed out that there are a lot of faults in the mining area, and room and pillar method is more suitable for this project. However, this proposal was not considered at all. And about duration of this project (Seriously affect the payback period of investment calculation), although Chinese experts have repeatedly reminded the plan in Australia is impossible to complete, this Australian chief engineer still believed it can be finished on time. As a result, the whole project has been postponed again and again. About work-face Sequence plan, these open pit mining experts did not consider the efficiency of equipment transportation and prevention of accidents. So, it is consume a lot of time to fix this problem when the accident happened. Eventually, the best time in the market was missed. Something like this has happened again and again and again...

Something else happened later and I will not talk about it. Overall, if this project is in China, Indonesia or any developing country, then Chinese companies can develop and manage this project in the "Chinese way". And I am pretty sure it is a very profitable coking coal project. What a pity!

Conclusion: Is it safe to invest in Australia, Canada and other countries with improved laws and regulations? The answer is not that simple. Instead, opportunities exist in countries people think it is a mess, the countries do not follow the rules, or even the countries where the mining laws are immature (most African countries for example). In there, you can develop and manage a project with low cost. You can make a profit. Even if one day the local government no longer supports your production for a variety of reason, it does not matter. Just quit because you have made a lot of money.

There are two extremes in China's mining investment. The one are speculators. They keep buying and selling mining rights and earn the difference. The others are dreamers. They think about big strategies, but they don't care about details.

There are no right or wrong for these two extremes. Whether it can make money depends on business level and a little bit luck.

"Cross the river by tossing stones."

"It doesn't matter whether the cat is black or white, as long as it catches mice."

Now think about these two sentences, and I found they are very philosophical. The same is true for mining investment. The mining investors and companies may develop the project and make money with low cost as first, and then seek long-term development opportunities. Probably, for the most mining company which want to develop good project, this is a better choice.

Email: luke.jiao@hot-mining.com

27. Midas Touch! How to Optimize the Investment Value of Mines by Exploring, Mining and Mineral Processing?

From prospecting to cash flow in the production of mines, only 6%!

Important note: *Engineering drawings and NPV data cannot be displayed, hope mine friends forgive me! Part of the three-dimensional map for the exploration model, the rest of the pictures are schematic.*

27.1 Project Profile

Project: a barite mine in Guizhou.

Minerals: mainly barite, associated with a small amount of fluorite, belonging to industrial minerals.

Reserves: The existing mineral rights within the estimated 500,000 tons of resources; of which about 65% can be taken. The ore body is stable and large scale, the ground 2-3km long visible ore. As the mineral rights below the elevation, there is a great possibility of mineralization, so the project has good prospects for deep prospecting.

Grade: the authority of its quality inspection, harmful impurities is very small, high brightness, density, and massive, containing up to 97% of barium.

Area: good traffic conditions, the road through the ore body, 5km from the county, the county has a lead in all directions of the highway, river and railway planning; farmland, woodland and other local relations less hidden.

Deposit type: low temperature hydrothermal vein deposit.

Vein formation: barite vein formation mainly to fill the main, accompanied by a small amount of metasomatism.

Development and utilization of performance: easy to adopt, easy to choose, low-cost, low pollution.

Infrastructure: water, electricity are very convenient.

27.2 The Profile of Investment

Type of company: Junior Mining Companies.

Development goals: 3 years to grow into a cash flow of small mineral company.

The main products: fluorite, barite.

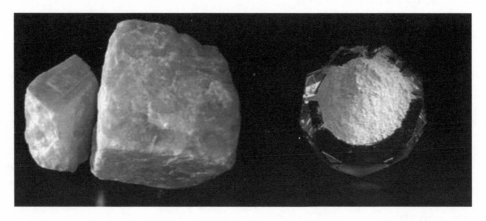

Figure 27.1 Schematic diagram of barite ore and meet the drilling packing standard products

27.3 Product Features

Products are industrial minerals, the main features:

• The added value is limited and the profit is relatively stable (compared with the precious metal / energy mineral ratio).

For example, borax, Rio Tinto's investment in the United States. Stable profit base metal company many times in history to make up for the low rate of return on investment profits. With boron placer.

• Fragile and the hardness is not high.

• The development and operation of the project is mainly based on small mineral company, which is less attractive to mainstream funds.

• The product pricing system is not transparent.

• The small scale mining, limited affected by mining cycle.

27.4 Exploration Work

27.4.1 Introduction of Ore Bodies

The outcrop elevation is 780-995m. Ore body and rock clear contact line, occurrence and fracture occurrence is consistent, toward NW, tend to NW 220 degrees, the angle of 71 – 78 degrees, with an average of 75 degrees. A length of about 1.43km, thickness of 1 1.66M, average 1.36M, NNE or SSW veins extending to after the pinch, belonging to epithermal ore deposits.

Figure 27.2 veins outcrop part

Picture, Courtesy by 9X Minerals LLC

27.4.2 No Drilling

No drilling, reason:

Barite / fluorite is soft surrounding dominated by limestone, difficult drilling coring, as shown in Figure 3.

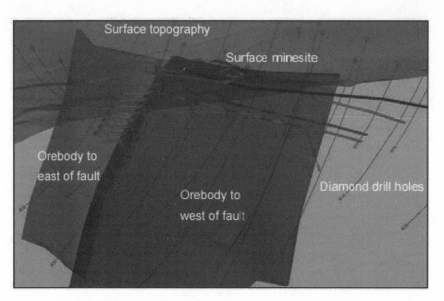

Figure 27.3 barite vein pouring drilling scenarios

Picture, Courtesy by Mine Boss Exploration Mining Holding Co Limited (Hong Kong)

A lode large angle, steep orebody, drilling angle is difficult to control, it is easy to penetrate the drilling veins, coring drilling results is not representative, basically no significance.

In addition, according to the following relevant national standards, the project can be used in other ways instead of drilling.

"GB / T 13908-2002 Solid Mineral Geological Survey Code"

"GB / T 17766-1999 Solid mineral resources / reserves classification"

If the terrain is favorable or ore body shape is complex, and drilling engineering is difficult to control, when collecting mineral processing large sample, we should select pit exploration project, to make full use of the old hole, mining pit for sample catalog.

Therefore, according to "barite, toxic heavy stone, fluorite, boron geology exploration norms" provides that the mine is classified as a type of exploration type III . The basic engineering spacing is 100×50m; the existing ore vein has a number of trench exploration, and stolen mining pits by the villagers before, to meet the relevant exploration requirements.

27.4.3 Summary of Exploration Methods

The existing ore vein has a number of trench exploration, and stolen mining pits by the villagers before, meet the relevant exploration requirements.

Veins are obvious, it is available to use pit exploration (development method with adit, Mining at the same time exploration)

Benefits: Save on exploration costs to achieve the same results.

27.5 Mining Methods

In order to reduce the investment risk, this barite ore mining will be developed along the veins, namely: adit mining (tunnel mining).

The exploration results coincide with the veins profile, the width of the vein is ideal; Barite / fluorite reserves are satisfactory. Developing along the veins and making full use of the high-grade ore profile will have a positive impact on the project's early cash flow.

See Figure 4, Figure 5, and Figure 6 for a schematic diagram of the development method with adit.

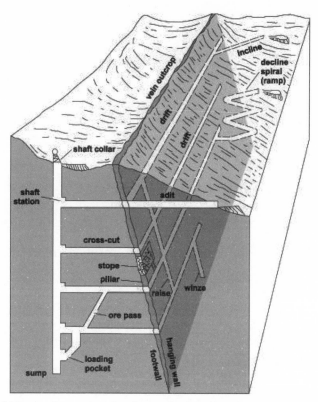

Figure 27.4 Three-dimensional schematic drawing of adit mining in tunneling

along the veins

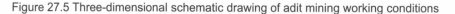

Figure 27.5 Three-dimensional schematic drawing of adit mining working conditions

Figure 27.6 A barite mine roadway

Reasons:

The ore bodies are mainly produced in the Ordovician limestone (hard rock) strata, the rocks on both sides of the veins are medium to thick layered limestone and a few dolomitic limestones. The rock is hard and has good stability, the contact surface is clear and stable, and the stability of surrounding rock is good. The ore body is controlled by the NW trending tensional fracture, which is inclined to output and the ore structure is simple. Therefore, the engineering geological conditions of the deposit are of simple type, which is favorable to the construction and exploitation of the deposit.

The vein extension mining method is in line with national safety standards and project acceptance requirements, in order to avoid safety accidents, there are more stringent requirements refer to the mine safety standards.

Compared with the local standard of the project, it is estimated to save RMB 4 million in the construction period and RMB 1 million in the production period per year according to the national standard.

Figure 27.7 Remote controlling LHD of a barite mine

This radio remote control system of LHD is innovated by Alpha Industrial Technology Pty Ltd (Australia)

27.6 Ellhead Confirmation

In order to reduce occupation of farmland and save construction cost, adit opening position is decided to be set at point 107 instead of point 117 (Figure 8). Because there is no village and farmland at point

107, road and industrial site construction is simpler than 117 points, cost is lower; it is also easy for post-mining.

27.6.1 Scheme Comparison of Pithead Position 880 VS 920

Table 25.1 Scheme Comparison of Pithead Position 880 VS 920

	880 Pithead Scheme	920 Pithead Scheme
Surface soil section	Same	Same
Three connections and one leveling	Short time consuming	Long time consuming (one more road needs to be built)
Villagers and community relations	Easy and simple	Hard (land and cropland requisition)
Duration	Steerable	Hard to control
Recoverable reserve	Many	Few
Karren	Possible	Possible
Investment recovery when construction	High possibility	Low possibility

27.6.2 Conclusion of Pithead Position Scheme

1) After field investigation, the temporarily chosen pithead position scheme is 880ML, GPS 57#.

2) The scheme that tunneling from the 960 or 920 inclined roadway is denied, to prevent the inclined roadway from hydrops.

3) After the 920ML ventilating shaft run-through, the fan is installed at the level of 920, however, after the 960ML air return way run-through, it's better to carry fan from 920ML to 960ML, in order to prevent the

forming of downriver ventilation and the pollution of underground air.

4) By calculating of the mineral reserves, it's hopeful that the investment could be recovered by extraction of minerals above 880ML.

5) Decrease the tunnel cross-section, design the tunnel H=2.8m and W=2.6m.H=2.8m W=2.6m. No driving, no pedestrian, there's no need to set apart the sidewalk. The height of cables and water pipe suspension should be 10cm higher than mine cars, to prevent collision during transportation. The hanging distance of celling lamp is about 30-50cm.

6) Simplify the roadway support, if the Protodyakonov Coefficient is between 10-12, then most of the tunnel needn't roof support, however, if there's separation layer, then it needs to be supported by roof bolter, if there's cracks, then it needs anchor nets support.

7) The mineral vein is assumed to be X. The problems might be, the mineral vein is not continuous, or the shape might be big-end-up, the metallogenic reason should be considered.

8) The treatment method of karren is, if there's karren during tunneling, the preliminary scheme is supporting by roof bolter, and advancing directly without detour.

27.7 Mineral Processing Part

Barite ore zone is lode deposit. Due to the main mineral is barite, secondary minerals are fluorite and a small amount of quartz and calcite. They are mostly related to the growth and decline. The massive structure mainly is ore, easy to hand sorting to get barite concentrate; However, a small amount of associated and paragenetic ores are not easy to be sorted by hand, only suitable for flotation separation.

The general contractor and product underwriting partner, Beijing HOT Mining Tech Co.,Ltd,there are cooperation of barite mineral processing working point where near the port of Guangxi.For saving construction costs, the ore will be transported to the vicinity of Guangxi port to dressing and grinding, then direct packaging and export in the processing plant.

Planning select site around the project and building a large barite fluorite ore dressing plant, purchasing other local ore mines with high value-added processing. Then export from the Guangxi port.

Figure 27.9 A barite ore grinding workshop, designed and delivered by HOT Mining

Client, 9X Minerals LLC, Guizhou, China

27.8 Project Plan

After the beginning of adit excavation, see the mine quickly to help the owner to achieve cash flow as soon as possible.

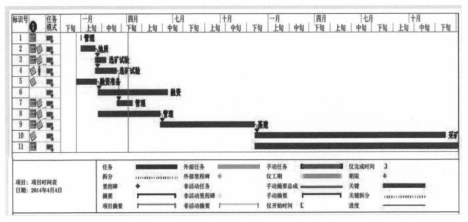

Figure 27.10 The barite mine project development plan

Current progress, has been obtained safety production permit and Notice To Proceed, about to start the construction (adit excavation). Project is expected to start after 3~4 months to achieve small-scale ore sales revenue.

27.9 HOT Mining's Value

± To help investors save cost (mine exploration method, mining method, concentrator installation etc.).

± Help the mine to realize the cash flow of the product sales, and make profit as soon as possible.

Summary: Only profitable stone is mine! Turning stone into gold which is HOT's mission!

27.10 Development Discussion

Why is it difficult for geologists to lead an exploration project into a mineral company with a steady cash flow?

Development of mining projects, what kind of team combination is the best?

What high value-added services are required by the general contractor to be more competitive?

28. Intelligent Mining Will Bringing Mining Industry New Era

Author, Kyle Lee, Project Coordinator, Alpha Industrial Technology Pty Ltd

Email: kyle.lee@alpha-technology.com.au

Science and technology are the first productive forces. Nowadays, mining market is sustained downturn, and the safe production situation of the mine is still grim. Therefore, strengthening the innovation of science and technology, reducing the cost and improve efficiency, and achieving environmental protection, has become a topic that the mining enterprises cannot avoid.

The characteristics of geological and mining conditions are complex, the production system is huge, the mining environment is changeable and so on, mining work is facing great challenges. As the mine intelligence has become a new breakthrough in the world revolution of science and technology after industrialization, electrification and informationalization, building green, intelligent and sustainable mines has become a new trend in the development of mining industry.

Three world famous intelligent mines

28.1 The world's largest underground mine-Kiruna Iron Mine

Kiruna Iron Mine, as the world's largest underground mine, is located in the north of Sweden. To Kiruna Iron Mine, the unmanned mine is no longer a new word, just like the high grade iron ore deposited here, has become the label of Kiruna Iron Mine. At present, Kiruna Iron Mine has basically realized the "unmanned intelligent mining", its smooth implementation, due to the following aspects:

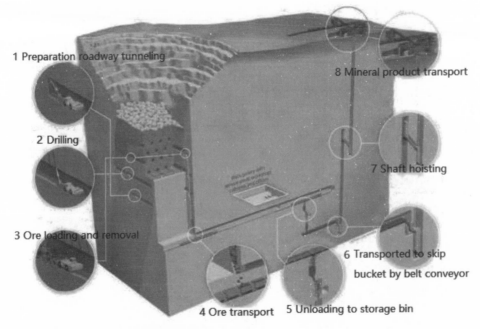

1 Preparation roadway tunneling

8 Mineral product transport

2 Drilling

7 Shaft hoisting

3 Ore loading and removal

6 Transported to skip bucket by belt conveyor

4 Ore transport   5 Unloading to storage bin

Figure 28.1 The world's largest underground mine-Kiruna Iron Mine

1.Reasonable and efficient mining technology

Non-pillar sublevel caving method is adopted, which is much beneficial to the large scale and mechanized mining of the mine.

2.Advanced rock drilling equipment

Stope drilling equipment is the Simba W469 Remote Control Drill Jumbo From Sweden Atlas company. This drill jumbo uses laser system for accurate positioning, it is unmanned, and can achieve 24h continuous circulation operation.

3.Automatic transport equipment, remotely control transport and lifting operation.

The loading and lifting of the ore have already realized intelligent and automated operations. The Atlas Toro2500E Remote Control LHD is used for ore loading, which adopts the automatic guidance function selected by the optical cable system and the remote control operation, to realize the unmanned driving. The belt conveyor automatically convey the ore from the crushing station to the metering device, after the shaft skip bucket stopped at the designated position, ore is automatically loaded into a skip bucket. Then, when the staff press the handle and the elevator is started, the skip bucket is lifted to the surface unloading station, and the bottom door of the skip is opened automatically to complete the unloading. The process of loading and unloading is remote control, and then through technological transformation, the lifting system is intellectualized.

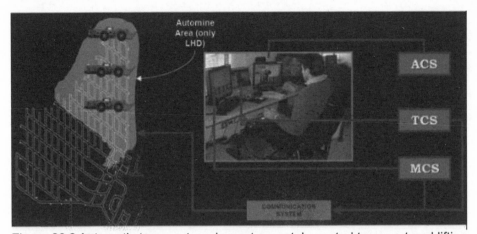

Figure 28.2 Automatic transport equipment, remotely control transport and lifting operation.

28.2 Chile Teniente Copper Mine

Chile Teniente Copper Mine adopting the "AutoMine System" form Sandvik. The system has realized automatic operation of the mine transportation system, including the machinery driving, ore loading and unloading process. The operator can remotely control equipment in the surface control room, and one person controls multiple LHD and truck. The operator can turn the LHD online to the remote control waiting, automatic or remote control operation at any time without shutting down the LHD. Also, its characteristics include operation state and production monitoring, traffic control, navigation system without infrastructure and strong applicability.

Figrue 28.3 Remote Control System Operation

At present, the AutoMine system is widely used in trucks and LHDs in Canada, Finland, Chile, South Africa and Australia.

28.3 The global mining giant – Rio Tinto Iron Mine

The 15 mines of the global mining giant, Rio Tinto, are distributed in the Pilbara mining area. If you are in the mining area, you can hear the roar of machinery, but you cannot see many workers there. The roar of the machinery comes from the intelligent machinery of the mine and why you cannot see many people is that the control center is in the city of Perth, which is more than 1000 kilometers away.

The "Transformers" in the mining area

At present, Rio Tinto is using unmanned trucks from Japan's Komatsu Company in 4 mines. This type of truck adopts coupling pulsed laser calibration guidance system and the global positioning system (GPS), which guides the truck along the predetermined route. If the truck deviates from the route, the control terminal will receive the warning information. That is to say, the truck can find the direction automatically and use the laser sensors and radar to find the obstacles.

Unmanned Mine Trucks

The "intelligent train system" independently developed by Rio Tinto in recent years is the first unmanned heavy haul train system in the world, which makes the ore transportation system more intelligent.

28.4 The "brain" of the mining system – Remote control center

More than 1000 kilometers away, in the remote control center of the city of Perth, the large and long screen at the top shows the progress of iron ore transportation process between 15 mines, 4 ports and 24 railways. For instance, it would show in real time that which train is loading (unloading) ore and how long it will take to complete it, which train is running and how long it is going to the port, which port is loading, and so on. Those operators, who sitting at the comfortable control center, manage the coordination operation of mines, processing plants, railways, electricity and port.

The intelligent mining in China is on the way, and still has a long way to go.

On the whole, because of the late start of intelligent mining in China, the technology is relatively backward. The mining enterprises still have insufficient attention, the investment in intelligence and informatization of mine is insufficient, and there is serious lack of interdisciplinary talents of this industry. The level of intelligence and informatization in domestic mining and metallurgical industry is low, which is far behind the other industries in China.

Just as is known to all, some countries with developed mining industry, just like Canada, Australia, South Africa and so on, now is popularizing mine intelligence in a large area and has achieved good results. But most of the countries are still in the process of transition. Only embrace the technology can embrace the future. Although the mining industry is sustained downturn, mining enterprises still need to develop digitization and intelligence of mining industry, to reduce the costs and improve efficiency by "Replace workers with machines by mechanization, reduce workers by intelligence"

Part 4 Abbreviation & Glossary

"China" or "PRC"	The People's Republic of China
"CHPP"	coal handling and preparation plant
UG	underground
UG Mining	Underground mining
"coke"	Bituminous coal from which the volatile components have been removed
"coking coal"	Coal used in the process of manufacturing steel. It is also known as metallurgical coal
"HOT" or "HOT Mining	Beijing HOT Mining Tech Co Ltd
"TBE" or "Techgart"	Techgart (Beijing) Engineering Ltd
"AIT" or "Alpha"	Alpha Industrial Technology Pty Ltd
"CSR"	Corporate Social Responsibility
"EUR"	Euro, the currency unit of the European Monetary Union

"USD"	US Dollar, the currency unit of the United States of America
"CNY"	Yuan RMB, the currency unit of China
"USA"	United States of America
"HCC"	Hard coking coal
"HR"	Human resources
"HSE"	Health, safety and environment
"JORC"	Joint Ore Reserves Committee of The Australasian Institute of Mining and Metallurgy, Australian Institute of Geoscientists and Minerals Council of Australia
"km"	Kilometres
"kt"	Kilotonnes
"LOM"	Life-of-Mine
"LTIFR"	Lost Time Injury Frequency Rate

"middlings"	thermal coal by-product of washed coal production
"Mt"	Million tonnes
"NBS"	National Bureau of Statistics of China
"open-pit"	The main type of mine designed to extract minerals close to the surface; also known as "open cut"
"ore"	A naturally occurring solid material from which a metal or valuable mineral can be extracted profitably
"probable coal reserve"	The economically mineable part of an indicated and, in some circumstances, a measured mineral resource demonstrated by at least a preliminary feasibility study. This study must include adequate information on mining, processing, metallurgical, economic and other relevant factors that demonstrate, at the time of reporting, that economic extraction can be justified.
"raw coal"	Generally means coal that has not been washed and processed
"ROM"	Run-of-mine, the as-mined material during room and pillar mining operations as it leaves the mine site (mined glauberite ore and out-of-seam dilution material)
"seam"	A stratum or bed of coal or other mineral; generally applied to large deposits of coal

"SSCC"	Semi-soft coking coal
"strip ratio" or "stripping ratio"	The ratio of the amount of waste removed (in bank cubic metres) to the amount of coal or minerals (in tonnes) extracted by open-pit mining methods
"thermal coal"	Also referred to as "steam coal" or "steaming coal", thermal coal is used in combustion processes by power producers and industrial users to produce steam for power and heat. Thermal coal tends not to have the carbonization properties possessed by coking coals and generally has lower heat value and higher volatility than coking coal
"tonne"	Metric tonne, being equal to 1,000 kilograms
"VAT"	Value added tax
"TBS"	Teetered Bed Separator, this special designed slurry separator can treat coal in the -3+0.25 mm size range, at cut points below 1.60.
"HTBS", or "H-TBS"	TBS which is innovated and produced by HOT Mining
"DM" or "HM"	Dense Medium, or Heavy Medium, the same meaning of a kind of separation
"DMS"	Dense Medium System

"DMC", "HMC"	Dense Medium Cyclone, or Heavy Medium Cyclone
"Coal Preparation Plant"	The coal preparation plant (CPP; also known as coal handling and preparation plant (CHPP), coal handling plant, prep plant, or coal wash plant, coal washery) is a facility that washes coal of soil and rock, crushes it into graded sized chunks (sorting), stockpiles grades preparing it for end users, e.g. thermal power plant, coking plant, chemical plant, cement plant, etc. The more of this waste material that can be removed from coal, the lower its total ash content, the greater its market value and the lower its transportation costs.
"shortwall mining"	The face length was therefore limited by the length of shuttle car cables then available, but in practice most shortwall faces were considerably shorter than this (<90m)
"longwall mining"	In the method of secondary extraction known as longwall mining a relatively long mining face (typically in the range 100 to 300m but may be longer) is created by driving a roadway at right angles between two roadways that form the sides of the longwall block, with one rib of this new roadway forming the longwall face.
"Complete Longwall System"	Longwall unit for longwall mining, they are shearer, BSL, AFC, roof support, monorail
"BSL"	Beam Stage Loader

"AFC"	Armored Face Conveyor
"UCG"	Underground Coal Gasification
"RFPA"	Rock Failure Process Analysis, a patent protection method innovated by Professor ChunAn Tang, used for rock engineering
"washed coal"	Coals that have been washed and processed to reduce its ash content
"Clean coal"	Coals that have been washed and processed to reduce its ash content